From Stress to Success DVD from Trivium Test Prep

Dear Customer,

Thank you for purchasing from Cirrus Test Prep! Whether you're looking to join the military, get into college, or advance your career, we're honored to be a part of your journey.

To show our appreciation (and to help you relieve a little of that test-prep stress), we're offering a **FREE *Praxis Chemistry Essential Test Tips DVD**** by Cirrus Test Prep. Our DVD includes 35 test preparation strategies that will help keep you calm and collected before and during your big exam. All we ask is that you email us your feedback and describe your experience with our product. Amazing, awful, or just so-so: we want to hear what you have to say!

To receive your **FREE *Praxis Chemistry Essential Test Tips DVD***, please email us at 5star@cirrustestprep.com. Include "Free 5 Star" in the subject line and the following information in your email:

1. The title of the product you purchased.
2. Your rating from 1 – 5 (with 5 being the best).
3. Your feedback about the product, including how our materials helped you meet your goals and ways in which we can improve our products.
4. Your full name and shipping address so we can send your **FREE *Praxis Chemistry Essential Test Tips DVD***.

If you have any questions or concerns please feel free to contact us directly at 5star@cirrustestprep.com.

Thank you, and good luck with your studies!

* Please note that the free DVD is not included with this book. To receive the free DVD, please follow the instructions above.

Praxis Chemistry Content Knowledge (5245) Study Guide

Comprehensive Review with Practice Test Questions for the Praxis II 5245 Exam

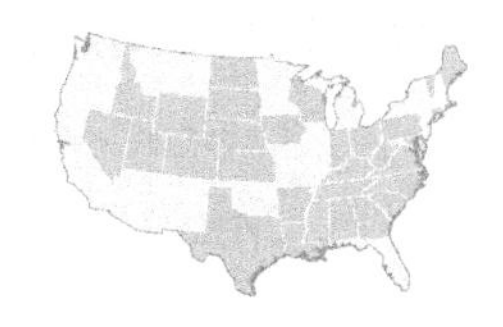

Table of Contents

Online Resources

To help you fully prepare for your Praxis Chemistry Content Knowledge (5245) Exam, Cirrus includes online resources with the purchase of this study guide.

Practice Test

In addition to the practice test included in this book, we also offer an online exam. Since many exams today are computer based, getting to practice your test-taking skills on the computer is a great way to prepare.

Flash Cards

A convenient supplement to this study guide, Cirrus's flash cards enable you to review important terms easily on your computer or smartphone.

From Stress to Success

Watch From Stress to Success, a brief but insightful YouTube video that offers the tips, tricks, and secrets experts use to score higher on the exam.

Reviews

Leave a review, send us helpful feedback, or sign up for Cirrus promotions—including free books!

Access these materials at:

www.cirrustestprep.com/praxis-chemistry-online-resources

Introduction

Congratulations on choosing to take the Praxis Chemistry: Content Knowledge (5245) Test! By purchasing this book, you've taken the first step toward becoming a chemistry teacher.

This guide will provide you with a detailed overview of the Praxis Chemistry test, so you know exactly what to expect on test day. We'll take you through all the concepts covered on the test and give you the opportunity to test your knowledge with practice questions. Even if it's been a while since you last took a major exam, don't worry; we'll make sure you're more than ready!

What is the Praxis Chemistry (5245) Test?

The Praxis Chemistry test measures aptitude in chemistry for teacher candidates looking to certify as chemistry teachers. This test must be taken *in addition to* the assessments in reading, writing, mathematics, and professional knowledge required in your particular state. The Praxis Chemistry test does not replace these other exams.

What's on the Praxis Chemistry (5245) Test?

The Praxis Chemistry test gauges college-level content knowledge in chemistry, as well as the necessary skills for chemistry. Candidates are expected to demonstrate thorough and extensive conceptual knowledge in principles of matter and energy, atomic and nuclear structures, chemical composition and nomenclature, chemical reactions, and solutions and solubility. You will also be expected to demonstrate mastery of key skills related to scientific inquiry. The content is divided into seven categories.

You will have two hours and thirty minutes to answer 125 selected-response questions.

What's on the Praxis Chemistry: Content Knowledge (5245) Test?

Content Category	Objectives
I. Basic Principles of Matter and Energy; Thermodynamics 17 questions	1. Organization of matter 2. Particulate structure of matter 3. Differences between chemical and physical properties and chemical and physical changes 4. Conservation of energy and the conservation of matter in chemical processes 5. Different forms of energy 6. Temperature, thermal energy, and heat capacity 7. Concepts and calculations involving phase transitions between various states of matter 8. Kinetic molecular theory and ideal gas laws 9. Energetics of chemical reactions 10. Relation of laws of thermodynamics to chemical reactions and phase changes
II. Atomic and Nuclear Structure 15 questions	1. Current model of atomic structure 2. Electron configuration of the elements 3. Radioactivity 4. Relationship between electron absorption and emission and electron energy levels
III. Nomenclature; Chemical Composition; Bonding and Structure 19 questions	1. Systematic names and formulas of simple inorganic compounds 2. Names of common organic compounds 3. Mole concept 4. Common properties of bonds 5. Types of bonds (ionic, covalent, metallic) 6. Structural formulas and molecular geometry 7. Polar and nonpolar molecules 8. Intermolecular interactions 9. Relationship between bonding and structure and physical properties

Content Category	Objectives
IV. Chemical Reactions; Periodicity 25 questions	1. Periodic table 2. Periodic trends in the elements 3. Balancing chemical equations 4. Stoichiometric calculations 5. Products of simple reaction types 6. Chemical kinetics 7. Chemical reaction equilibrium 8. Oxidation-reduction reactions 9. Biochemical compounds 10. Common organic compounds
V. Solutions and Solubility; Acid-Base Chemistry 19 questions	1. Solution terminology and calculations 2. Solubility and dissolution rate 3. Solution phenomena based on colligative properties 4. Equilibrium in ionic solutions 5. Acids and bases 6. pH scale 7. Acid-base titrations 8. Equilibrium relations in acid-base chemistry
VI. Scientific Inquiry and Social Perspectives of Science 15 questions	1. Processes involved in scientific inquiry 2. Experimental design 3. Nature of scientific knowledge 4. Major historical developments and figures in chemistry 5. Impact of chemistry and technology on society and the environment 6. Applications of chemistry in daily life 7. Pros and cons of different types of energy production
VII. Scientific Procedures and Techniques 15 questions	1. Collection, evaluation, manipulation, interpretation, and reporting of data 2. Units of measurement, notation systems, conversions, and chemistry-related mathematics 3. Basic error analysis 4. Proper preparation, use, storage, and disposal of materials 5. Proper preparation, use, maintenance, and calibration of laboratory equipment 6. High school chemistry lab safety procedures and precautions

Category I assesses your understanding of matter and energy as well as the basic principles and methods of thermodynamics. You must demonstrate mastery of the organization and processes of matter and identify different forms of energy. You also must be able to explain how chemical processes impact the conservation of energy and matter. In addition, you must be able to conduct calculations involving temperature and phase transitions, and explain the kinetic molecular theory and the ideal gas laws. Finally, you must show you understand how chemical reactions work, the difference between endothermic and exothermic reactions, and how the laws of thermodynamics relate to these reactions.

Category II assesses your understanding of the structure of atoms and electron configurations. You should be able to properly describe the current atomic model and explain the electron configuration of the elements based on the periodic table. You should also be able to demonstrate understanding of radioactivity, including decay processes and nuclear reactions, and the absorption and emission spectra of electrons and how they relate to frequency and wavelength.

Category III assesses your understanding of nomenclature, bonding, and structure. You should be able to name basic inorganic compounds (along with the chemical formulas) and common organic compounds. You also should be able to define and apply the mole concept. In terms of bonding, you must be able to identify types of bonds and their common properties. You should be able to describe different structural formulas, including their molecular geometry, and explain how both structure and bonding correlate with physical properties. Finally, you should be able to differentiate between polar and nonpolar molecules and explain different types of intermolecular interactions.

Category IV assesses your understanding of periodicity and chemical reactions. In terms of the first, you must demonstrate mastery of the periodic table, including its basis, its general layout, and trends in the physical and chemical properties of the elements (e.g. atomic/ionic radius, electron affinity, chemical reactivity, etc.). You must also show that you can interpret and solve equations and calculations related to chemical reactions. This means balancing chemical equations, including those involving oxidation-reduction; completing stoichiometric calculations; applying chemical kinetics; and determining oxidation states. Finally, you must demonstrate your understanding of biochemistry and organic chemistry.

Category V assesses your understanding of solubility and acids and bases. In addressing solubility, you must be able to use proper terminology and conduct accurate calculations. You must also understand the different factors that can affect a substance's solubility and dissolution rate and the various phenomena that can occur based on the colligative properties of a substance. Furthermore, you must be able to identify certain acids and bases, as well as their properties, and demonstrate mastery of the pH scale. Finally, you must understand the equilibrium relationships in acid-base chemistry and be able to complete calculations involving acid-base titrations.

Categories VI and VII emphasize the process of doing science. The material addresses formulating and investigating scientific questions; it also approaches experiment design and implementation, from proper handling of data to mastery of key equipment. Additionally, Category VI assesses your understanding of chemistry in a broader historical and current social context, with a particular focus on current methods of energy production.

How is the Praxis Chemistry (5245) Test Scored?

Your scores on your Praxis Chemistry test will become available online on a predetermined release date ten to eleven days after the close of your testing window. For more information, check https://www.ets.org/praxis. Your scores will be available for one year after your test date. In order to have your scores sent to a particular institution, you must make a request when you register for the exam. You can select up to four institutions to receive your scores.

Each multiple-choice question is worth one raw point. The total number of questions you answer correctly is added up to obtain your raw score, which is then converted to a number on a scale of 100 – 300. The passing score is determined by each state and can be found here: https://www.ets.org/praxis/states.

There will be some questions on the test that are not scored; however you will not know which ones these are. Praxis uses these to test out new questions for future exams.

There is no guess penalty on the Praxis, so you should always guess if you do not know the answer to a question.

How is the Praxis Chemistry (5245) Test Administered?

The Praxis Chemistry Test is a computer-based test offered in pre-determined testing windows at a range of universities and testing centers. Check out https://www.ets.org/praxis/ for more information.

You will need to print your registration ticket from your online account and bring it, along with your identification, to the testing site on test day. You will not need a calculator for the test and will be provided with the periodic table and other information during the test. No pens, pencils, erasers, printed or written materials, electronic devices, or calculators are allowed. You also may not bring any kind of bag or wear headwear (unless for religious purposes). You may take the test once every twenty-one days.

About Cirrus Test Prep

Cirrus Test Prep study guides are designed by current and former educators and are tailored to meet your needs as an incoming educator. Our guides offer all of the resources necessary to help you pass teacher certification tests across the nation.

Cirrus clouds are graceful, wispy clouds characterized by their high altitude. Just like cirrus clouds, Cirrus Test Prep's goal is to help educators "aim high" when it comes to obtaining their teacher certification and entering the classroom.

About This Guide

This guide will help you master the most important test topics and also develop critical test-taking skills. We have built features into our books to prepare you for your tests and increase your score. Along with a detailed summary of the test's format, content, and scoring, we offer an in-depth overview of the content knowledge required to pass the test. Our sidebars provide interesting information, highlight key concepts, and review content so that you can solidify your understanding of the exam's concepts. Test your knowledge with sample questions and detailed answer explanations in the text that help you think through the problems on the exam and practice questions that reflect the content and format of the Praxis Chemistry test. We're pleased you've chosen Cirrus to be a part of your professional journey!

Basic Principles of Matter

Matter is the physical foundation for all the processes in the universe. **Matter**, by definition, is anything that has mass and occupies space. Soil, trees, water, engines, all living beings, and even the air that surrounds us are examples of matter.

The Particulate Structure of Matter

All matter is composed of **atoms**. Atom, in turn, are made up of subatomic particles. **Protons**, which are positive, and **neutrons**, which are negative, form the nucleus of the atom. Negative particles called **electrons** orbit the nucleus.

A neutral atom will have an equal number of protons and electrons. When a neutral atom loses or gains electrons, it gains or loses charge accordingly, forming an **ion**. An ion with more protons than electrons has a positive charge and is called a **cation**. An ion with more electrons than protons has a negative charge and is considered an **anion**.

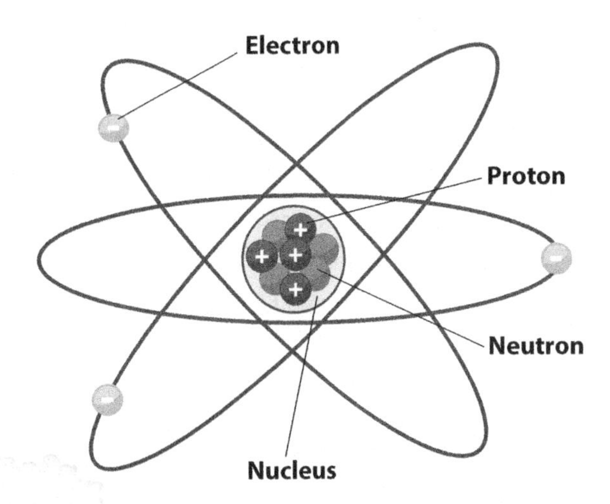

Figure 1.1. Structure of an Atom

For example, the element nitrogen has seven protons and seven electrons (and so has an atomic number of 7 in the periodic table). A neutral nitrogen atom is represented as N. However, if there are seven protons and eight electrons instead, it is called an anion form of nitrogen and has a charge of –1. This nitrogen anion with a charge of –1 is represented as N^-.

All atoms with the same number of protons are the same **element** and cannot be further reduced to a simpler substance by chemical processes. The number of protons in an atom is that atom's **atomic number**. A **molecule** is formed when two or more atoms combine chemically.

SAMPLE QUESTIONS

1) **What is the charge of an atom with five protons and seven electrons?**

A. 12

B. −12

C. 2

D. −2

Answers:

D. **Correct.** There are five protons and seven electrons in the atom. The total charge of an atom is calculated by the difference of the number of protons and electrons. Subtracting the number of electrons from the number of protons results in −2 (total charge of atom = 5 − 7 = −2).

2) **If an atom has seventeen protons and sixteen electrons, it is**

A. a cation.

B. an anion.

C. neutral.

D. a molecule.

Answers:

A. **Correct.** The charge of an atom is found by subtracting the number of electrons from the number of protons. This atom has seventeen protons and sixteen electrons. Since 17 − 16 = +1, a positive number, this atom has a positive charge and is therefore a cation.

B. Incorrect. The atom has a positive charge as it has more protons than electrons. Therefore, it cannot be an anion.

C. Incorrect. The atom has a positive charge; it is not neutral.

D. Incorrect. A molecule is composed of two or more atoms.

States of Matter

Matter can exist in a solid, liquid, gas, or plasma state. The state of a substance is determined by the various properties of the matter, and is largely dependent on the forces holding the atoms or molecules together.

In **solids**, the atoms or molecules are packed close together. The force that holds the particles together is strong, providing very little freedom for movement. Particles in solids have thermal energy associated with them, which leads to the vibration of the particles. However, because the atoms are packed very close to each other, the movement caused by vibration is negligible and does not force the molecules to move apart. As a result, solids are rigid and have a definite shape and volume.

> HELPFUL HINT
>
> Important properties of solids include solubility, conductivity, melting point, and density.

Solids can be categorized as **crystalline solids**, in which the positions of the atoms or molecules are fixed on a lattice, or **amorphous solids**, in which atoms or molecules are randomly arranged. Crystalline solids can further be categorized as either molecular, network, metallic, or ionic solids.

- Molecular solids are composed of discrete molecules held together by weak intermolecular forces.
- Network solids are composed of atoms held together by covalent bonds.
- Ionic solids are composed of cations and anions held together by ionic bonds.
- Metallic solids are composed of metal atoms bound together by metallic bonds.

In a **liquid** state, particles are not tightly bound and take the shape of the container used to keep them. They still have a definite volume and can flow and change shape depending on the shape of the container.

Two special properties of liquids are surface tension and viscosity. **Surface tension** is the force of attraction by the particles at the surface by the bulk of the liquid, which results in minimum surface area. This property is the reason water forms drops that are spherical in shape. **Viscosity** is the internal resistance that inhibits the flow of liquids.

In a **gas** state of matter, the force between the particles is weak (compared to solids and liquids). Due to this weak force of attraction, the gaseous form of matter does not have a defined shape or volume. Instead, a gas will expand to take the shape of the closed container in which it is stored. The properties of gas—such as pressure, volume, and temperature—are interrelated and discussed in greater detail in a later section.

Table 1.1. States of Matter

	Solid	**Liquid**	**Gas**
Volume	Definite volume	Definite volume	Volume of container
Shape	Definite shape	Takes shape of container	Expands to take shape of closed container
Particle Arrangement	Close together	Random but still close	Random and far apart

Table 1.1. States of Matter (continued)

	Solid	Liquid	Gas
Interparticle Interaction	Extremely strong	Strong	Extremely weak
Particle Movement	Extremely slow (vibration)	Moderate	Fast
Example	Ice, wood, iron rod	[illegible]	Water [illegible]

Finally, **plasma** can be defined as ionized gas, where electrons become free from the atoms or molecules, allowing the electrons and positive ions to coexist. Plasma can occur either in partially ionized or fully ionized form.

Plasma is produced by subjecting gases to a strong electromagnetic field. Unlike the solid, liquid, and gas phases, plasma does not exist naturally under normal conditions, but it can be generated artificially from neutral gases. Plasmas can be categorized as artificially produced (plasma display TV screens), terrestrial (lightning, polar winds), and space and astrophysical (sun and stars, solar winds). Plasmas occur in auroras, lightning, and flames.

SAMPLE QUESTION

3) **Which of the following is true of plasma?**

A. It has molecules that are closely packed together.

B. It can only be artificially produced in a laboratory setting.

C. It is an ionized gas.

D. It has fixed volume and shape.

Answers:

A. Incorrect. The molecules of solids are closely packed together.

B. Incorrect. Plasma is produced in natural settings such as stars and lightning.

C. **Correct.** Plasma is an ionized gas.

D. Incorrect. Solids have fixed volume and shape.

Special Properties of Water

In general, particles in a solid are closer to each other than the particles in liquid. However, there is an exception to this rule. In ice, the solid form of water, the molecules are farther apart than the molecules in water's liquid form. Because of this unique property, ice is less dense than water and will float instead of sinking.

Ice has hydrogen bonding among its molecules and an open structure with empty space between the molecules. The structure breaks down as ice melts, and molecules fill up the empty space. As a result, ice takes up more space than the water formed when it melts; this is unlike the behavior of other solids, which increase in volume on melting. Likewise, the hydrogen bonding of the liquid structure expands when water freezes, while most liquids contract on freezing.

The rigid hydrogen bonded structure remains present until 4°C. In the temperature range from 0°C to 4°C, the density of water increases because molecules free themselves and occupy less space. At temperatures above 4°C, the molecules move apart and density falls.

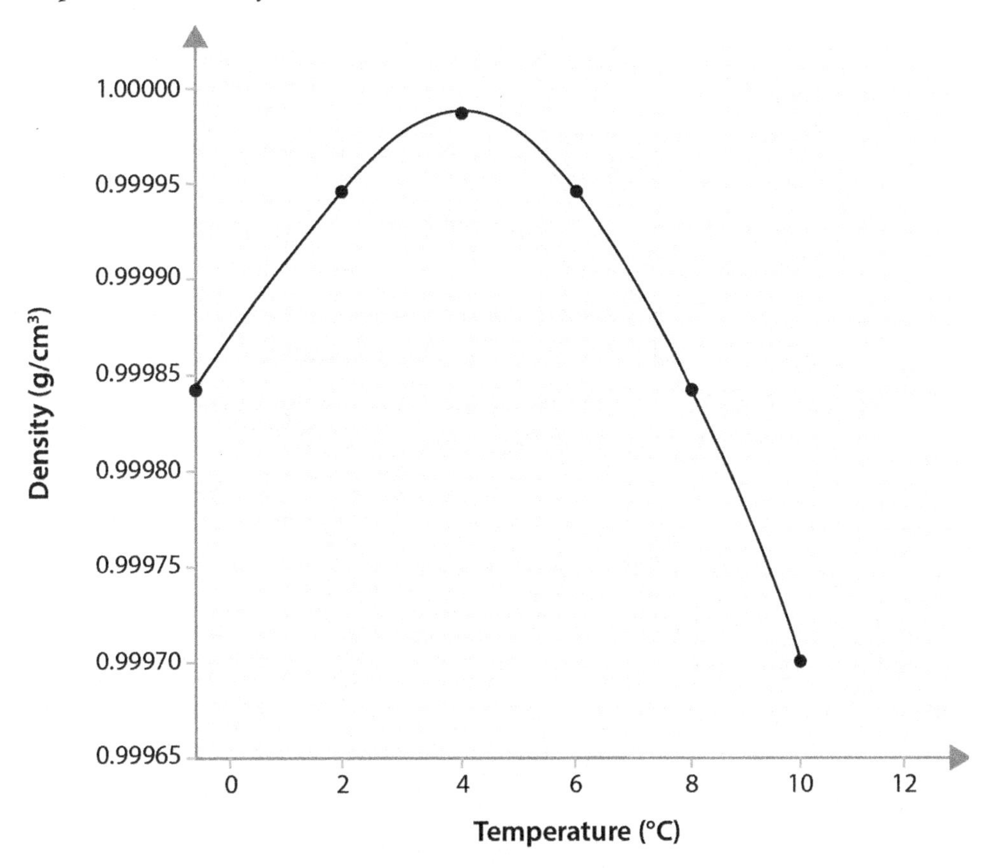

Figure 1.2. Density versus Temperature Plot for Water

Water has a number of other properties that make it unique. It has unusually high boiling and freezing points and a high heat capacity, meaning it takes a great deal of energy to change temperature or state. This property makes it ideal for supporting life in a wide variety of climates, and explains why water exists naturally on Earth in all three states.

In addition, water molecules are **cohesive**, meaning they are attracted to each other, and **adhesive**, meaning they are attracted to other substances. Cohesion is responsible for water's high surface tension, which is caused by the attraction of water molecules on the surface of a liquid. Adhesion is the property behind

capillary action, the process by which water climbs against gravity in narrow spaces such as glass tubes and plant xylem.

SAMPLE QUESTION

4) **Which of the following is true of solid water?**

A. The molecules in solid water are more closely packed together than the molecules in liquid water.

B. Water remains solid at all temperatures below 4°C.

C. The density of solid water is less than the density of liquid water.

D. Molecules of solid water have a large amount of kinetic energy.

Answers:

A. Incorrect. Unlike solids, molecules are not closely packed together in ice.

B. Incorrect. Water is at its most dense at 4°C, but it only freezes to become a solid at 0°C.

C. Correct. This is called the anomalous behavior of water, and because it has less density than water, ice floats on water.

D. Incorrect. Although the molecules are not tightly packed, they do not possess high kinetic energy and are at fixed positions.

Classifying Matter

There are two kinds of matter on the macroscopic scale: pure substances and mixtures. These can further be divided into subcategories: mixtures can be homogeneous or heterogeneous, and pure substances can be elements or compounds.

A **pure substance** has a constant composition with fixed chemical as well as physical properties. A pure substance cannot be broken down further by physical processes. There are two categories of pure substances: elements and compounds.

HELPFUL HINT

All compounds are molecules but not all molecules are compounds.

An **element**, as discussed in the previous section, can be defined as a pure substance composed of one type of atom that cannot be further reduced to a simpler substance by chemical means. A **compound** can be defined as a pure substance composed of two or more elements combined in fixed proportion that can be broken down into simpler matter chemically but not physically.

- examples of elements: lead (Pb), copper (Cu), gold (Au)
- examples of compounds: water (H_2O), salt (NaCl)

A **mixture** is a physical combination of two or more pure substances (elements or compounds) mixed together in any ratio. Different combination ratios of substances (1:2 versus 1:1 versus 1:3) result in a mixture with different properties and compositions. Also, each component involved in the mixture retains its original characteristics. The ease or difficulty of separating the substances in a mixture depends on their properties, such as solubility, particle size, electrical charge, and density. Mixtures can be separated by processes such as filtration, evaporation, chromatography, and distillation.

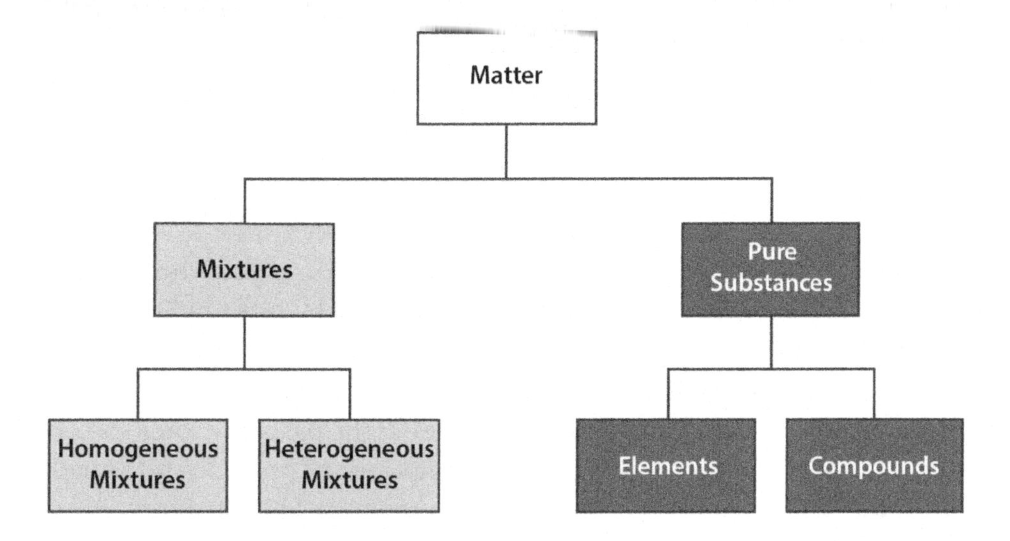

Figure 1.3. Classification of Matter

Some examples of mixtures include:

- alloy mixtures: brass (zinc and copper), cupronickel (copper and nickel)
- food mixtures: tea, lemonade
- other mixtures: air, smog

Mixtures are further classified into homogeneous and heterogeneous mixtures. **Homogeneous mixtures** have the following characteristics:

- uniform composition, that is, uniform properties and appearance throughout
- uniform distribution of different components of the mixture, making it difficult to see them
- can be separated using chromatography and distillation techniques
- can also be called solutions, if they have certain characteristics
- can be solid, liquid, or gas

Examples of homogeneous mixtures include air (a gaseous solution), salt dissolved in water (a liquid solution), and brass (a solid solution).

Heterogeneous mixtures have the following characteristics:

- nonuniform composition, that is, different properties and appearance throughout
- different components of the mixture are separated into regions with different properties, making those different components visible
- substances present in the mixture do not lose their properties
- easy to separate using the physical properties of different parts of the mixture
- can be emulsions (liquid-liquid), suspensions (solid-liquid), or aerosols (solid-gas)

Examples of heterogeneous mixtures include soda (a liquid solution), and oil and vinegar dressing (an emulsion).

A **solution** is a homogeneous mixture with a certain set of properties. It has small particle size and uniform distribution of molecules or ions, which makes it difficult to see different parts of the solution. The solute can pass through the filter paper, which implies the solution cannot be separated by filtration. (For instance, sugar in a water solution—sugar as solute and water as solvent—cannot be separated by filter paper. Nothing will settle on the filter paper; instead the entire solution will pass through.) There is no scattering when light passes through a solution. Also, components present in the solution cannot be separated by filtration or centrifugation, but they can be separated using techniques like distillation.

A **suspension** is a heterogeneous mixture. Unlike a solution, particle size is not very small, and it is easy to see different parts of the suspension as the distribution is nonuniform. Suspensions can be separated by filtration—particles can pass through the filter paper. (For instance, if sand mixed with water is made to pass through filter paper, sand will deposit on the filter paper and not pass through it.) If a suspension can stand for a while, then the particles settle and separate out.

HELPFUL HINT

Two or more substances combined chemically in fixed ratio → compound

Two or more substances combined physically in any ratio → mixture

SAMPLE QUESTION

5) Which of the following statements about classifying matter is true?

A. All pure substances are atoms.

B. All atoms are molecules.

C. All molecules are compounds.

D. All compounds are molecules.

Answers:

A. Incorrect. Pure substances can be atoms or molecules.

B. Incorrect. Atoms make up molecules.

C. Incorrect. O_2 is an example of a molecule that is not a compound.

D. Correct. This is true—all compounds are also molecules.

PHYSICAL AND CHEMICAL PROPERTIES OF MATTER

One of the important ways of classifying matter is based upon its set of physical and chemical properties. A **physical property** of a substance can be measured or observed without changing its composition or changing the chemical nature of the substance. Examples of the physical properties of substances include:

- color
- odor
- density
- hardness
- melting point
- boiling point
- refractive index
- ionization energy
- atomic radius
- ductility
- malleability
- allotropes

Physical properties can help categorize matter in different ways. For example, metals and nonmetals can be grouped based on the physical properties they exhibit. Metals are malleable and ductile, whereas nonmetals do not exhibit these physical properties. However, even though all metals might exhibit a certain set of physical properties, they can be further categorized by other properties such as melting point, density, and so on.

Physical properties can be classified as intensive and extensive properties. **Intensive properties** of a substance are not dependent on the size or mass of the sample and cannot be determined by simply looking at the substance. Intensive properties of a substance do not change unless the substance itself is changed. Examples of intensive properties of a substance include boiling point, melting point, density, temperature, and pressure.

Extensive properties of a substance are dependent on the amount of matter present in each sample. Examples of extensive properties of a substance include mass and volume.

Chemical properties of a substance can only be determined by changes in the chemical identity of the substance. Chemical properties describe how a substance will change when it reacts with other substances. For example, properties like flammability, heat of combustion, enthalpy of formation, toxicity, oxidation states, and so on, are all associated with chemical changes in the substance.

SAMPLE QUESTION

6) **Which of the following describes a physical change?**

A. Water becomes ice.

B. Batter is baked into a cake.

C. A firecracker explodes.

D. Neutralizing an acid with a base.

Answers

A. Correct. When water changes form, it does not change the chemical composition of the substance. Once water becomes ice, the ice can easily turn back into water.

B. Incorrect. During a chemical change, the chemical composition of the substance changes and cannot be reversed. Baking a cake is an example of a chemical change.

C. Incorrect. Setting off fireworks causes a chemical change.

D. Incorrect. Neutralizing an acid with a base is a chemical change.

The Periodic Table

Elements are arranged in the **periodic table** by increasing atomic number. Each block on the table includes an element's atomic number and the one or two letters that represent the element. The table also includes an element's **mass number**, the sum of its protons and neutrons. Atoms of the same element may have different numbers of neutrons, resulting in **isotopes**. Oxygen, for example, has three stable isotopes: oxygen-16, oxygen-17, and oxygen-18 (the attached number is the isotope's mass number). On the periodic table, an element's mass number is a weighted average of the element's most common isotopes.

HELPFUL HINT

The superscript on an element symbol is its mass number, and the subscript is its atomic number. Subtracting the bottom number from the top gives the number of neutrons in the atom.

$^{18}_{8}O$

protons + neutrons = 18

protons = 8

neutrons = 10

The rows of the periodic table are called **periods**, and the vertical columns are called **groups**. Each group contains elements with similar chemical properties, and the groups are labeled 1 – 18 from left to right. Groups IA through VIIIA contain the main group elements, and groups IB through VIIIB contain the **transition elements**, commonly referred to as the *transition metals*.

The majority of the elements in the periodic table are metals. **Metals** have the following properties:

1	2	3	4	5	6	7	8	9	10	11	12	13	14	15	16	17	18
1 H Hydrogen 1.008																	2 He Helium 4.0026
3 Li Lithium 6.941	4 Be Beryllium 9.0122											5 B Boron 10.81	6 C Carbon 12.011	7 N Nitrogen 14.007	8 O Oxygen 15.999	9 F Fluorine 18.998	10 Ne Neon 20.180
11 Na Sodium 22.990	12 Mg Magnesium 24.305											13 Al Aluminum 26.982	14 Si Silicon 28.085	15 P Phosphorus 30.974	16 S Sulfur 32.06	17 Cl Chlorine 35.45	18 Ar Argon 39.948
19 K Potassium 39.098	20 Ca Calcium 40.078	21 Sc Scandium 44.956	22 Ti Titanium 47.867	23 V Vanadium 50.942	24 Cr Chromium 51.996	25 Mn Maganese 54.938	26 Fe Iron 55.845	27 Co Cobalt 58.933	28 Ni Nickel 58.963	29 Cu Copper 63.546	30 Zn Zinc 65.38	31 Ga Gallium 69.723	32 Ge Germanium 72.64	33 As Arsenic 74.922	34 Se Selenium 78.971	35 Br Bromine 79.904	36 Kr Krypton 83.798
37 Rb Rubidium 85.468	38 Sr Strontium 87.62	39 Y Yttrium 88.906	40 Zr Zirconium 91.224	41 Nb Niobium 92.906	42 Mo Molybdenum 254	43 Tc Technetium 98	44 Ru Ruthenium 101.07	45 Rh Rhodium 102.91	46 Pd Palladium 106.42	47 Ag Silver 107.87	48 Cd Cadmium 112.41	49 In Indium 114.82	50 Sn Tin 118.71	51 Sb Antimony 121.75	52 Te Tellurium 127.60	53 I Iodine 126.90	54 Xe Xenon 121.29
55 Cs Caesium 132.91	56 Ba Barium 137.33	57-71	72 Hf Hafnium 178.49	73 Ta Tantalum 183.84	74 W Tungsten 183.84	75 Re Rhenium 186.21	76 Os Osmium 190.23	77 Ir Iridium 192.22	78 Pt Platinum 195.08	79 Au Gold 196.97	80 Hg Mercury 200.59	81 Tl Thallium 204.38	82 Pb Lead 207.2	83 Bi Bismuth 208.98	84 Po Polonium 209	85 At Astatine 210	86 Rn Radon 222
87 Fr Francium 223.020	88 Ra Radium 226	89-103	104 Rf Rutherfordium 267	105 Db Dubnium 268	106 Sg Seaborgium 271	107 Bh Bohrium 272	108 Hs Hassium 277	109 Mt Meitnerium 276	110 Ds Darmstadtium 281	111 Rg Roentgenium 280	112 Cn Copernicium 285	113 Uut Ununtrium Unknown	114 Fl Flerovium 254	115 Uup Ununpentium Unknown	116 Lv Livermorium 291	117 Uus Ununseptium Unknown	118 Uuo Ununoctium Unknown

Lanthanide	57 La Lanthanium 138.905	58 Ce Cerium 140.12	59 Pr Praseodymium 140.91	60 Nd Neodymium 144.24	61 Pm Promethium 144.913	62 Sm Samarium 150.36	63 Eu Europium 151.96	64 Gd Gadolinium 157.25	65 Tb Terbium 158.93	66 Dy Dysprosium 152.50	67 Ho Holmium 154.930	68 Er Erbium 167.259	69 Tm Thulium 168.934	70 Yb Ytterbium 173.065	71 Lu Lutetium 174.967
Actinide	89 Ac Actinium 227.028	90 Th Thorium 232.038	91 Pa Protactinuim 231.036	92 U Uranium 238.029	93 Np Neptunium 237.048	94 Pu Plutonium 244.064	95 Am Americium 243.061	96 Cm Curium 247.070	97 Bk Berkelium 247.070	98 Cf Californium 251.080	99 Es Einsteinium 254	100 Fm Fermium 257.095	101 Md Mendelevium 258.1	102 No Nobelium 259.101	103 Lr Lawrencium 262

Key: Atomic Number / Symbol / Name / Atomic Mass

Alkali Metal | Alkaline Earth Metal | Transition Metal | Basic Metal | Metalloid | Nonmetal | Halogen | Noble Gas | Lanthanide | Actinide

Figure 1.4. The Periodic Table

- They are ductile and malleable.
- They conduct electricity.
- They can form alloys.
- They are thermally conductive.
- They are hard, opaque, and shiny.
- With the exception of mercury, they are solids.

Solid metals usually consist of tightly packed atoms, resulting in fairly high densities. Metals begin on the left side of the periodic table and span across the middle of the table, almost all the way to the right side. Examples of metals include gold (Au), tin (Sn), and lead (Pb).

Nonmetals are elements that do not conduct electricity and tend to be more volatile than metals. They can be solids, liquids, or gases. The nonmetals are located on the right side of the periodic table. Examples of nonmetals include sulfur (S), hydrogen (H), and oxygen (O).

Metalloids, or semimetals, are elements that possess both metal and nonmetal characteristics. For example, some metalloids are shiny but do not conduct electricity well. Many metalloids are semiconductors. Metalloids are located between the metals and nonmetals on the periodic table. Some examples of metalloids are boron (B), silicon (Si), and arsenic (As).

The groups are discussed in more detail in Chapter 3.

SAMPLE QUESTIONS

7) **Which of the following is the correct symbol for the isotope of boron that contains 6 neutrons?**

A. $^{5}_{6}B$

B. $^{11}_{5}B$

C. $^{11}_{6}B$

D. $^{6}_{0}B$

Answer:

B. Correct. The periodic table shows that boron has 5 protons, giving it an atomic number of 5. With 6 neutrons, it will then have a mass number of 6 + 5 = 11. The atomic number (5) is written as the subscript, and the mass number (11) is written as the superscript.

8) **Bismuth is a**

A. metal.

B. nonmetal.

C. metalloid.

D. transition element.

Answer:

A. **Correct.** Bismuth is a metal.

GASES

KINETIC MOLECULAR THEORY

The **kinetic molecular theory** of gases is used to describe the macroscopic properties of a gas (such as pressure and temperature) based on the behavior of its microscopic components (i.e., atoms). This theory explains why the temperature, pressure, volume, and number of moles of gas are all related, and can be used to predict the behavior of gases.

The kinetic molecular theory describes the behavior of an **ideal gas**, which is a theoretical model of a gas with the following assumptions:

- The gas particles exert no attractive forces on each other or the surroundings; that is, gas particles do not attract or repel each other.
- Compared to the volume of the container, the volume occupied by individual particles is negligible.
- Molecules of a gas are in a constant state of random motion, and they travel in a straight line until they collide.
- Molecules only interact in collisions, and these collisions do not change the average kinetic energy of the molecules.
- The average kinetic energy of molecules of gas is directly proportional to absolute temperature, meaning all gases have the same average kinetic energy at the same temperature.

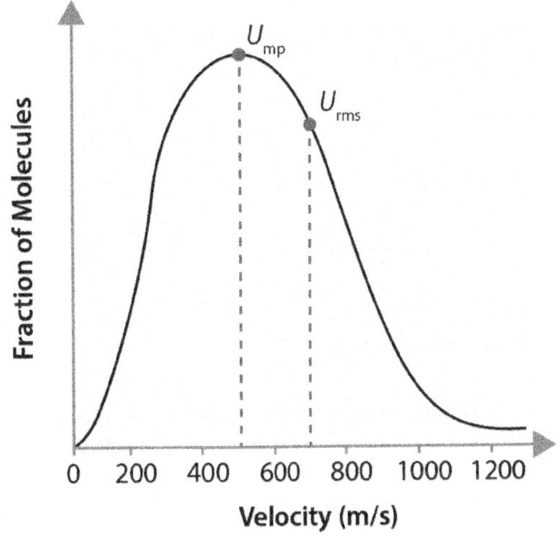

Figure 1.5. Molecular Speed Distribution

Although the molecules in a gas have a constant average kinetic energy, each molecule moves at a different (and changing) speed. The speed of molecules in a gas is shown on a molecular speed distribution curve. The peak of the curve shows the most probable speed of the molecules (u_{mp}). The curve will also show the **root-mean-square speed** (u_{rms}), which is the speed of a molecule with the same kinetic energy as the entire sample's average kinetic energy. The shape of the curve depends on the substance and the sample's temperature.

SAMPLE QUESTION

9) **Kinetic molecular theory includes all of the following assumptions EXCEPT**

A. Gas molecules neither attract nor repel each other.

B. All molecules in a gas move with a uniform velocity.

C. The kinetic energy of gas molecules is proportional to temperature.

D. Gas molecules occupy a negligible amount of space in their container.

Answer:

B. Correct. The molecules in a gas do not all have the same velocity. The speed of individual particles varies and is clustered around the speed that corresponds to the molecules' average kinetic energy.

Gas Laws

The kinetic molecular theory can be used to explain many properties of gases, including the relationship between pressure, temperature, volume, and amount of a substance. These relationships are described in the gas laws.

HELPFUL HINT

The gas laws describe the behavior of all gases, regardless of their chemical composition.

Kinetic molecular theory assumes that average kinetic energy of gas particles is dependent on the temperature of the gas. At constant volume, an increase in the temperature leads to more forceful and frequent collisions between the molecules, and thus creates a higher pressure. This relationship is described in **Amonton's law**:

$$\frac{P_1}{T_1} = \frac{P_2}{T_2}$$

where P_1 is initial pressure, P_2 is final pressure, T_1 is initial temperature, and T_2 is final temperature.

When temperature is increased and pressure is held constant, the volume of the gas will expand. The extra space will prevent the number of collisions between molecules from increasing due to their higher average kinetic energy. This relationship is described in **Charles's law:**

$$\frac{V_1}{T_1} = \frac{V_2}{T_2}$$

where V_1 is initial volume, V_2 is final volume, T_1 is initial temperature, and T_2 is final temperature.

When the volume of the gas is decreased without changing the temperature, the particles of the gas are compressed, resulting in more collisions among the gas particles. This, in turn, increases the pressure of the gas. This relationship is described in **Boyle's law**:

$$P_1V_1 = P_2V_2$$

where V_1 is initial volume, V_2 is final volume, P_1 is initial pressure, and P_2 is final pressure.

Avogadro's law is derived from the observation that equal volumes of gases at the same temperature and pressure will have the same number of molecules. Accordingly, increasing the number of moles of a gas will increase its volume:

$$V = kn$$

where V is volume, k is a constant, and n is the number of moles.

HELPFUL HINT

1 atmosphere = 101,325 Pa

1 bar = 100 kPa = 100,000 Pa

Dalton's law of partial pressures states that the total pressure of the gas mixture is equal to the sum of the partial pressures of the individual gases. Dalton's law can be written as:

$$P_t = P_1 + P_2 + P_3 + ...$$

where P_t is the total pressure and P_n is the partial pressure of each gas.

Combining Amonton's, Charles's, Boyle's, and Avogadro's laws gives the **ideal gas law**:

$$PV = nRT$$

where P is pressure, V is volume, T is temperature, R is the gas constant, and n is the number of moles.

The variables in the ideal gas law can be expressed in different combinations of units, and the value of R will depend on the units used in the equation (as shown in Table 1.2).

Table 1.2 The Gas Constant

Value of R	Units
8.314	$\frac{J}{K \cdot mol}$
	$\frac{m^3 \cdot Pa}{K \cdot mol}$
	$\frac{L\,kPa}{K^{-1} \cdot mol^{-1}}$
	$\frac{cm^3\,MPa}{K^{-1} \cdot mol^{-1}}$
	$\frac{cm^3\,bar}{K^{-1} \cdot mol^{-1}}$
8.314×10^{-6}	$\frac{m^3\,MPa}{K^{-1} \cdot mol^{-1}}$
8.314×10^{-5}	$\frac{m^3\,bar}{K^{-1} \cdot mol^{-1}}$
8.314×10^{-2}	$\frac{L\,bar}{K^{-1} \cdot mol^{-1}}$
83.14	$\frac{cm^3\,bar}{K^{-1} \cdot mol^{-1}}$

Table 1.2 The Gas Constant (continued)

Value of R	Units
8.314×10^3	$\frac{cm^3\,kPa}{K^{-1} \cdot mol^{-1}}$
8.314×10^6	$\frac{cm^3\,Pa}{K^{-1} \cdot mol^{-1}}$
1.987×10^{-3}	$\frac{kcal}{K^{-1} \cdot mol^{-1}}$
8.206×10^{-5}	$\frac{m^3\,atm}{K^{-1} \cdot mol^{-1}}$
8.206×10^{-2}	$\frac{L\,atm}{K^{-1} \cdot mol^{-1}}$
82.06	$\frac{cm^3\,atm}{K^{-1} \cdot mol^{-1}}$

SAMPLE QUESTIONS

10) What is the final volume of a sample of gas with an initial volume of 4 L and an initial temperature of 28°C if the temperature is raised to 305.15 K?

Answer:

$V_1 = 4\text{ L}$	Define the initial volume of the system.
$T_1 = 28°\text{C} = 28 + 273 = 301\text{ K}$	Define the initial temperature.
$T_2 = 32°\text{C} = 32 + 273 = 305\text{ K}$	Define the final temperature.
$\frac{V_1}{T_1} = \frac{V_2}{T_2}$ $V_2 = \frac{V_1 T_2}{T_1}$ $= \frac{(4\text{ L})(305\text{ K})}{301\text{ K}}$ $= \mathbf{4.05\text{ L}}$	The final volume can be calculated using Charles's law.

11) What is the volume of 3 moles of O_2 at 25°C if it has a pressure of 1 atm?

Answer:

Use the ideal gas law.

$$PV = nRT$$

$$P = \frac{nRT}{V}$$

$$= \frac{(3\text{ mol})(8.206 \times 10^{-5}\text{ L atm K}^{-1}\text{ mol}^{-1})(605.15\text{ K})}{4\text{ L}} = \mathbf{0.37\text{ m}^3}$$

Atomic and Nuclear Structure

The Evolution of the Atomic Model

Understanding of the atom has developed and improved over the course of many centuries. With each new discovery about the structure of the atom, a new atomic model was developed. That model, in turn, was tested and improved upon. The current model of atomic structure incorporates many of the features of previous models.

The first model of the atom was based on philosophical ideas that can be traced to ancient Greek and Indian cultures. The Indian sage Acharya Kanada (b. 600 BCE) first postulated the idea of a particle that was indivisible, and referred to it as a *parmanu* or *anu*. Democritus (460 – 370 BCE) theorized that objects can be divided into smaller pieces until a point is reached where the object cannot be divided any further. This led to his conclusion that all matter is made up of particles that cannot be broken apart; these particles are called **atoms**, derived from the Greek word *atomos*, meaning indivisible. Democritus had no experimental evidence to support his claims, but scientists have worked since then to better understand the structure of matter and the atom.

Table 2.1. Evolution of the Atomic Model

Model	Shape	Description
John Dalton 1803		Stated that atoms are indivisible, atoms belonging to same element are identical, and atoms combine in whole number ratios to form compounds.

Table 2.1. Evolution of the Atomic Model (continued)

Model	Shape	Description
J.J. Thomson 1904		Confirmed the existence of electrons with the cathode ray experiment.
Ernest Rutherford 1911		Showed that the atom includes a positively charged core at the center—the nucleus—with the gold foil experiment.
Niels Bohr (also called the Rutherford-Bohr model) 1913	M K L	Proposed that electrons orbit the nucleus in specific energy levels.
Erwin Schrödinger (Quantum Mechanical Model) 1926		Showed that electrons move in orbitals and not in defined paths.

Dalton's Model of the Atom

John Dalton's (1766 – 1844) atomic model expanded on Democritus's idea that the atom is indivisible. According to his model, atoms belonging to the same element have the same mass, whereas atoms of different elements have different masses. The main postulates of Dalton's atomic theory are:

- All matter is made up of indivisible, minute particles called atoms.
- Atoms belonging to a single element are identical and have the same size and mass; atoms belonging to different elements have different sizes, masses, and properties.
- When atoms belonging to different elements combine in whole number ratios, compounds are formed. The types of atoms in a given compound are always the same.
- Atoms are neither created nor destroyed in a chemical reaction; they are only reorganized. Additionally, atoms of one element cannot be changed into atoms of another element.

Dalton's theory addressed several important laws that had previously been established. His theory explained the law of conservation of mass (that matter cannot be created or destroyed) and the law of definite proportions (that the relative numbers of different kinds of atoms is constant in a compound). Despite this success, Dalton's model had a number of problems:

- The theory did not explain why atoms belonging to different elements had different sizes and masses.
- The theory did not explain what types of forces hold the atoms together.
- The theory did not explain how atoms belonging to different elements combined to form compounds.
- The theory did not explain the law of gaseous volume, which states that the ratio between the volumes of reactant gases and the gaseous products in a reaction can be expressed in simple whole numbers.

SAMPLE QUESTION

1) **Which of the following was NOT explained by Dalton's model of the atom?**

A. the law of conservation of mass
B. the law of definite proportions
C. the law of multiple proportions
D. the law of gaseous volume

Answers:

A. Incorrect. Dalton's theory proposed that atoms are neither created nor destroyed during reactions, but instead are reorganized.

B. Incorrect. Dalton's theory proposed that atoms of different elements combine in whole number ratios to create compounds.

C. Incorrect. Dalton's theory explained the law of multiple proportions, which applies the law of definite proportions to different compounds composed of the same elements.

D. Correct. Dalton's law did not explain the law of gaseous volume, which states that the ratio between the volumes of reactant gases and the gaseous products in a reaction can be expressed in simple whole numbers. His theory only addressed the ratio of elements in a compound.

THOMSON'S MODEL OF THE ATOM

In 1897, J.J. Thomson (1856 – 1940) discovered the existence of electrons while examining the properties of **cathode rays**, which are produced when a high voltage is applied to electrodes in a vacuum tube. Thomson found that these particles could be deflected by a negatively charged plate, and thus were negatively charged. He also found that changing the material of the cathode did not change the properties of the resulting cathode ray. He proposed that cathode rays were composed of a stream of negatively charged particles that became known as electrons. Further experimentation by Thomson determined an electron's charge-to-mass ratio to be 1.76×10^8 coulombs per gram.

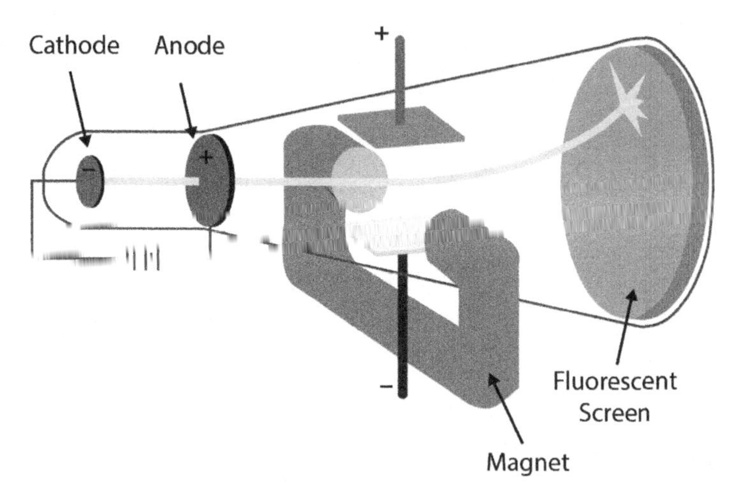

Figure 2.1. Cathode Ray Experiment

Thomson incorporated the electron into a new model of the atom. He proposed that the atom had a spherical shape with a uniformly distributed positive charge. The electrons, which made up only a small portion of the atom's mass, were uniformly embedded in the positive mass. This would provide a stable arrangement in which the negative charges canceled out the positive charges. This model is also called the **plum pudding model**.

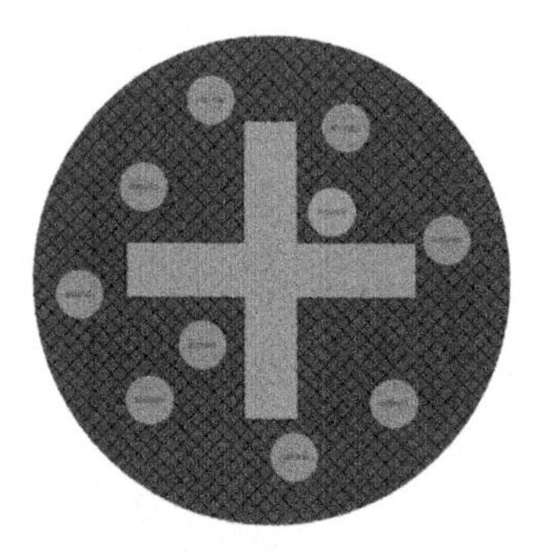

Figure 2.2. Plum Pudding Model

SAMPLE QUESTION

2) Which of the following statements about J.J. Thomson's cathode ray experiment is NOT true?

A. Cathode rays were negatively charged.

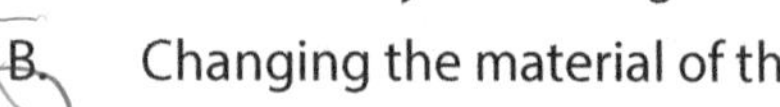

B. Changing the material of the cathode changed the properties of the resulting cathode ray.

C. Cathode rays are produced by applying a high voltage to electrodes in a vacuum.

D. The particles in the cathode ray could be deflected by a negatively charged plate.

Answers:

A. Incorrect. Cathode rays, composed of electrons, are negatively charged.

B. Correct. Changing the material of the cathode did not change the properties of the resulting cathode ray.

C. Incorrect. Cathode rays are produced by applying a high voltage to electrodes in a vacuum.

D. Incorrect. The negatively charged particles were deflected by a negatively charged plate.

RUTHERFORD'S MODEL OF THE ATOM

Ernest Rutherford (1871 – 1937) built on Thomson's model of the atom by introducing the concept of the nucleus. During his gold foil experiment, he observed that positively charged alpha particles fired through gold foil did not always follow a straight path, as they would have if Thomson's model was accurate. Instead, a small number of particles were deflected at large angles, including back in the direction they were originally traveling. If Thomson's model had been accurate, all the alpha particles would have passed straight through the foil because the charge of that atom was balanced throughout. As Rutherford described in his experiment, "It was almost as incredible as if you fired a 15-inch shell at a piece of tissue paper and it came back and hit you." This suggested there was a very dense region in the atom.

HELPFUL HINT

Rutherford used different types of foils like lead, aluminum, and iron; however, his experiment with gold foil is most widely discussed.

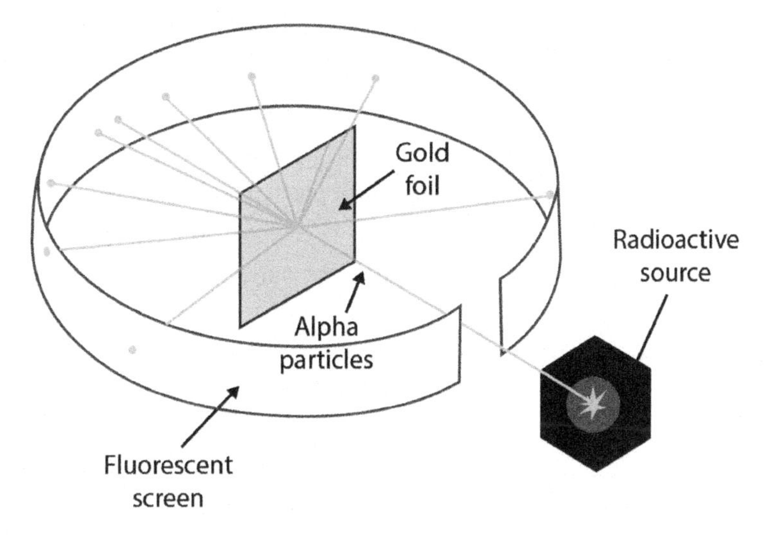

Figure 2.3. Gold Foil Experiment

From this experiment, Rutherford concluded that an atom is not just empty space with electrons distributed inside it. Instead, an atom has a positively charged nucleus that contains most of its mass. Because so few alpha particles bounced back, he also concluded that the positively charged nucleus of the atom was tiny compared to the size of the entire atom.

Rutherford's atomic model includes the following:

- An atom consists of a nucleus, which is a densely concentrated mass that exists in an extremely small region and has a positive charge.
- Electrons surround and move around the nucleus at high speed, in circular paths called orbits.
- Strong electrostatic forces hold the nucleus and electrons together.

There were limitations to Rutherford's model. According to the laws of physics, when a body moves in an orbit at constant speed, it is accelerating. An electron accelerating in an orbit would constantly emit radiation (Maxwell's electromagnetic theory) and hence would lose energy and eventually collide with the nucleus. It would take just 10^{-8} seconds for electrons to collapse into the nucleus. Because this does not happen, the stability of the atom described by Rutherford's model was questioned. Rutherford's model also does not explain the arrangement of electrons around the nucleus and the energies associated with them.

HELPFUL HINT

The radius of an atom is 10^{-10} m, and the radius of its nucleus is just 10^{-15} m.

SAMPLE QUESTION

3) **Which of the following statements about Ernest Rutherford's gold foil experiment is NOT true?**

A. The alpha particles shot at the gold foil did not always follow a straight path.

B. A few alpha particles were deflected at large angles, including straight back.

C. The alpha particles took a straight path but were occasionally deflected.

D. The alpha particles took a parabolic path.

Answers:

A. Incorrect. Some of the particles were deflected or even directed back in the direction they were originally traveling.

B. Incorrect. Some of the particles were deflected or even directed back in the direction they were originally traveling.

C. Incorrect. Most of the particles took a straight path but some were occasionally deflected.

D. Correct. None of the alpha particles took a parabolic path.

BOHR'S MODEL OF THE ATOM

Niels Bohr (1885 – 1962) addressed the problem of stability in Rutherford's model by proposing that electrons did not simply orbit the nucleus in circular paths. Instead, electrons could only exist in certain orbits that have a specific energy state; electrons in that state would not lose energy, and thus would not collide with the nucleus.

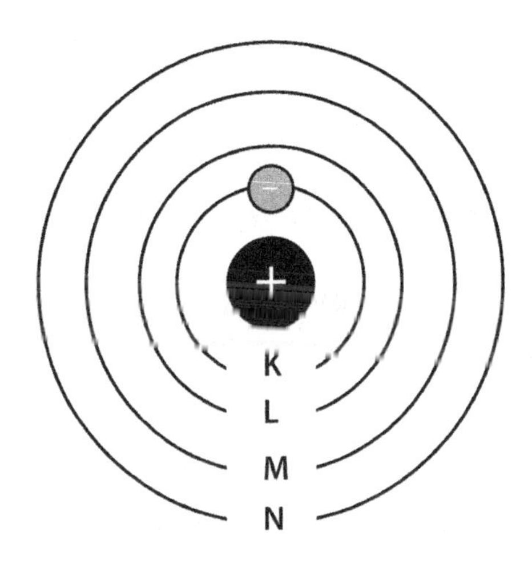

Figure 2.4. The Bohr Model of the Atom

Bohr based his model on his observations of the **line spectrum** of hydrogen. When a high voltage is applied to a gas, it emits a characteristic color, which can then be broken down into a spectrum showing its component wavelengths. Hydrogen has a simple line spectrum that includes only four wavelengths of visible light. Bohr proposed that hydrogen's line spectrum resulted from the emission of discrete amounts of energy that were released when electrons moved from a high to a low energy orbit.

According to the Bohr model, electrons must gain or lose energy in specific amounts (or quanta) called **photons** in order to move between orbits. The energy of a photon is given by the equation $E = h\nu$ where h = Planck's proportionality constant (6.626×10^{-34} joule-sec.) and v is the frequency of the radiation. Electrons in the lowest energy orbit are in their **ground state**. When they absorb a photon, they are **excited** and "jump" to a higher energy orbit. Conversely, when electrons "fall" to a lower energy orbit, they release a photon and emit electromagnetic radiation at a wavelength inversely proportional to the energy released.

> HELPFUL HINT
>
> Electromagnetic radiation absorbs and releases energy in small "packets" called **quanta**. Thus, a change in energy is not continuous (like a ramp), but instead occurs in discrete bursts (like stairs).

Bohr's model was able to explain the stability of the atom that Rutherford's model could not. However, just like other models of the atom, Bohr's model had some limitations:

- The model was based on experiments with the hydrogen atom and did not explain the behavior of atoms with more than one electron.
- The model did not explain why electrons did not simply fall into the nucleus.
- The model was two dimensional and suggested that electrons move in defined circular paths, which later models would show was not accurate.

SAMPLE QUESTION

4) Which of the following questions did Bohr's model of the atom NOT answer?

A. Why do electrons not fall into the nucleus?

B. Why does hydrogen have a distinctive line spectrum?

C. Why do electrons emit energy with discrete wavelengths when going from a higher energy level to a lower energy level?

D. Why do different elements produce different line spectra?

Answers:

A. **Correct.** The model did not explain what prevented the electrons from falling into the nucleus.

B. Incorrect. Bohr proposed that electrons in a hydrogen atom "falling" to a lower energy level emit electromagnetic radiation with a discrete wavelength that is dependent on the spacing of energy levels in hydrogen. These wavelengths are responsible for hydrogen's line spectrum.

C. Incorrect. Bohr proposed that electrons release discrete packets of energy called photons that have a discrete wavelength inversely proportional to the energy they release.

D. Incorrect. In Bohr's model, each element has a unique spacing of energy levels, resulting in emission spectra that can be likened to a fingerprint since a characteristic emission spectrum is obtained for each type of element.

The Quantum Mechanical Model of the Atom

Probability Densities and Orbitals

The discovery that matter can act like a wave led to the next step in the development of the atomic model. According to Werner Heisenberg's (1901 – 1976) **uncertainty principle**, the wave-like nature of electrons means that it is impossible to know both an electron's momentum (i.e., its velocity) and its position at the same time. While its momentum may be known with greater accuracy, it is at the expense of its location and vice versa. Thus, it is only possible to find the *probability* that an electron will be found in a specific position, not its exact location.

HELPFUL HINT

The uncertainly principle applies to all matter. However, the magnitude of the uncertainty is inconsequential compared to the size of everyday objects, which is why their momentum and location can be found using the equations in Newtonian mechanics.

The probability that an electron will be in a given location is found using Erwin Schrödinger's (1887 – 1961) **wave functions**, which are denoted with the

Greek letter psi, Ψ, (the functions themselves are complex and will not be covered here). The value Ψ^2, called the **probability** or **electron density**, represents the probability that an electron will be found at any given location. The collection of wave functions for an atom yields a set of **orbitals**, which are the areas around the nucleus where an electron is most likely to be found.

This quantum mechanical model of the atom corrected the Bohr model by explaining that electrons do not orbit the nucleus. Instead of following a set circular trajectory, electrons exist in "clouds" around the nucleus

SAMPLE QUESTION

5) **According to the uncertainty principle, what properties of an electron can never be known at the same time?**

A. momentum and velocity
B. velocity and position
C. momentum and wavelength
D. wavelength and velocity

Answers:

A. Incorrect. Because the mass of an electron is known, it is possible to calculate its velocity from its momentum ($p = mv$).

B. Correct. Because the magnitude of the uncertainty is large compared to the size of an electron, it is only possible to know either the momentum (which gives velocity) or position of an electron, not both.

C. Incorrect. The uncertainly principle does not address an electron's wavelength, which can be found using the DeBroglie equation.

D. Incorrect. The uncertainly principle does not address an electron's wavelength, which can be found using the DeBroglie equation.

QUANTUM NUMBERS

Schrödinger's wave functions result in three quantum numbers that describe the position and shape of an orbital. Another quantum number is used to describe the rotation of an electron around its axis, resulting in four total quantum numbers for each electron in an atom:

- n: principal quantum number
- l: azimuthal or orbital angular momentum quantum number
- m_l: magnetic quantum number
- m_s: spin magnetic quantum number

The **principal quantum number** (n) describes the energy level of an orbital. It has positive integer values (1, 2, 3, ...), with increasing numbers that denote an increase in the orbital's energy. Larger numbers also describe larger orbitals in which electrons spend more time farther away from the nucleus. All the orbitals with the same principal quantum number are called a **shell.**

The secondary quantum number, called the **azimuthal quantum number** (*l*), gives the shape of the orbital. It can have values from zero to (n – 1), but each numerical value is usually described using letters as shown in Table 2.2. As with the principal quantum number, the energy of orbitals increases as the secondary quantum number increases. All of the orbitals that share a primary and secondary quantum number (n and l) are called **subshells.**

Table 2.2. Secondary Quantum Number Notation	
Azimuthal Quantum Number	**Letter Notation**
0	*s*
1	*p*
2	*d*
3	*f*
4	*g*

The **magnetic quantum number** (m_l) describes the orientation of the orbitals around the nucleus. Its value ranges from $-l$ to $+l$ (including zero). The relationship between the first three quantum numbers is shown in Table 2.3.

Table 2.3. The First Three Quantum Numbers

Principal quantum number, *n* *shell*	**Azimuthal quantum number, *l*** *subshell*		**Magnetic quantum number, m_l** *orientation*	**Number of orbitals in subshell**	**Number of orbitals in shell**
1	0	1*s*	0	1	1
2	0	2*s*	0	1	4
	1	2*p*	–1, 0, 1	3	
3	0	3*s*	0	1	9
	1	3*p*	–1, 0, 1	3	
	2	3*d*	–2, –1, 0, 1, 2	5	
4	0	4*s*	0	1	16
	1	4*p*	–1, 0, 1	3	
	2	4*d*	–2, –1, 0, 1, 2	5	
	3	4*f*	–3, –2, –1, 0, 1, 2, 3	7	

Each electron in an atom rotates on its axis, producing the final quantum number—the **spin magnetic quantum number** (m_s). Electrons can **spin** in one of two opposite directions, yielding two possible values for m_s: $+\frac{1}{2}$ and $-\frac{1}{2}$.

For atoms containing more than one electron, the energy of an orbital depends on both its principal and azimuthal quantum numbers (n and l). Because inner electrons **screen**, or shield, outer electrons from the attraction of the nucleus, orbitals within a shell do not all have the same energy. The energy of orbitals in a shell increases with l: $s < p < d < f$. The energy of the $2p$ orbital, for example, is greater than the energy of the $2s$ orbital. In other words, an s-orbital electron is more tightly bound to the nucleus than a p-orbital electron. As discussed above, each orbital within a subshell is **degenerate**, meaning it has the same energy.

HELPFUL HINT

In a hydrogen atom, which has only one electron, the energy level of an orbital depends only on its principal quantum number, n:
$1s < 2s = 2p < 3s = 3p = 3d < 4s = 4p = 4d = 4f$

SAMPLE QUESTION

6) **Which set of the following quantum numbers is correct?**

A. $n = 4, l = 3, m_l = 3, m_s = +\frac{1}{2}$

B. $n = 1, l = 1, m_l = 1, m_s = +\frac{1}{2}$

C. $n = 3, l = 1, m_l = 2, m_s = -\frac{1}{2}$

D. $n = 2, l = 1, m_l = 1, m_s = 0$

Answer:

A. $n = 4, l = 3, m_l = 3, m_s = +\frac{1}{2}$

B. l must be at least one less than n

C. m_l ranges from $+l$ to $-l$

D. m_s must be $+\frac{1}{2}$ or $-\frac{1}{2}$

ORBITAL SHAPES

The shape of orbitals is determined using electron densities, which use the wave function to show the likelihood that an electron will be found in a specific position. The dots on the electron density distribution represent the probability of finding an electron in that region. To approximate the shape of the orbital, **boundary surface diagrams** are drawn to enclose a certain percentage of the probability density.

HELPFUL HINT

All orbitals except the s-orbital have an electron density of zero at the nucleus. An area where the electron density is zero is called a node.

The shape of the **s-orbital** is a sphere, implying that the probability of finding an electron at a certain distance in all directions is equal. It has $n - 1$ nodes where n is the principal quantum number. As the value of n increases, the size of the s-orbital increases.

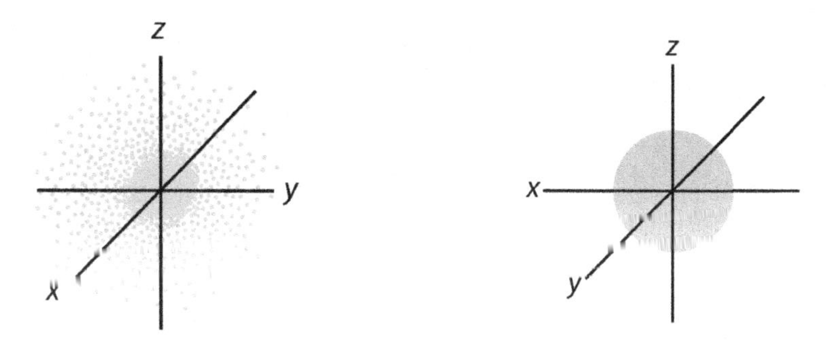

Figure 2.5. Electron-Density Distribution

Figure 2.6. *s*-orbital

Each ***p*-orbital** has two lobes with a radial node at the nucleus (represented as the origin on the diagrams below). Each shell has three p-orbitals (for the magnetic quantum numbers –1, 0, 1) that have the same shape, energy, and size. It has $n - 1$ total nodes ($n - 2$ radial and 1 angular). The only difference between the orbitals is their orientation, and the orbitals are named by the axis with which they align: $2p_x$, $2p_y$, and $2p_z$. As with the s-orbital, the energy and size of these orbitals increase with increasing values of n.

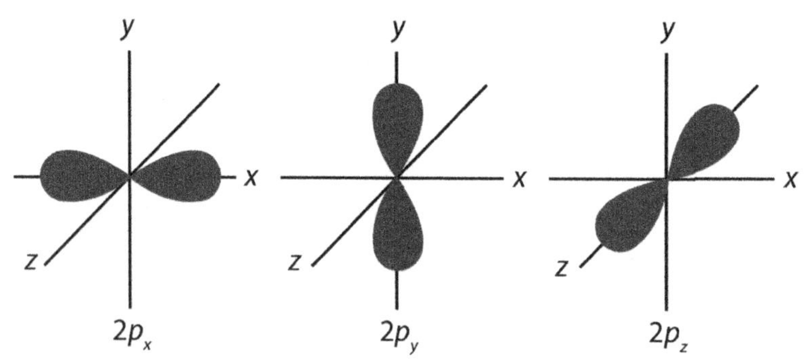

Figure 2.7. *p*-orbital

The five ***d*-orbitals** (for the magnetic quantum numbers –2, –1, 0, 1, 2) have two different shapes. Four of the orbitals have four lobes that meet at the nucleus. The fifth orbital has two lobes surrounded by a donut shape at the nucleus. The orbitals are written as d_{xy}, d_{yz}, d_{xz}, $d_{x2 - y2}$, and d_{z2}. As with the other shells, the orbital's energy and size increase with each increase in n. It has a total of $n - 1$ nodes ($n - 3$ radial and 2 angular).

The shape of the seven ***f*-orbitals** is too complex to be covered here, but each orbital has a different number and orientation of lobes and donuts. Like the d-orbitals, the f-orbitals in a shell have the same energy and size, both of which increase with each increase in n.

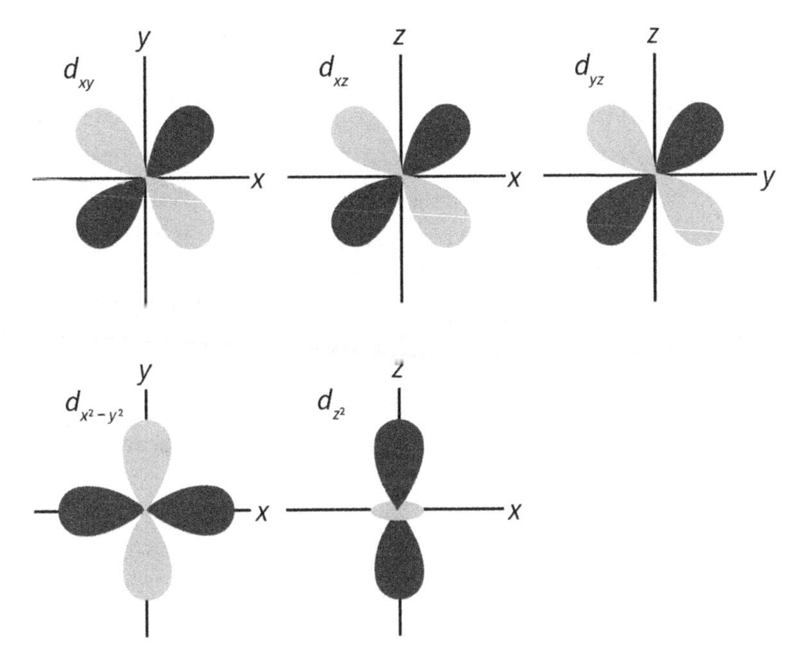

Figure 2.8. *d*-orbital

SAMPLE QUESTION

7) **How many nodes does a 2*p* orbital have?**

A. 0
B. 1
C. 2
D. 3

Answer:

B. Correct. The total number of nodes for *p*-orbitals is one less than its principal quantum number *n*.

ELECTRON CONFIGURATION

Electron configuration describes the way in which electrons in an atom are arranged in orbitals. It is written in the form nl^x, where n is the principal quantum number, l is the azimuthal quantum number, and x is the number of electrons in the orbital. The electron configuration for hydrogen, for example, is written as $1s^1$ because its one electron occupies the $1s$ orbital.

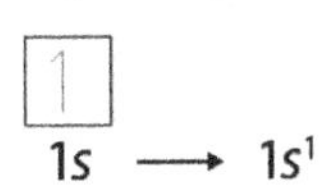

Figure 2.9. Orbital Diagram and Electron Configuration for Hydrogen

An atom's electron configuration can be shown visually using an **orbital diagram**, which includes a box for each orbital and half-arrows representing electrons. The arrows point up or down to indicate spin.

The **Pauli exclusion principle** states that no electrons in an atom may have the same four quantum numbers. In practice, this means that orbitals can hold a maximum of two electrons, and that those two electrons will have opposite spins. Thus, an *s*-shell will hold only 2 electrons. A *p*-shell, which has three orbitals, will hold 6 electrons, the *d*-shell will hold 10, and the *f*-shell will hold 14.

Table 2.4. Electron Configuration and Orbital Diagrams for the Four Subshells

Subshell	Electron Configuration When Full	Orbital Diagram When Full
s	ns^2	[↑↓]
d	nd^6	[↑↓] [↑↓] [↑↓]
p	np^{10}	[↑↓] [↑↓] [↑↓] [↑↓] [↑↓]
f	nf^{14}	[↑↓] [↑↓] [↑↓] [↑↓] [↑↓] [↑↓] [↑↓]

According to the **aufbau principle**, electrons fill the orbital with the lowest available energy. Because of screening, however, the energy of orbitals does not simply increase with each shell. Instead, orbitals increase in energy as shown in Figure 2.10. All degenerate orbitals within a subshell must be filled before electrons will begin to fill the next orbital.

Hund's rule of maximum multiplicity states that when orbitals of equal energy (i.e., degenerate orbitals), are available, electrons first occupy all the orbitals singly before pairing up. Electrons repel each other if they are present in the same subshell with parallel spin, so the repulsion has to be minimized by placing electrons as far apart as possible.

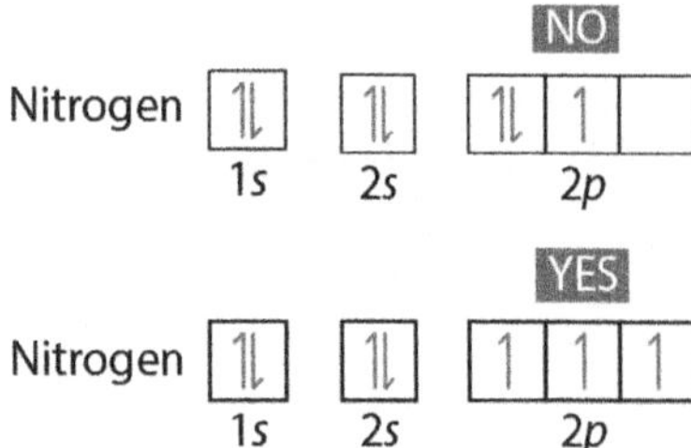

Figure 2.11. Hund's Rule

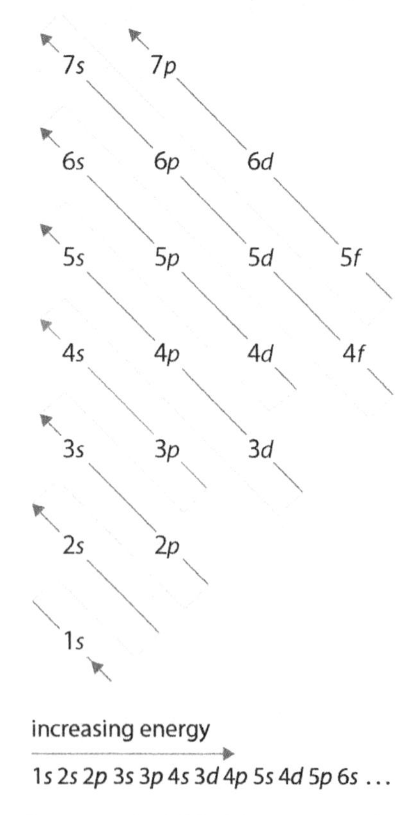

Figure 2.10. Orbital Energy Levels

Using these rules, it is possible to find electron configurations for all the elements. Consider a sulfur atom, which has sixteen electrons. Starting with 1*s*, electrons fill orbitals following the pattern shown in Figure 2.10: $1s^2\ 2s^2\ 2p^6\ 3s^2$. In the last subshell, 3*p*, two orbitals contain only one electron each (both with the same spin), in accordance with Hund's rule.

> **HELPFUL HINT**
>
> In a condensed electron configuration, core electrons are replaced with a corresponding noble gas to shorten the notation.
>
> Tin: $[1s^2 2s^2 2p^6 3s^2 3p^6 4s^2 3d^{10} 4p^6] 5s^2 4d^{10} 5p^2 \rightarrow [Kr] 5s^2 4d^{10} 5p^2$

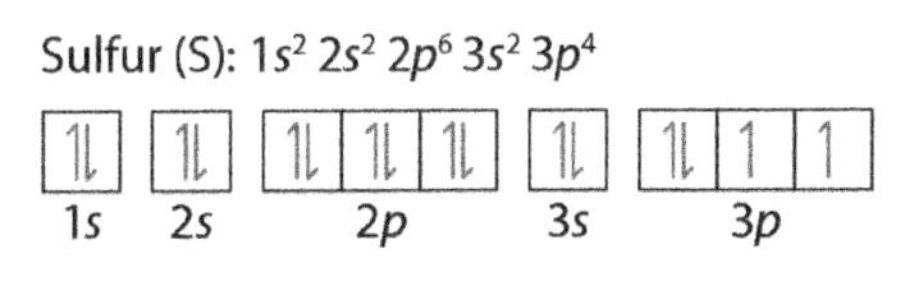

Figure 2.12. Electron Configuration of Sulfur

The electrons in the outermost shell of an atom are the **valence electrons**. In sulfur, shown at left, the six electrons in the $n = 3$ shell (3*s* and 3*p*) are the valence electrons. Atoms are most stable when they have a configuration of ns^2np^6—8 total electrons—in their outer shell. Atoms that are close to having a complete valence shell are extremely reactive: atoms with one extra electron will lose it easily, and atoms that need only one atom to complete their shell will gain it easily. Atoms with full valence shells (the noble gases) are inert. Electrons that are not in the valence shell are the **core electrons**.

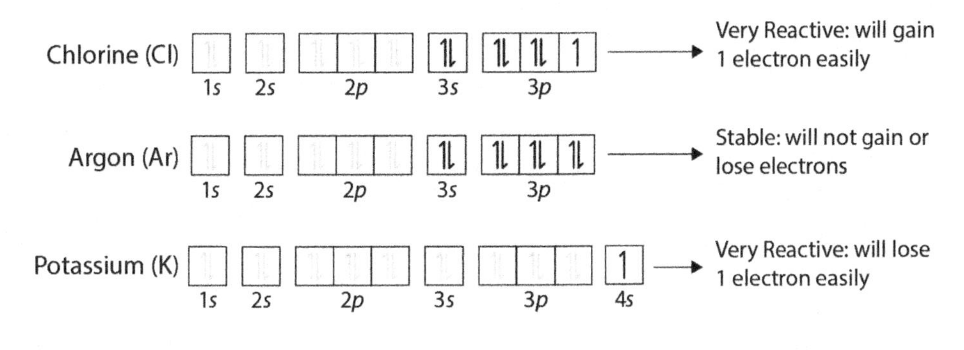

Figure 2.13. Valence Electrons

SAMPLE QUESTIONS

8) Which of the following electron configurations does NOT follow the aufbau principle?

A. $1s^2\ 2s^2\ 2p^6\ 3s^1$

B. $1s^2\ 2s^2\ 2p^6\ 3s^2$

C. $1s^1\ 2s^2\ 2p^6\ 3s^1$

D. $1s^2\ 2s^2\ 2p^6\ 3s^2\ 3p^1$

Answer:

C. Correct. $1s^1\ 2s^2\ 2p^6\ 3s^1$

The 1*s* orbital is not completely filled.

9) **Which of the following is the correct electron configuration for phosphorus (P)?**

A. $1s^2\ 2s^2\ 2p^6\ 3s^2\ 3p^2$

B. $1s^2\ 2s^2\ 2p^6\ 3s^2\ 3p^4$

C. $1s^1\ 2s^2\ 2p^6\ 3s^2\ 3p^4$

D. $1s^2\ 2s^2\ 2p^6\ 3s^2\ 3p^3$

Answers:

A. Incorrect. This configuration has the wrong number of electrons.

B. Incorrect. This configuration has the wrong number of electrons.

C. Incorrect. This configuration has a half-filled 1*s* orbital.

D. Correct. This configuration has the correct number of electrons in the correct orbitals.

Electron Configuration and the Periodic Table

The periodic table is arranged in order of increasing atomic number, meaning the table is organized by the number of electrons in an atom. This arrangement makes it possible to easily identify the number of valence electrons in each element, as shown in Figure 2.14. All the elements in a group have the same number of valence electrons, with the number of the period corresponding to the principal quantum number of the valence shell.

HELPFUL HINT

Reading the periodic table from left to right and top to bottom gives the order in which orbitals are filled: 1*s*, 2*s*, 2*p*, 3*s*, 3*p*, 4*s*, 3*d*, 4*p*, and so on.

Because valence electrons determine the reactivity of elements, the members of a group on the table all share similar properties. Group 1 (IA) contains the **alkali metals**, which create alkaline aqueous solutions. Group 2 (IIA) contains the **alkali earth metals**, which are extracted from minerals and create alkaline solutions. Both groups contain very reactive metals and, as such, the metals are found only in compounds in nature, not in their free metallic forms.

Groups 13 (IIIA) through 17 (VIIA) do not have special names, but they do contain the most abundant elements in the earth's crust and atmosphere. Groups 14 (IVA), 15 (VA), and 16 (VIA) each begin with at least one nonmetal, include a metalloid, and end with a metal. Group 17 (VIIA) contains the **halogens**, which are highly reactive. The word *halogen* comes from two Greek words: *hals* (salt) and *genes* (forming). The halogen elements all form salts upon reacting with metals. Group 18 (VIIIA) contains the **noble gases**, which are the least reactive elements.

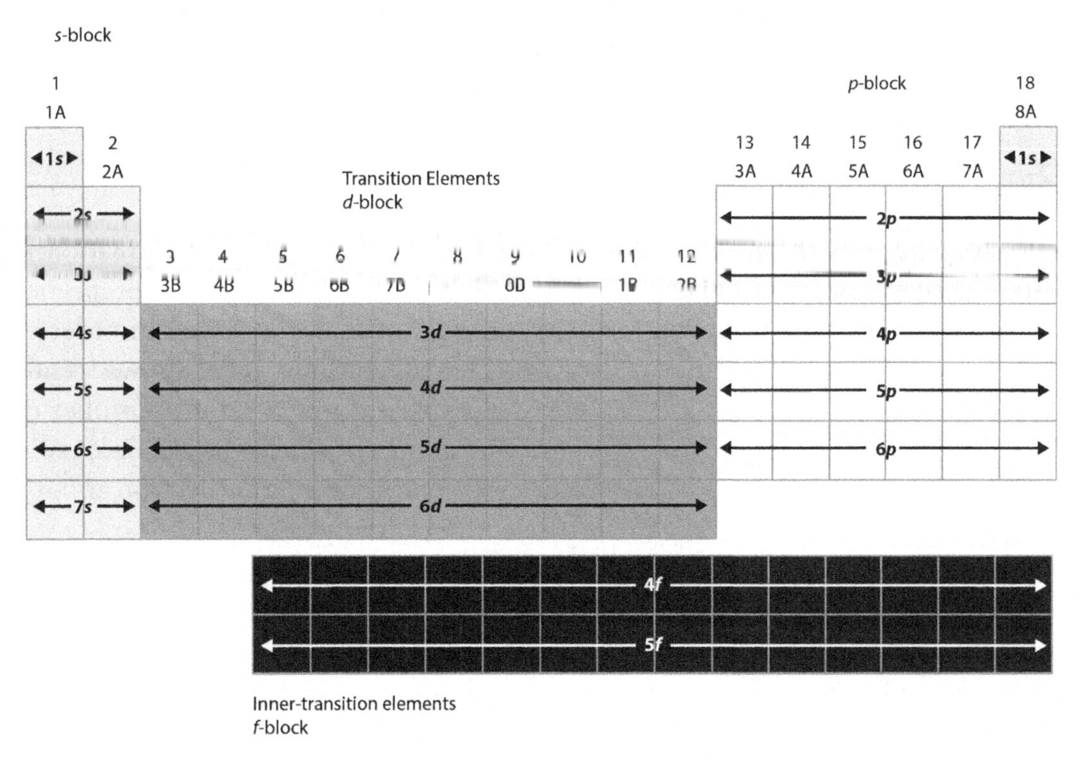

Figure 2.14. Valence Electron Configuration in the Periodic Table

The two rows at the bottom of the periodic table contain the **lanthanides** and **actinides**. They are separated to keep the periodic table from becoming too wide. Their location in the periodic table is indicated by the two blocks below Scandium (Sc) and Yttrium (Y).

HELPFUL HINT

While the number of valence electrons typically increases sequentially across a period, there are some exceptions to this in the *d*- and *f*-blocks. These exceptions occur because of the significant increase in stability for an element with a half-filled valence shell.

SAMPLE QUESTION

10) Which of the following groups are included in the *f*-block elements?

A. alkali metals

B. alkaline earth metals

C. halogens

D. lanthanides

Answers:

A. Incorrect. The alkali metals are group 1, which is in the *s*-block.

B. Incorrect. The alkaline earth metals are group 2, which is in the *s*-block.

C. Incorrect. The halogens are group 17, which is in the *p*-block.

D. Correct. The lanthanides are in the *f*-block because they all contain partially filled *f*-orbitals.

Periodic Properties of Elements

The elements in the periodic table are arranged in order of increasing atomic number because of the **law of chemical periodicity**, which states that the properties of the elements are periodic and predictable when they're arranged in order of increasing atomic number. Because of this law, the periodic table shows trends across groups and periods for a number of important properties, including atomic radii, ionic radii, ionization energy, electron affinity, and electronegativity.

> HELPFUL HINT
>
> left to right → electron added to same valence shell → atomic radii decrease
>
> top to bottom → electron added to a different shell → atomic radii increase

Atomic radius is a measure of the size of an atom from the nucleus to the boundary of the surrounding electron cloud. In the periodic table, the atomic radii increase going down a group as more electrons are added. It decreases going across a period from left to right as the attraction between the nucleus and the increasing number of electrons grows stronger.

The trend for the ionic radii is the same as that for the atomic radii. Positive and negative ions of elements in the same group increase in size down a group. The cation radius of an element is smaller than the anion radius of the element because a cation can hold the electron cloud of the atom more tightly.

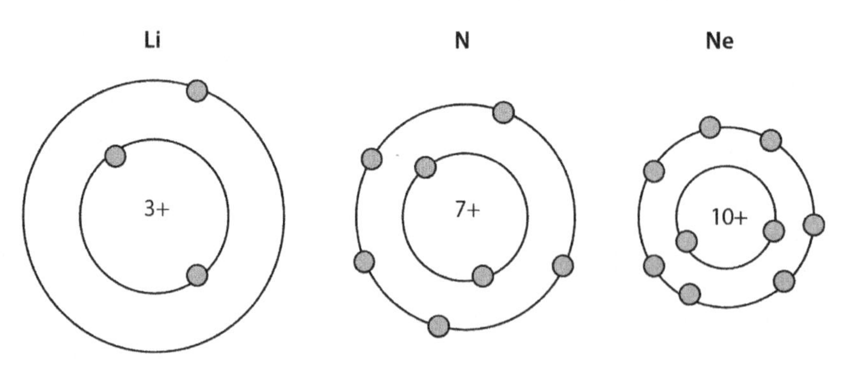

Figure 2.15. Atomic Radii Left to Right Within a Period

The **ionization energy** of an element is the energy required to remove an electron from an atom of the element in the gas phase. The more energy that is required to remove the electron, the greater the ionization energy. Ionization energies tend to decrease down a group and increase across a period. When moving down a group, the atoms become larger and the valence electrons are farther away from the nucleus, making it easier to remove electrons. However, when moving across a period, the atoms have more protons, which more strongly attract the electrons to the nucleus and make it harder to remove an electron.

The **electron affinity** of an element is the change in energy when a –1 ion is formed; it indicates the attraction an atom has for an electron. Atoms with a negative electron affinity value have a higher electron affinity than atoms with a positive value. This is because atoms that become more stable with the addition of an electron decrease in potential energy, resulting in a negative value. When atoms become less stable with the addition of an electron, the potential energy increases, resulting in a more positive electron affinity value. The electron affinity tends to increase across a period, with the halogens having the largest electron affinity.

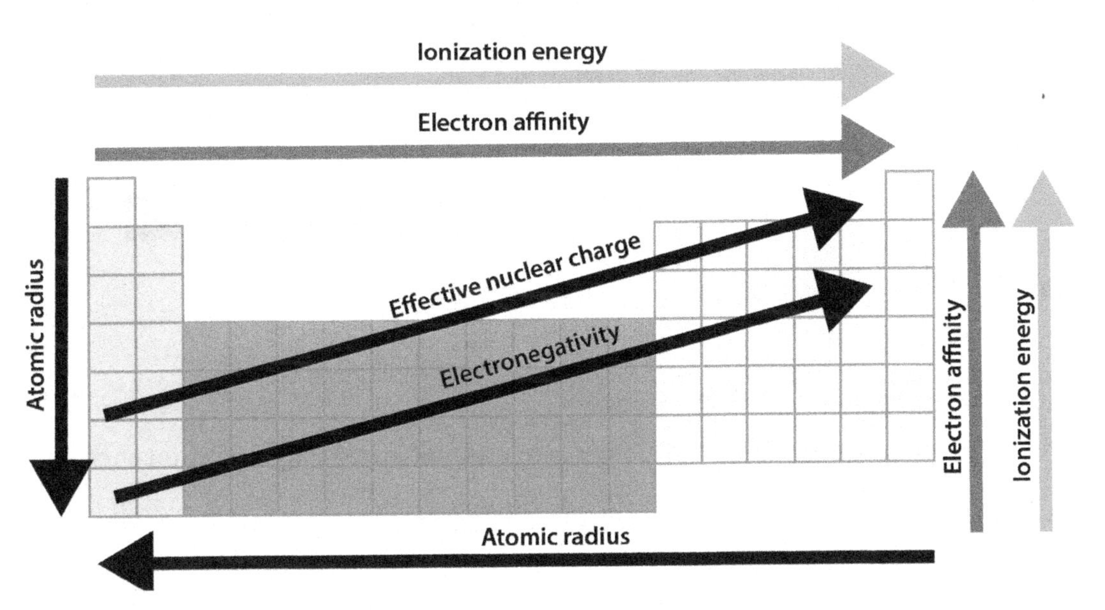

Figure 2.16. Trends of the Periodic Table

The **electronegativity** of an element is the ability of an atom in a covalent bond to attract the shared electrons. On the periodic table, the electronegativity increases diagonally upward and to the right. That is, electronegativity increases across a period because of a stronger attraction for electrons as the nuclear charge increases; it decreases down a group because of the increased distance between the nucleus and the valence electron shell.

> HELPFUL HINT
>
> While they are mostly inert, the noble gases Krypton and Xenon can be made to react with highly electronegative atoms, so both elements have an electronegativity value.

Effective nuclear charge (Z_{eff}) is the net positive charge experienced by an electron in a multi-electron atom. It is described by the equation

$$Z_{eff} = Z - S$$

where Z_{eff} is the effective nuclear charge, Z is the number of protons, and S is the screening constant. The value of S is close to the number of core electrons, whose charge shields valance electrons from the nucleus. Effective nuclear charge increases from left to right across periods as the number of protons increases, but the number of core electrons remains constant.

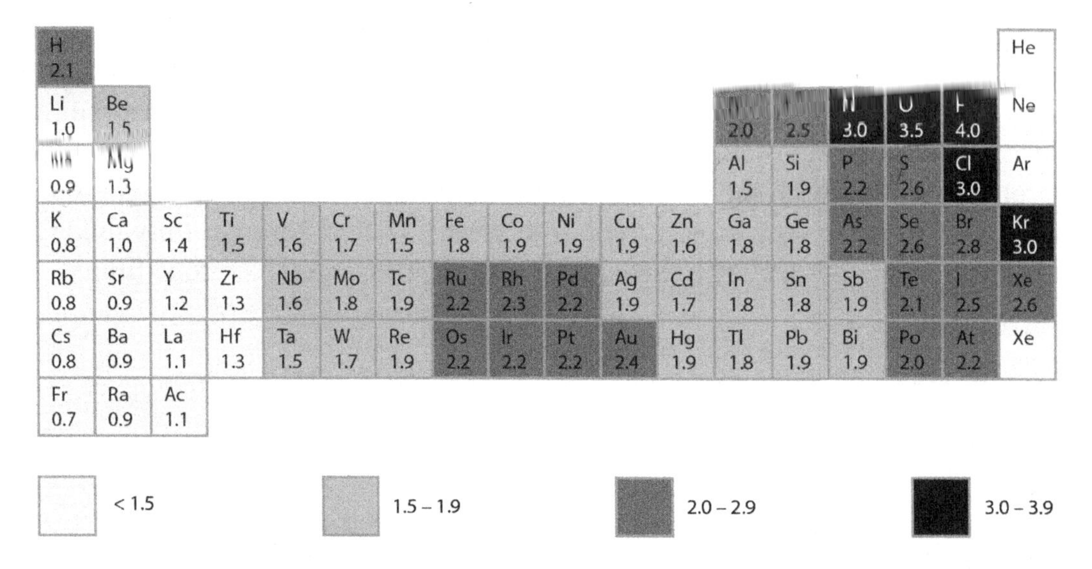

Figure 2.17. Electronegativity

SAMPLE QUESTIONS

11) Arrange the following elements in order of increasing ionization energy: Al, S, Na, and Mg.

A. Mg < Na < S < Al

B. Na < Mg < Al < S

C. Na < Al < Mg < S

D. Al < Na < Mg < S

Answer:

B. Correct. Na < Mg < Al < S

The ionization energy of elements increases across a period (row).

12) Arrange the following elements in order of increasing electronegativity: C, F, N, and O.

A. C < N < O < F

B. F < N < O < C

C. F < O < N < C

D. C < N < F < O

Answer:

A. Correct. C < N < O < F

Electronegativity increases across a period (row).

NUCLEAR CHEMISTRY

RADIOACTIVITY

In a chemical reaction, such as combustion or acid-base neutralization, it is only the number of electrons in an atom that changes—the nucleus remains unaffected. Conversely, in a **nuclear reaction**, changes occur in an atom's nucleus, altering the number of protons, neutrons, or both. In a nuclear reaction, unstable atoms called **radioisotopes** spontaneously emit particles and energy.

> HELPFUL HINT
>
> A **nuclide** is a nucleus that contains a specific number of protons and neutrons.

Table 2.5. Particles and Emissions in Nuclear Reactions

Particle	Symbol
Proton	$^{1}_{1}p$
Neutron	$^{1}_{0}n$
Electron	$^{0}_{-1}e$
Alpha particle	$^{4}_{2}\alpha$
Beta particle	$^{0}_{-1}\beta$
Gamma particle	$^{0}_{0}\gamma$
Positron	$^{0}_{1}e$

In **alpha decay**, atoms emit **alpha (α) particles**, which contain two protons and two neutrons. Alpha particles are written as $^{4}_{2}\alpha$ or $^{4}_{2}He$ because they are identical to a helium nucleus. They have a high ionization power (100 times higher than beta particles and 10,000 times higher than gamma radiation), meaning they have the potential to cause severe damage to biological tissue. However, their penetrating power is low: they can only travel a few centimeters through the air, and they cannot penetrate even thin surfaces.

> HELPFUL HINT
>
> A **radioactive series** is a sequence of nuclear reactions that create a stable nucleus from a previously unstable one. There are three naturally occurring radioactive sequences: thorium-232 to lead-208, uranium-235 to lead-207, and uranium-238 to lead-206.

Alpha decay can be described using a **nuclear equation**, which includes the element symbols of each atom or particle along with their atomic and mass numbers.

In a nuclear equation, the number of neutrons and protons must balance on each side. To balance a nuclear reaction or find a missing part of the equation, make sure that the sum of the top numbers is equal and that the sum of the bottom numbers is equal.

The equation below shows the decay of radium-226 to create radon and an alpha particle. Note that the top and bottom numbers balance:

$${}^{226}_{88}Ra \rightarrow {}^{222}_{86}Ra + {}^{4}_{2}\alpha$$

$$226 = 222 + 4$$

$$88 = 86 + 2$$

Beta decay releases **beta (β) particles**, which have the charge of an electron but can be thought of as fast-moving electrons emitted by the nucleus. Beta particles are written as ${}^{0}_{-1}e$ or ${}^{0}_{-1}\beta$ or , so the resulting element will have a higher atomic number. They have a low ionization power (about 1/100th the power of an alpha particle), but are highly penetrative (100 times more than alpha particles). The nuclear equation below shows the decay of carbon-14 to nitrogen-14:

$${}^{14}_{6}C \rightarrow {}^{14}_{7}N + {}^{0}_{-1}\beta$$

Gamma (γ) radiation consists of high-energy, short wavelength photons that are often released with other radioactive particles during decay. They are written as ${}^{0}_{0}\gamma$ and do not change the number of protons or neutrons in the atom. Their penetrating power is greater than alpha and beta particles, but their ionization power is much lower.

HELPFUL HINT

When positrons collide with electrons, they create gamma rays: ${}^{0}_{1}e + {}^{0}_{-1}e \rightarrow {}^{0}_{0}\gamma$

A **positron** has a charge of +1 and the same mass as an electron, so it is written as ${}^{0}_{1}e$. The nuclear equation below shows the decay of sodium-22, which produces a neon atom.

$${}^{22}_{11}Na \rightarrow {}^{22}_{10}Ne + {}^{0}_{1}e$$

Electrons themselves can also be taken into the nucleus during **electron capture**. The equation below shows the decay of beryllium to produce lithium caused by electron capture; note that the electron appears on the left side of the equation.

$${}^{7}_{4}Be + {}^{0}_{-1}e \rightarrow {}^{7}_{3}Li$$

The type of radioactive decay an element undergoes is determined by the ratio of neutrons to protons in its nucleus. Because neutrons are needed to counteract the attraction between protons, larger atoms require more neutrons. The optimum neutron to proton ratio lies in the **belt of stability** shown in Figure 2.18. An element's position relative to the belt determines its radioactivity:

- Elements above the belt will experience beta decay and move closer to the belt by increasing their number of protons.

- Elements below the belt will undergo either positron emission or electron capture; they move closer to the belt by decreasing their number of protons.
- Nuclei with more than 84 protons will undergo alpha decay, which moves them closer to the belt by decreasing the numbers of both protons and neutrons.

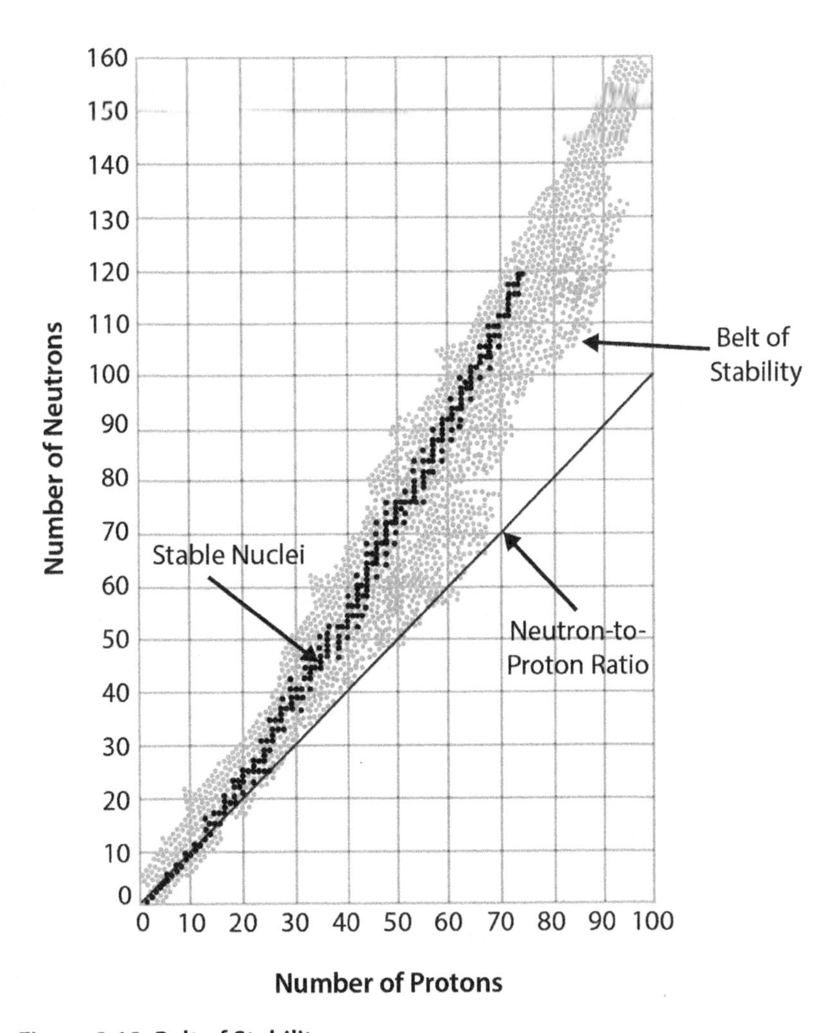

Figure 2.18. Belt of Stability

SAMPLE QUESTIONS

13) What type of particle is released when thorium-232 undergoes decay to form radon-228?

A. alpha particle
B. beta particle
C. gamma particle
D. positron

Answer:

A. **Correct.** Write the nuclear equation and set up two equations to find the missing values:

$^{232}_{90}\text{Th} \rightarrow {}^{228}_{88}\text{Ra} + {}^{a}_{b}X$

$232 = 228 + a$

$a = 4$

$90 = 88 + b$

$b = 2$

The decay releases an **alpha particle**:

$^{232}_{90}\text{Th} \rightarrow {}^{228}_{88}\text{Ra} + {}^{4}_{2}\alpha$

14) What type of particle is released when cesium-137 undergoes decay to form barium-137?

A. alpha particle

B. beta particle

C. gamma particle

D. positron

Answer:

B. **Correct.** Write the nuclear equation and set up two equations to find the missing values:

$^{137}_{55}\text{Cs} \rightarrow {}^{137}_{56}\text{Ba} + {}^{a}_{b}X$

$137 = 137 + a$

$a = 0$

$55 = 56 + b$

$b = -1$

The decay releases a **beta particle**:

$^{137}_{55}\text{Cs} \rightarrow {}^{137}_{56}\text{Ba} + {}^{0}_{-1}\beta$

HALF-LIFE

The time it takes for substances to decay varies widely—some radioisotopes decay completely in only a few seconds, while others decay over millions of years. The time it takes for half of a radioactive sample to decay is that substance's **half-life** (h or $t_{\frac{1}{2}}$). The equation for half-life is written as

$$A = A_0\left(\frac{1}{2}\right)^{\frac{t}{h}}$$

where A is the final amount, A_0 is the initial amount, t is the time, and h is the half-life.

Half-life is also described using the first-order rate constant, k:

$$\ln\frac{N_t}{N_0} = -kt$$

where N_t is the remaining number of nuclei, N_0 is the original number of nuclei, k is the **decay constant**, and t is time.

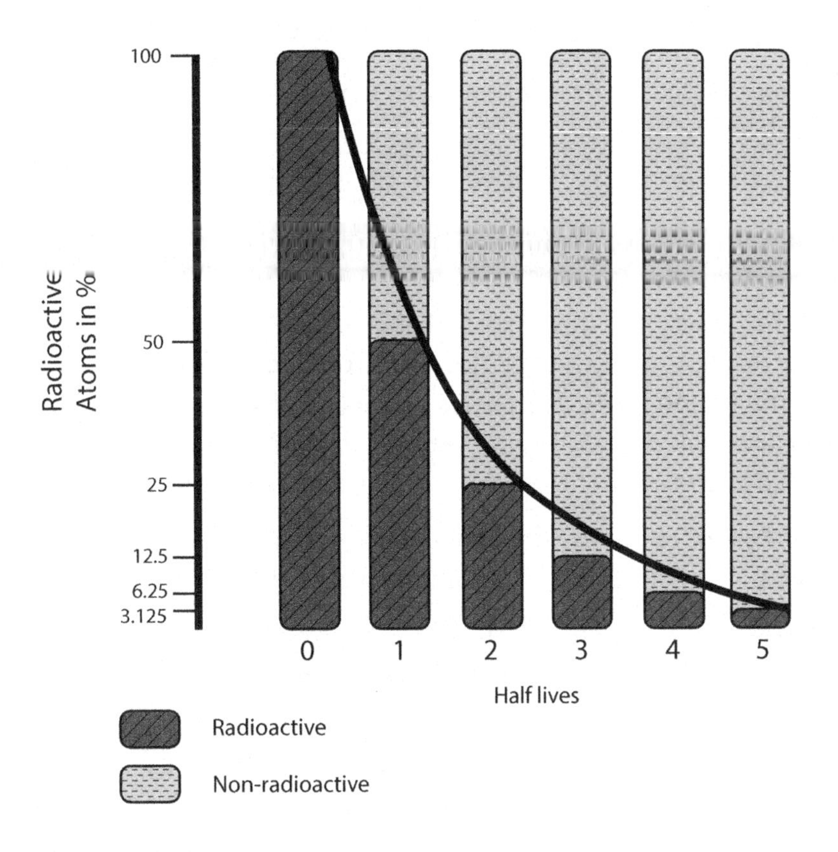

Figure 2.19. Half-Life Decay

Half-life and the decay constant are related by the equation

$$k = \frac{0.693}{t_{\frac{1}{2}}}$$

SAMPLE QUESTION

15) What is the half-life of uranium-235 if $k = 1.65 \times 10^{-10}$ yr^{-1}?

A. 1.65×10^9 years

B. 8.25×10^{10} years

C. 4.20×10^9 years

D. 4.50×10^{10} years

$\frac{1.65 \times 10^{-10}}{yr} = \frac{.693}{t_{\frac{1}{2}}} \Rightarrow t_{\frac{1}{2}} = \frac{.693\ yr}{1.65 \times 10^{-10}}$

$t_{1/2} = 4{,}200{,}000{,}000 = 4.2 \times 10^9$ yr

Answer:

C. Correct. Use the equation for the decay constant.

$$t_{\frac{1}{2}} = \frac{0.693}{k} = \frac{0.693}{1.65 \times 10^{-10}\ \text{yr}^{-1}} = \mathbf{4.20 \times 10^9\ years}$$

Nuclear Energy of an Atom

Nuclear fission occurs when a nucleus splits into two or more light nuclei after being bombarded by particles such as protons, neutrons, or alpha particles. Fission occurs to heavy nuclei with atomic numbers greater than 230. For example, when uranium is bombarded with low energy thermal neutrons, it splits into two smaller nuclei and releases neutrons:

$$^{1}_{0}n + ^{235}_{92}U \rightarrow ^{141}_{56}Ba + ^{92}_{36}Kr + 3\,^{1}_{0}n$$

The neutrons released during fission can in turn lead to more fission reactions, ultimately setting off a series of nuclear fission reactions called a **chain reaction**. When the chain reaction is **uncontrolled**, it is self-sustaining and gives off energy at a rapidly increasing rate. If the reaction is **controlled** so that only a single neutron emitted during fission leads to another fission, the fission rate stays constant and energy is steadily released. Nuclear fission is used in atomic bombs and to power nuclear power plants.

Nuclear fusion happens when two or more light nuclei fuse to form a single heavy nucleus. Below is an example of the fusion of hydrogen nuclei into helium nuclei, a process that is believed to power most stars:

$$^{1}_{1}H + ^{1}_{1}H \rightarrow ^{2}_{1}H + ^{0}_{1}e$$

$$^{2}_{1}H + ^{2}_{1}H \rightarrow ^{3}_{2}He + ^{1}_{0}n$$

$$^{2}_{1}H + ^{2}_{1}H \rightarrow ^{3}_{1}H + ^{1}_{1}H$$

These reactions only occur under extremely high heat and pressure. Such conditions have been created in thermonuclear (or hydrogen) bombs, but nuclear fusion is not currently used for other purposes.

SAMPLE QUESTION

16) Which of the following is an example of nuclear fission?

A. $^{2}_{1}H + ^{3}_{1}H \rightarrow 2 + ^{1}_{0}n$

B. $4\,^{1}_{1}H \rightarrow ^{4}_{2}He + 2\,^{0}_{1}e$

C. $^{2}_{1}H + ^{3}_{2}He \rightarrow ^{4}_{2}He + ^{1}_{1}H$

D. $^{1}_{0}n + ^{239}_{94}Pu \rightarrow ^{134}_{54}Xe + ^{103}_{40}Zr + 3\,^{1}_{0}n$

Answer:

D. Correct.

$^{1}_{0}n + ^{239}_{94}Pu \rightarrow ^{134}_{54}Xe + ^{103}_{40}Zr + 3\,^{1}_{0}n$

Some of the products have a lower mass number and lower atomic number, meaning larger atoms were split into smaller ones.

Bonding

Ionic Bonds

Ionic bonds tend to form between elements toward the left side of the periodic table, which have low ionization energies, and elements on the right side, with large negative electron affinities. Both the atoms losing electrons and those gaining electrons are stabilized by attaining a full outer shell, or octet configuration, of s^2p^6, except for Li and Be, which yield a $1s^2$ filled outer shell.

The attraction between the positive and negative ions results in the formation of a regular crystal, or lattice, in which each positive ion interacts with several negative ions around it, and vice versa. The energy released by the stabilizing effect of lattice formation is called the **lattice energy**. The formation of ionic compounds is exothermic due to the stabilizing effects of a full outer electron shell and a lattice that balances the attractive and repulsive forces of the ions. Sodium chloride, NaCl, is a typical ionic compound. Na loses an electron to Cl, and the resulting Na^+ and Cl^- ions form a lattice in which each ion is surrounded by six ions of the opposite charge.

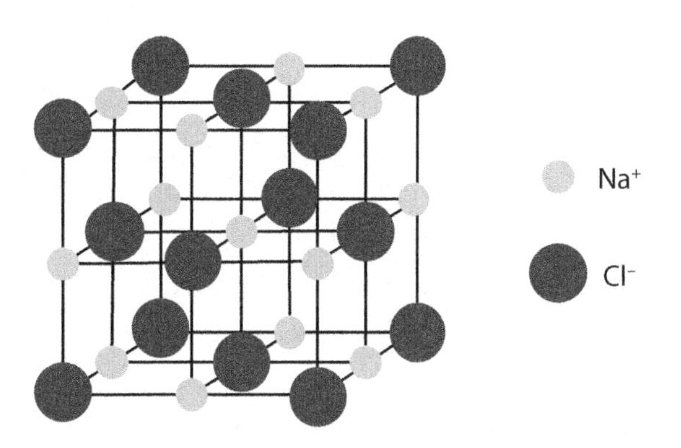

Figure 3.1. A Lattice of Na^+ and Cl^- ions

To form a filled outer shell, elements in family 1 lose one electron and form ions with a charge of 1^+. Elements in family 2 lose two electrons and form 2^+ cations. Cations are smaller than the corresponding neutral atom. The halogens accept an electron to form anions

> HELPFUL HINT
>
> The noble gases are highly stable because they have filled outer shells and do not ionize.

with a charge of 1^-. Atoms in family 16 tend to accept two electrons to form anions with a charge of 2^-. Anions are larger than the corresponding atoms.

The transition metals also form cations. Most of them can have multiple charges. They lose their outer *s* electrons first and then their outer *d* electron(s).

QUICK REVIEW

Explain the changes in atomic size when electrons are gained or lost in terms of the change in electron-electron repulsion in the outer orbitals.

In addition to ions formed by single atoms, there are also polyatomic ions, such as NH_4^+, CO_3^{2-} and CrO_4^{2-}. Most are negatively charged and contain oxygen. The atoms within these ions are covalently bonded, and the whole molecule has a charge and can bond with oppositely charged ions.

SAMPLE QUESTION

1) **Which of the following pairs of atoms is most likely to form an ionic bond?**

A. O and H

B. Li and F

C. Be and Ne

D. Ni and Cu

Answers:

A. Incorrect. Both oxygen and hydrogen are in the upper right corner of the periodic table and do not form ionic bonds.

B. **Correct.** Lithium is an alkali metal and forms the ion Li^+, and fluorine is a halogen that forms the ion F^-. The two ions form an ionic bond to make LiF.

C. Incorrect. Neon is a noble gas and does not form ionic bonds.

D. Incorrect. Both nickel and copper are metals and do not form ionic bonds.

Covalent Bonds

In **covalent** molecules, electrons are shared between atoms. Nonmetals occupying the top of family 13 and extending down and across the periodic table to encompass all the halogens are capable of forming covalent bonds. Covalent bonding stabilizes the molecule by giving each participant in the bond a completely filled outer octet. Hydrogen also forms covalent bonds, resulting in two electrons filling its *s* shell.

POLARITY

Covalent bonds may be nonpolar or polar. In a **nonpolar bond**, electrons are shared equally between the atoms. Diatomic gases, such as Cl_2 and N_2, exhibit nonpolar bonding.

When one of the atoms has a stronger attraction for electrons than the other, it attracts more of the electron density toward itself, resulting in a **polar bond**. Atoms with high ionization energies and high electron affinities have a high attractive force for electrons, or electronegativity, in bonds.

HELPFUL HINT

The chemical interactions of polar molecules are dependent on the orientation of the molecules, so a little arrow is often drawn over the molecule to show the direction of charge. Nonpolar molecules have no dipole (and no arrow), so the interaction is less dependent on the orientation of the molecule.

C ——— Cl

δ + δ –

Figure 3.2. Dipole Moment

Polar bonds can be visualized as **dipoles**, where there is a partial negative charge on the more electronegative atom and a partial positive charge on the less electronegative atom. **Dipole moment** is a measure of the strength of a dipole and is expressed in a unit called a debye. The formula for dipole moment is $\mu = \delta d$, where δ is the effective charge and d is the distance between the charges. The charge δ is a function of the difference in electronegativity between the atoms participating in the dipole. Longer distances between charges translate into larger dipole moments.

A molecule is considered polar if it contains polar bonds that do not balance each other out. In other words, it has a net dipole moment. CH_3Cl is polar, but, in contrast, CCl_4 is not. Although the C—Cl bond is polar, in CCl_4, the bonds are symmetrically distributed around the central carbon and are all equally polar so there is no net dipole moment. Likewise, the linear molecule O=C=O has no dipole moment because the two opposing C=O dipoles cancel each other out.

SAMPLE QUESTION

2) **Put the bonds C—H, H—F, and H—Br in order of increasing polarity.**

A. C—H, H—F, H—Br

B. C—H, H—Br, H—F

C. H—Br, C—H, H—F

D. H—Br, H—F, C—H

Answer:

B. Correct. The difference in electronegativities of the halogens and hydrogen is much greater than the difference between carbon and hydrogen. Fluorine is higher in family 17 than bromine and more electronegative.

HYBRIDIZATION

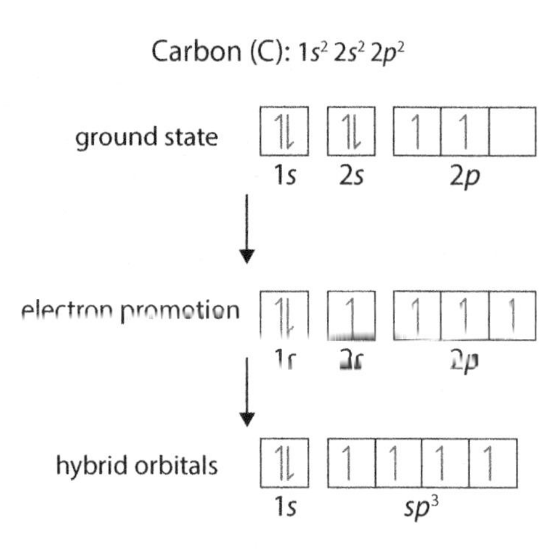

Figure 3.3. Electron Promotion and Hybrid Orbitals

When electrons are shared between atoms, the outer atomic orbitals can hybridize to form orbitals that are of the same average energy as the atomic orbitals from which they formed. For this to happen, atoms "promote" paired electrons to higher-energy orbitals, freeing unpaired electrons for covalent bonds. Carbon, for example, promotes one electron from its 2*s* orbital to its 2*p* orbital, creating four orbitals with one electron each. These orbitals hybridize to form four sp^3 orbitals of equal energy.

Mixing a certain number of orbitals results in the same number of hybrid orbitals. An *s* orbital can hybridize with one, two, or three *p* orbitals, and *d* orbitals may also hybridize with *s* and *p* orbitals for elements in period 3 and below. These hybridizations result in the following hybrid orbitals:

- $s + p$ = two *sp* orbitals
- $s + p + p$ = three sp^2 orbitals
- $s + p + p + p$ = four sp^3 orbitals
- $s + p + p + p + d$ = five sp^3d orbitals
- $s + p + p + p + d + d$ = six sp^3d^2 orbitals

SAMPLE QUESTION

3) **In BeF_2, the orbitals of the Be atom hybridize to form**

A. two *sp* orbitals.
B. three sp^2 orbitals.
C. four sp^3 orbitals.
D. five sp^3d orbitals.

Answer:

A. Correct. Be promotes one electron from its filled 2*s* shell to its empty 2*p* shell, creating two *sp* orbitals.

SIGMA (σ) AND PI (π) BONDS

Sigma (σ) bonds are formed by two orbitals lined up end to end. They are usually single bonds, and are the strongest type of covalent bond.

Sigma bonds can be formed from regular or hybrid orbitals. The diatomic molecule H_2, for example, includes a σ bond between the *s* orbitals on each atom. In the molecule CH_4, the four sp^3 orbitals bond with the *s* orbital of the hydrogen atoms, giving the molecule a tetrahedral structure that minimizes electron-electron repulsion.

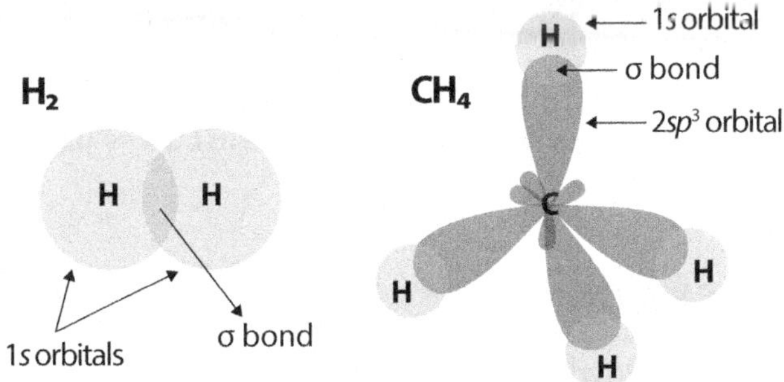

Figure 3.4. Sigma Bonds in Hydrogen Gas and Methane

Pi (π) bonds are formed by the lateral overlap of two *p* or *d* orbitals, and are usually formed between atoms after a σ bond has already formed. A double bond consists of one σ and one π bond; a triple bond consists of one σ bond and two π bonds. For example, in ethene (C_2H_4), the carbons undergo sp^2 hybridization. The sp^2 orbitals overlap to form three σ bonds: one with each hydrogen atom, and one with the other carbon. The remaining *p* orbitals overlap to form a π bond—the second bond of the double bond. In ethyne, two sets of *p* orbitals overlap to form two π bonds (see Figure 3.6).

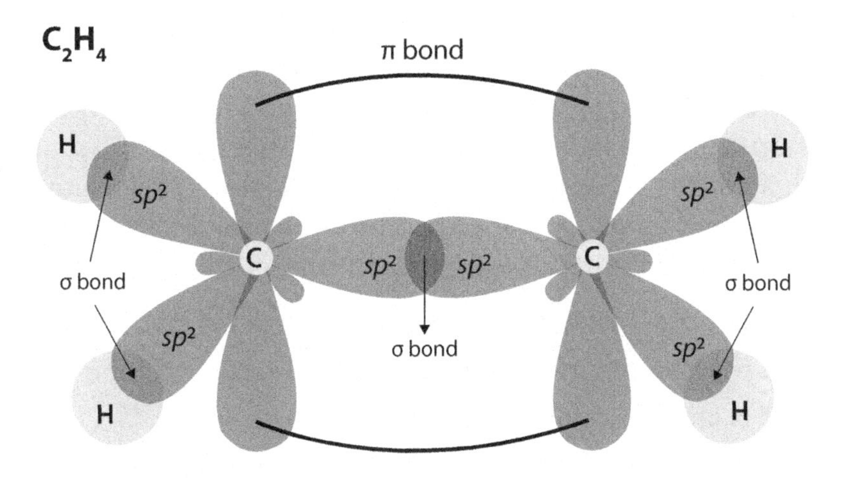

Figure 3.5. sp^2 Hybridization with a π Bond in Ethene (Trigonal Planar)

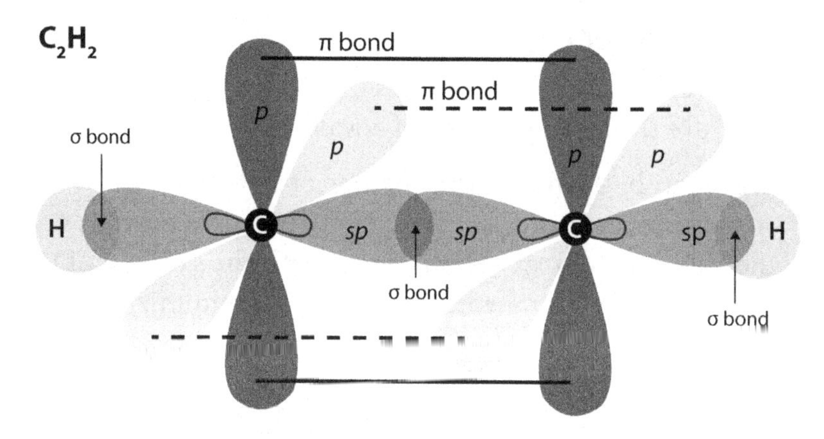

Figure 3.6. *sp* Hybridization with Two π Bonds in Ethyne (Linear)

SAMPLE QUESTION

4) **Which of the following compounds does NOT contain a π bond?**

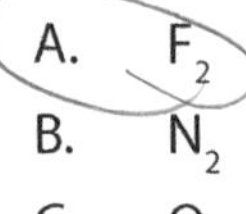

A. F_2

B. N_2

C. O_2

D. C_2H_4

Answer:

A. **Correct.** F_2 includes a single covalent bond. The other three compounds all include a double or triple bond, which is a π bond.

Lewis Structures

It can often be difficult to figure out the bonding structure of complex covalent compounds simply from their chemical formulas. **Lewis structures** and formal charge are means of determining the most stable and therefore likely configuration. Lewis structures are based on the octet rule—that atoms will share electrons so that each atom has a complete set of eight of electrons in its outer shell. This configuration mimics the very stable electron configuration of the nearest noble gas. The steps in determining a Lewis structure are as follows:

1. Calculate the total number of valence electrons for all the atoms.
2. Place the least electronegative atom in the center position.
3. Place H and F in terminal positions.
4. Connect the terminal atoms to central atoms with single bonds.
5. Calculate the remaining number of electrons.
6. Place lone pairs of electrons around the terminal atoms to give an octet—except for H, which gets two electrons.

7. Place any remaining electrons around the central atom as lone pairs.
8. Check the number of electrons around each atom.
9. Move electrons from terminal atoms to the central atom, creating multiple bonds if necessary to achieve an octet on the central atom.

In some cases, it is possible to draw multiple nonequivalent Lewis structures for a molecule. Formal charge is used to determine which structure is correct. **Formal charge** (FC) is the difference between the number of valence electrons of a free atom and the number of electrons assigned in the Lewis structure. It is calculated for each atom in the molecule, and the structure that yields the lowest formal charge value is the most stable. Formal charge is calculated for each atom as:

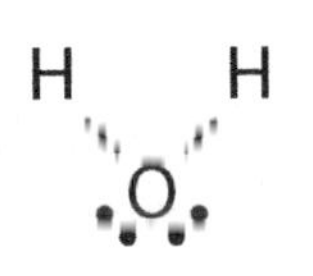

Figure 3.7. Lewis Structure of H_2O

$$FC = \text{valence electrons} - \text{lone pair electrons} - \frac{1}{2}\,\text{bonding electrons}$$

Sometimes there is more than one equivalent Lewis structure, called **resonance structures**, for a molecule. For example, SO_2 can be drawn two ways. In these cases, the electron density is on average evenly divided between the two bonds, so the true structure is an average of the two forms.

HELPFUL HINT

Boron has only six electrons in its outer shell. Therefore, BF_3 tends to react with molecules, such as NH_3, that can donate two electrons to form a bond.

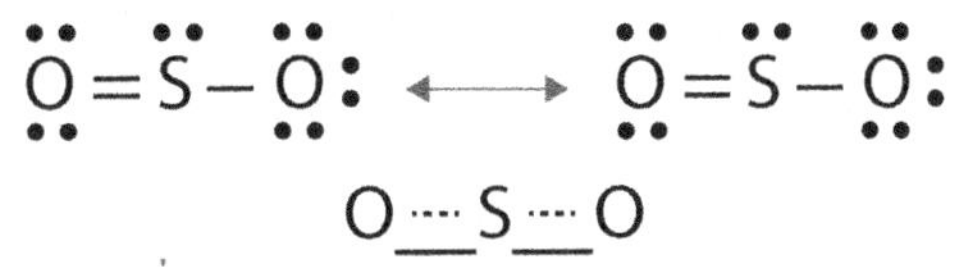

O=S–O: ⟷ O=S–O:

O⋯S⋯O

Figure 3.8. Resonance Forms of SO_2

There are three exceptions to the octet rule. These exceptions have Lewis structures that do not always follow the rules given above.

- ▶ Incomplete octets—these usually form with F or H. Fluorine is too electronegative to donate electrons to a double bond. Hydrogen can only accommodate two electrons in its outer and only shell. An example of a compound with an incomplete octet is BF_3.

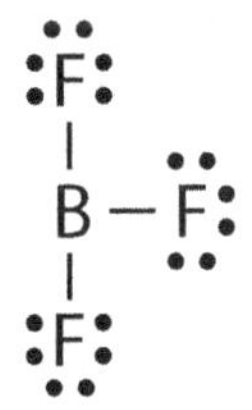

:F:
|
B–F:
|
:F:

Figure 3.9. Incomplete Octet in BF_3

- ▶ Molecules with odd numbers of electrons. An example is NO_2.

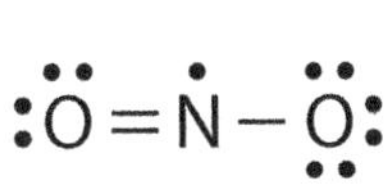

:O=N–O:

Figure 3.10. Odd Numbers of Electrons in NO_2

- ▶ Elements with an expanded valence shell—elements in the third period and below—have empty *d* orbitals and can accommodate more than an octet around the central atom. An example is PCl_5, which has ten electrons around phosphorus.

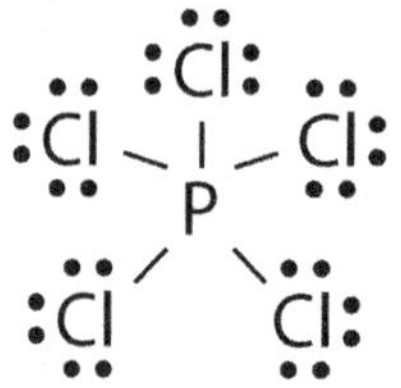

Figure 3.11. Lewis Structure of PCl_5

SAMPLE QUESTIONS

5) **Draw the Lewis structure for CO_2.**

A.  O::C::O

B. :O–C–O:

C. :O–C–O:

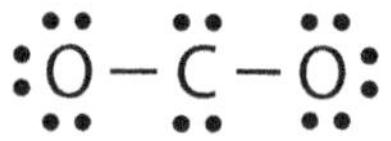

D. 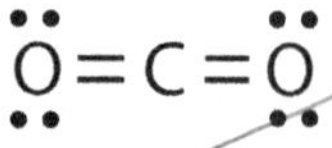 O=C=O

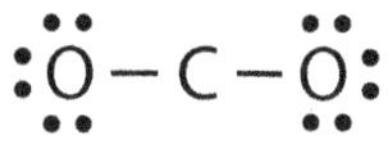

O=C=O

Answers:

A. Incorrect. Lines are used to denote bonds rather than electron pairs.

B. Incorrect. Carbon only has four electrons. It should have an octet.

C. Incorrect. The least electronegative atom goes in the center. Also, there are too many electrons—twenty. C, O, and O only have a total of sixteen valence electrons.

D. Correct. The less electronegative carbon is in the center. Placing single bonds between the atoms and placing the remaining lone pairs on the oxygen atoms leaves carbon with only four electrons. A lone pair is donated from each oxygen to form two double bonds, giving carbon an octet.

6) **Which Lewis structure is correct for $COCl_2$?**

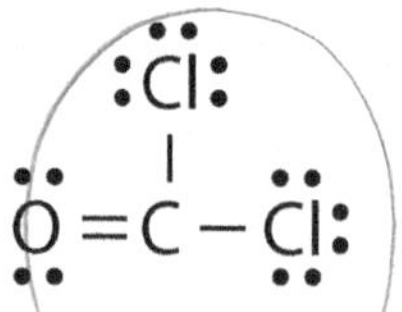

Structure A: O=C(–Cl)–Cl or Structure B: O–C(–Cl)=Cl

Structure A or Structure B

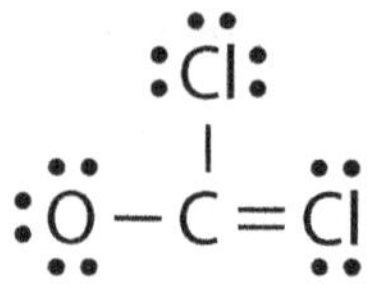

Answers:

A. **Structure A is correct.** Structure A minimizes the formal charges—all are zero.

O has 6 valence electrons – 4 lone pair electrons – ½ of 4 bonding electrons = 0.

C has 4 valence electrons – no lone pairs – ½ of 8 bonding electrons = 0.

Cl has 7 valence electrons – 6 lone pair electrons – ½ of 2 bonding electrons = 0.

B. Structure B is incorrect.

For O: 6 valence electrons – 6 lone pair electrons – ½ of 2 bonding electrons = –1.

For C: Same as in structure A: 0.

For singly bonded Cl: same as in structure A: 0.

For doubly bonded Cl: 7 valence electrons – 4 lone pair electrons – ½ of 4 bonding electrons = 1.

THE VSEPR MODEL

The valence shell electron pair repulsion (VSEPR) model predicts **molecular geometry** based on Lewis structures. Valence electrons are both attracted to the central nucleus and repelled by each other. VSEPR places both the bonding electrons and the lone pairs around the central atom in the geometric arrangement that minimizes the repulsion between them. The model predicts the measured bond angles of many molecules perfectly and is a good approximation for most others.

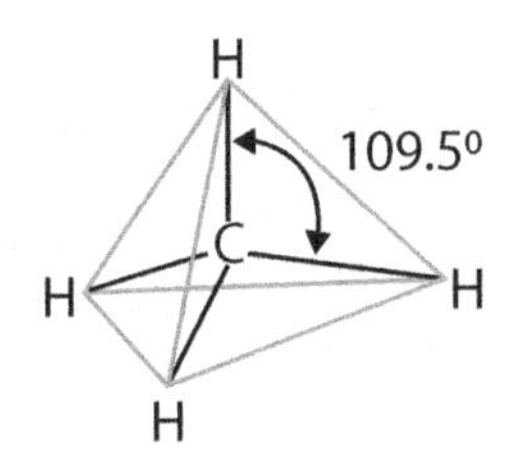

Figure 3.12. VSEPR Structure of Methane

For the simple molecule CH_4, VSEPR predicts a tetrahedral arrangement that places each bonding pair as far as possible from its nearest neighbor. The angles in a tetrahedron are 109.5 degrees, and that is the measured bond angle for CH_4.

The VSEPR model holds that lone pairs of electrons occupy more space than bonding pairs because the bonding pairs are attracted to two nuclei, whereas the lone pairs only experience the attractive force of the central nucleus. Therefore, lone pairs repel bonding pairs a bit more than bonding pairs repel each other. This effect can be seen in the geometry of NH_3 shown next.

QUICK REVIEW

Carbon has four valence electrons and is the element that makes up diamond and graphite. Graphite is a two-dimensional sheet, where three valence electrons are equally spaced (at angles of 120°) in a plane while the fourth is perpendicular to the plane. In diamond, the valence electrons are equally spaced in a three-dimensional crystal. What are the ideal bond angles for diamond?

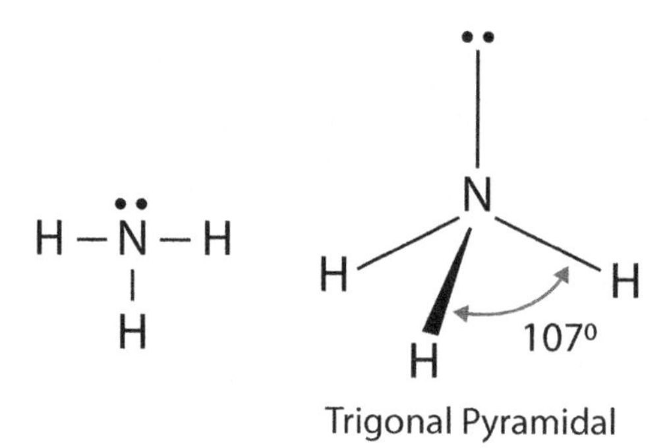

Figure 3.13. Lewis Structure and Molecular Geometry of NH^3

The bond angles are 107 degrees rather than 109.5 degrees because the lone pair repels the bonding electrons more strongly than they repel each other. The description of the molecule as "trigonal pyramidal" refers to the position of the bonded atoms and does not include the position of the lone pair. Spectroscopy and diffraction are used to determine the actual positions of the atoms and bond angles.

When there are double bonds or triple bonds, they are treated like single bonds except that they are expected to take up somewhat more space and will push out adjacent bonds a bit more.

Table 3.1 shows the VSEPR geometries predicted for various Lewis structures. The steric number is the number of atoms bonded to the central atom plus the number of lone pairs on the central atom.

Table 3.1. VSEPR Molecular Geometries

Bonding Electron Pairs	Lone Pairs	Electron Domains (Steric Number)	Shape Name	Ideal Bond Angle	Example	Shape
4	0	4	tetrahedral	109.5°	CH_4	
6	0	6	octahedral	90°, 180°	SF_6	
9	0	9	tricapped trigonal prismatic		$ReHg^{2-}$	

Bonding Electron Pairs	Lone Pairs	Electron Domains (Steric Number)	Shape Name	Ideal Bond Angle	Example	Shape
2	1	3	bent	120° (119°)	SO_2	
2	2	4	bent	109.5° (104.48°)	H_2O	
2	0	2	linear	180°	CO_2	
2	3	5	linear	180°	XeF_2	
7	0	7	pentagonal bipyramidal	90°, 72°, 180°	IF_7	
5	2	7	planar pentagonal	72°, 144°	XeF_5^-	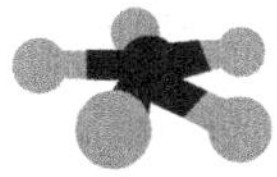
6	1	7	pentagonal pyramidal	72°, 90°, 144°	$XeOF_5^-$	
3	1	4	trigonal pyramidal	109.5° (107.8°)	NH_3	

Table 3.1. VSEPR Molecular Geometries (continued)

Bonding Electron Pairs	Lone Pairs	Electron Domains (Steric Number)	Shape Name	Ideal Bond Angle	Example	Shape
4	1	5	seesaw	ax-ax 180° (173.1°) eq-eq 120° (101.6°) ax-eq 90°	SF_4	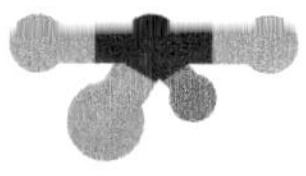
8	0	8	square antiprismatic		XeF_8^{2-}	
4	2	6	square planar	90°, 180°	XeF_4	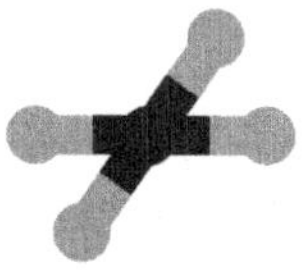
5	1	6	square pyramidal	90° (84.8°)	BrF_5	
3	2	5	T-shaped	90° (87.5°), 180° (175°)	ClF_3	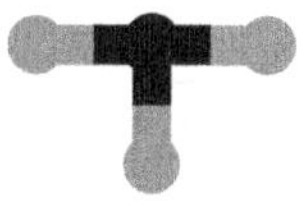
3	0	3	trigonal planar	120°	BF_3	
5	0	5	trigonal bipyramidal	90°, 120°, 180°	PCl_5	

SAMPLE QUESTION

7) Why is BF_3 trigonal planar as opposed to trigonal pyramidal like NH_3?

A. The B—F bond is stronger than the N—H bond.

B. NF_3 has a lone electron pair while BF_3 does not.

C. F is more electronegative than H.

D. The B—F bond is more polar than the N—H bond.

Answers:

A. Incorrect. The overall shape is not related to bond strength.

B. Correct. For BF_3, a planar structure with 120-degree bond angles minimizes the repulsion between the three B—F bonding pairs. There is no lone pair. For NH_3, the lone pair occupies the fourth axis of a tetrahedron with the three N—H bonds forming the other three axes. The shape formed by the three N—H bonds is trigonal pyramidal.

C. Incorrect. Electronegativity does not determine overall shape.

D. Incorrect. The polarity of a molecule does not determine its shape (although its shape can influence the strength and direction of its dipole moment).

METALLIC BONDS

Elements in families 1 and 2, as well as the transition metals and some of the heavier members of families 3–6, can form tightly packed arrays in which each atom is in close contact with many neighbors. So many atomic orbitals overlap with each atom that they form very large molecular orbitals that in turn overlap with each other, creating a continuous band in which electrons can move. This type of delocalized bonding is called **metallic bonding**.

Any excitation, such as an electrical current, can cause the electrons to move throughout the array. The high electrical and thermal conductivity of metals is due to this ability of electrons to move throughout the lattice. Metals are ductile—or can be bent without breaking—because the atoms can slide past each other without breaking the delocalized bonds.

SAMPLE QUESTION

8) The valence electrons in a metallic bond are NOT

A. evenly distributed.

B. held in place by their attraction to the cations.

C. shared between two atoms.

D. free to move.

Answers:

A. Incorrect. This statement is true—valence electrons in a metallic bond are evenly distributed throughout the metal.

B. Incorrect. This statement is true—while they are free to move within the metal, valence electrons in a metallic bond are held within the metal by their attraction to the cations.

C. Correct. The valence electrons in a metallic bond are shared equally by all the atoms in the metal.

D. Incorrect. This statement is true—valence electrons in a metallic bond can move freely, as happens when a voltage is applied to the metal.

Bond Strength and Bond Length

The strength of a chemical bond is reflected in the **bond length**, with stronger bonds tending to be shorter because the attractive force between atoms is greater. Bond length can be measured by X-ray diffraction in crystals and by spectroscopy. Bond lengths are related to the atomic radii of the bonded atoms and tend to decrease going across the periodic table and increase going down families.

Bond strength can be measured as the energy required to break apart a bond and is known as the **bond energy**. Stronger bonds are harder to break and make a more stable molecule.

Covalent molecules have characteristic bond strengths based on the atoms participating in the bonds, and, to a smaller extent, on the rest of the molecule. When atoms form double and triple bonds with each other, bond strength increases as more electrons are shared between the atoms. In general, as bond strength goes up, bond length gets shorter, as the atoms are more tightly held together. So bonds between smaller atoms tend to be shorter and stronger than those between larger atoms.

SAMPLE QUESTION

9) How would the bond lengths and bond strengths of C—C, C=C, and C≡C compare?

A. Bond length: C—C > C=C > C≡C
Bond strength: C—C > C=C > C≡C

B. Bond length: C—C > C=C > C≡C
Bond strength: C—C < C=C < C≡C

C. Bond length: C—C < C=C < C≡C
Bond strength: C—C > C=C > C≡C

D. Bond length: C—C < C=C < C≡C
Bond strength: C—C < C=C < C≡C

Answer:

B. **Correct.** Triple bonds are shorter and stronger than double bonds, which in turn are shorter and stronger than single bonds.

INTERMOLECULAR FORCES

TYPES OF INTERMOLECULAR FORCES

Covalent molecules experience a variety of intermolecular forces due to electrostatic interactions between molecules. These forces are responsible for the physical properties of liquids and solids.

Table 3.2. Intermolecular Forces

Force	Strength	Occurs Between
Hydrogen	High	Permanent dipoles in molecules with an H and an F, O, or N
Dipole-Dipole	Medium	Permanent dipoles in polar molecules
Dipole-Induced Dipole	Medium	Temporary dipoles induced in nonpolar molecules by polar molecules
London	Low	Temporary dipoles in nonpolar molecules

The strongest of the forces between polar molecules is **hydrogen bonding**. It occurs in molecules that have N—H, O—H, and F—H bonds. These bonds are quite polar, with N, O, and F being much more electronegative than H. An attraction is produced between the relatively positive H and the unpaired electrons on N, O, and F so that hydrogen bonds of the form X—H—X form, where X can be N, O, F or an anion. The molecule containing the relatively positive H is called the donor, and the molecule containing the electronegative atom bonding to H is called the acceptor.

HELPFUL HINT

Water is often called the *universal solvent* because of its strong intrinsic dipole and hydrogen bond. Materials that don't dissolve in water (oil is a common example) have forces holding them together that are stronger than the van der Waals forces from water that could separate them.

Hydrogen bonding is the reason that H_2O has a high boiling point and is a liquid at room temperature, while H_2S, H_2Se, and H_2Te, the larger hydrides of family 16, are all gases. Hydrogen bonding is also the reason ice floats, a property necessary for aquatic life. When water freezes, the molecules adopt a regular structure that maximizes the number of hydrogen bonds. There are regular spaces in the structure, causing water, unlike most substances, to be less dense in the solid phase than the liquid phase. Hydrogen bonding plays an important role in biological systems, holding the DNA double helix together and causing proteins to fold into globular shapes.

There are three weaker intermolecular forces collectively called **van der Waals forces**. They are dipole-dipole interactions, dipole-induced dipole forces, and London forces.

Dipole-dipole interactions occur between polar molecules resulting from the attraction between the negative and positive ends of dipoles. When a dipole comes close to a nonpolar molecule or atom, it can induce a dipole by distorting the electron cloud, creating a **dipole-induced dipole force**. Electrons will be repelled from the negative end of a dipole and attracted to the positive end. Such interactions are important in allowing some nonpolar molecules to dissolve in water. For instance, the negative dipole on H_2O can induce a dipole on O_2 gas, allowing it to dissolve.

London forces refer to the ability of any atom or molecule to induce a temporary dipole in another atom or molecule that is very close. It arises because electrons are constantly in motion. Although on average the electrons are evenly distributed, at any given moment a temporary dipole may occur where there is more electron density on one side of an atom or molecule. This may in turn induce dipoles and result in attraction between adjacent atoms or molecules.

The London force increases with atomic and molecular weight because the electrons are farther from the nucleus and more easily distorted. In general, boiling points increase as atomic and molecular size increase due to increased London forces. The shape of the molecule also has an effect. The boiling point of n-pentane is 27 degrees higher than that of neopentane. The straight chain of n-pentane allows for more London interactions between molecules than the relatively spherical shape of neopentane.

SAMPLE QUESTION

10) Which intermolecular force causes n-pentane to be a liquid at room temperature, while neopentane, also known as 2,2-dimethylpropane, is a gas?

A. dipole-induced dipole

B. dipole-dipole

C. hydrogen bonding

D. London force

Answers:

A. Incorrect. Both molecules are nonpolar and do not have significant dipole interactions.

B. Incorrect. Both molecules are nonpolar.

C. Incorrect. Neither molecule contains —OH, —NH, or —FH bonds, so there is no hydrogen bonding.

D. **Correct.** London forces operate between all molecules and generally increase with increasing molecular weight. Molecular shape also affects them. Although n-pentane and neopentane have identical molecular weights, n-pentane is a long chain where multiple interactions with nearby molecules are possible along the length of the molecule. Neopentane is roughly spherical with fewer opportunities for intermolecular interaction.

INTERMOLECULAR FORCES AND PHYSICAL PROPERTIES

The combinations of bonding and intermolecular interactions determine the physical properties of compounds, including their boiling and melting points. To boil a liquid, heat has to provide molecules with the kinetic energy needed to overcome the intermolecular forces holding them together so the molecules can enter the gas phase. Thus, the stronger the intermolecular forces are in a substance, the higher that substance's boiling point will be. Similarly, the application of heat gives ions and molecules the kinetic energy to overcome the strong stabilizing and attractive forces in a solid and begin to melt. The stronger those attractive forces, the higher the substance's melting point.

Ionic compounds, because of the strong attraction between ions and the stabilizing effect of the lattice energy, have very high melting points, typically several hundred to a 1,000°C. In molten salts, there are still strong attractions between oppositely charged ions. These attractions must be overcome for vaporization, so salts have low equilibrium vapor pressures and boiling points in the thousands of degrees Celsius. Ionic attractions are stronger when the ionic radii are smaller, with more concentrated charge and closer interactions leading to higher melting and boiling points. Higher nominal values of charge also produce stronger attractions and higher melting and boiling points.

The intermolecular interactions between covalent molecules are much weaker than the attractions between ions, so covalent compounds have much lower melting and boiling points. For compounds with similar structures, as molecular weight increases, melting and boiling points increase and equilibrium vapor pressure decreases due to attractive London forces. Introducing polar groups increases boiling and melting points due to dipole-dipole and dipole-induced dipole forces. Introducing hydrogen bonding significantly increases the boiling and melting points of otherwise similar compounds.

Table 3.3. Effects of Dipole-Dipole Interactions on Boiling Point

Formula	Molecular Mass (amu)	Dipole Moment (D)	Boiling Point (K)
$CH_3CH_2CH_3$	44	0	231
CH_3OCH_3	46	1.3	249
CH_3CHO	44	2.7	293

In terms of polarity, like tends to dissolve like. Nonpolar liquids tend to be miscible with each other, being stabilized by London forces. Polar liquids tend to dissolve in water because of dipole-dipole interactions between the polar molecules and water. Compounds that form hydrogen bonds with water tend to be soluble, especially when a large proportion of the molecule participates in the hydrogen bonding.

Electrostatic interactions also play a role in solubility. Simple gases tend to become more soluble in water as molecular weight increases due to greater London forces.

SAMPLE QUESTIONS

11) **$CH_3CH_2CH_3$, CH_3OCH_3, and CH_3CHO have similar molecular weights with dipole moments of 0, 1.3, and 2.7 D, respectively. Put them in order of increasing boiling points.**

↑ polarity

A. $CH_3CH_2CH_3$, CH_3CHO, CH_3OCH_3

B. CH_3CHO, CH_3OCH_3, $CH_3CH_2CH_3$

C. $CH_3CH_2CH_3$, CH_3OCH_3, CH_3CHO

D. CH_3OCH_3, CH_3CHO, $CH_3CH_2CH_3$

Answers:

A. Incorrect. CH_3CHO is more polar than CH_3OCH_3.

B. Incorrect. $CH_3CH_2CH_3$ is nonpolar.

C. **Correct.** The compounds are in order of increasing polarity and so increasing dipole-dipole attraction, leading to increasing boiling points.

D. Incorrect. $CH_3CH_2CH_3$ is nonpolar.

12) **Which is more soluble in water—ethanol or n-butanol?**

A. ethanol

B. n-butanol

Answers:

A. **Correct.** The —OH group constitutes a larger part of the molecule for ethanol.

B. Incorrect. n-butanol has a larger nonpolar chain so would be less soluble. Compounds that react with water tend to be more soluble than expected due to intermolecular interactions.

Naming Compounds

The practice and advancement of science requires that scientists have a common language to describe their work. As early as the nineteenth century, chemists from around the world recognized the need for a standardized naming system for chemical compounds. A committee formed in 1860 to develop a standard nomenclature for organic compounds; this committee evolved into the International Union of Pure and Applied Chemistry or **IUPAC**, the organization responsible for naming elements, molecules, and compounds.

Nomenclature and Chemical Composition

Inorganic Compound Nomenclature

A chemical compound by definition is composed of more than one element. **Ionic binary compounds** consist of two elements: a cation, which is positively charged, and an anion, which is negatively charged. They are generally formed between metals and nonmetals. When naming a binary ionic compound, the name of the cation comes first followed by the root of the name of the anion with an *-ide* suffix. For example, NaCl is called sodium chloride, and $MgBr_2$ is named magnesium bromide.

> **CONSIDER THIS**
>
> The most abundant mineral on the Earth's surface is quartz, which is a primary component of sand and is used to make glass. Its chemical formula is SiO_2—what is its IUPAC name?

Most of the transition metals, except for Ag^+, Zn^{2+}, and Sc^{3+} can have more than one charge. A Roman numeral is used to denote the charge in this case. For example, CuCl is written as *copper(I) chloride*, whereas $CuCl_2$ is *copper(II) chloride*. $ZnCl_2$ would simply be zinc chloride.

For covalent binary compounds, which are generally formed between nonmetals, the name of the element that is further left in the periodic table comes first. If the elements are in the same column, the one that is lower comes first. The second element gets an *–ide* suffix as with ionic compounds. The Greek prefixes *mono–*, *di–*, *tri–*, *tetra–*, *penta–*, *hexa–*, etc., are used to denote the number of atoms of each element. For example, P_2O_5 is named *diphosphorus pentoxide*.

Acids are compounds that yield a proton, H^+, when dissolved in water. For binary acids, the prefix *hydro–* and suffix *–ic* are added to the root of the anion followed by the word *acid*. For example, HF is *hydrofluoric acid*.

Ternary acids are composed of hydrogen and polyatomic anions. Most of these acids form from oxyanions. In the most common case, an oxyanion that ends in *–ate*, like carbonate, yields an oxyacid that ends in *–ic acid*, like carbonic acid. Some elements form multiple oxyanions. The nomenclature for an oxyacid is related to the names of the oxyanions. For each element that forms multiple oxyanions, there is a most common oxyanion that ends in *–ate*. For instance, sulfate, SO_4^{2-}, is the most common oxyanion of sulfur, but it also forms SO_3^{2-}, SO_2^{2-}, and SO_5^{2-}. (Table 4.1 explains how compounds formed from oxyanions are named.) Some common oxyanions include:

- SO_4^{2-} Sulfate
- NO_3^- Nitrate
- PO_4^{3-} Phosphate
- ClO_3^- Chlorate
- BrO_3^- Bromate
- IO_3^- Iodate
- CO_3^{2-} Carbonate
- $CH_3CO_2^-$ Acetate

Table 4.1. Naming Oxyanions

Number of Oxygen Atoms	Name of Oxyanion	Name of Oxyacid
2 < most common	hypo– (root) –ite	hypo– (root) –ous acid
1 < most common	(root) –ite	(root) –ous acid
most common	(root) –ate	(root) –ic acid
1 > most common	per– (root) –ate	per– (root) –ic acid

Example: Naming Sulfur Compounds

Oxyanion Formula	Name of Oxyanion	Acid Formula	Name of Acid
SO_2^{2-}	hyposulfite	H_2SO_2	hyposulfous acid
SO_3^{2-}	sulfite	H_2SO_3	sulfous acid
SO_4^{2-}	sulfate	H_2SO_4	sulfuric acid
SO_5^{2-}	persulfate	H_2SO_5	persulfuric acid

Bases yield hydroxide ions (OH^-) when dissolved in water. The naming of bases is similar to the naming of binary ionic compounds. The name of the cation formed when the base dissociates comes first followed by the word *hydroxide*. NaOH is *sodium hydroxide*. $Ca(OH)_2$ is *calcium hydroxide*. NH_3 has the common name *ammonia* and is a weak base. NH_4OH is *ammonium hydroxide*.

Salts are ionic compounds formed when an acid neutralizes a base yielding water and the salt. The name of the salt is the name of the cation followed by the name of the anion. Some examples are NaCl, which is called sodium chloride, and NH_4NO_3, which is called ammonium nitrate. For transition metals, which can have multiple charges, Roman numerals denote the charge, as with $FeCO_3$, which is *iron(II) carbonate*.

EXCEPTIONS TO THE RULE

Note the bottom 2 acids in Table 4.1 have a *-ur* added to the root. Similarly, phosphoric acid (not *phosphic* acid) is formed from the phosphate ion.

Hydrates are salts bound in a specific ratio to water molecules within a crystal. The name of the salt is followed by a Greek prefix indicating the number of water molecules bound. For instance, $CoCl_2 \cdot 6H_2O$ is expressed as *cobalt(II) chloride hexahydrate*.

SAMPLE QUESTIONS

1) **What is the name of the acid HNO_2?**

A. nitrous acid

B. nitric acid

C. pernitric acid

D. nitrite

Answers:

A. **Correct.** NO_2^- has one less oxygen atom than the most common oxyanion of nitrogen, NO_3^-. So NO_2^- is nitrite and the corresponding acid, HNO_2, is nitrous acid.

B. Incorrect. Nitric acid is HNO_3 formed from the most common oxyanion of nitrogen NO_3^-.

C. Incorrect. Pernitric acid is HNO_4 with one more oxygen than nitric acid.

D. Incorrect. Nitrite is an oxyanion, not an acid.

2) **What is the name of $ZnSO_4 \cdot 7H_2O$?**

A. zinc(II) sulfate heptahydrate

B. zinc sulfate pentahydrate

C. zinc sulfate heptahydrate

D. zinc(II) sulfite heptahydrate

Answers:

A. Incorrect. Zn, Ag, and Sc are the three transition metals that can have only one charge, so it is not necessary to denote the charge.

B. Incorrect. Pentahydrate indicates five H_2O, not seven.

C. **Correct.** Heptahydrate indicates seven H_2O bound, and it is unnecessary to denote the charge on zinc, as it can only have one charge of +2.

D. Incorrect. The anion is sulfate, not sulfite.

Organic Compound Nomenclature

Organic compounds contain carbon and are the basis of life. The simplest organic molecules contain just carbon and hydrogen and are called *hydrocarbons*. Carbon participates in four bonds and hydrogen participates in one bond. Hydrocarbons that are composed of all single bonds are called **alkanes**. The nomenclature for alkanes is based on the number of carbons in the molecule.

Table 4.2. Naming Alkanes

Chemical Formula	Name	Chemical Formula	Name
CH_4	methane	$C_{11}H_{24}$	undecane
C_2H_6	ethane	$C_{12}H_{26}$	dodecane
C_3H_8	propane	$C_{13}H_{28}$	tridecane
C_4H_{10}	butane	$C_{14}H_{30}$	tetradecane
C_5H_{12}	pentane	$C_{15}H_{32}$	pentadecane
C_6H_{14}	hexane	$C_{16}H_{34}$	hexadecane
C_7H_{16}	heptane	$C_{17}H_{36}$	heptadecane
C_8H_{18}	octane	$C_{18}H_{38}$	octadecane
C_9H_{20}	nonane	$C_{19}H_{40}$	nonadecane
$C_{10}H_{22}$	decane	$C_{20}H_{42}$	eicosane

```
    H          H  H         H  H  H          H  H  H  H
    |          |  |         |  |  |          |  |  |  |
 H—C—H     H—C—C—H     H—C—C—C—H     H—C—C—C—C—H
    |          |  |         |  |  |          |  |  |  |
    H          H  H         H  H  H          H  H  H  H

 Methane     Ethane       Propane          Butane
```

Figure 4.1. Alkanes

Starting with butane, there are multiple configurations possible for the same chemical composition, as shown in Figure 4.2. As the number of carbons in the molecule increases, there are too many possible configurations to use common names. It becomes necessary to have a naming system, which the IUPAC has defined.

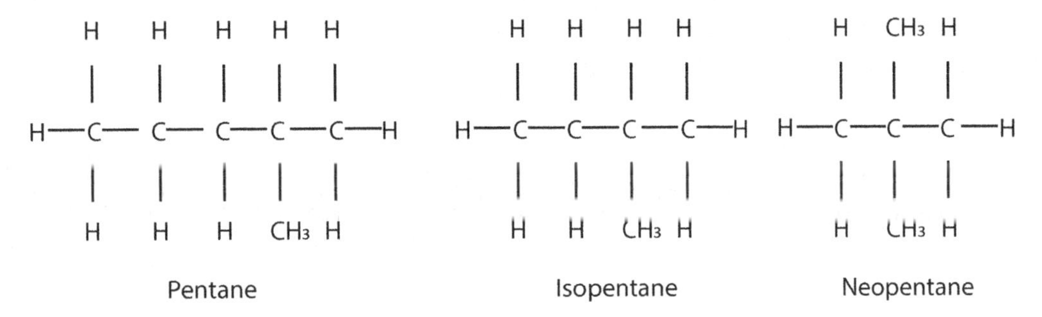

Figure 4.2 Isomers of Pentane

For branched alkanes, the groups attached to the longest chain are called alkyl groups and are named with the same roots as above but end in *-yl* as opposed to *-ane*. Common names of branched groups are also converted from *-ane* to *-yl*, such as isopropyl, isobutyl, etc. For alkyl groups of six or fewer carbons, common names are often intermingled with IUPAC conventions for the overall molecule. There is a common convention of prefixes for the alkyl groups that depends on the configuration of the group and how many carbons are bonded to the carbon at the point of attachment to the main chain:

- *n–* refers to a straight chain.
- *iso–* refers to the configuration $(CH_3)_2CH$—.
- *sec–* refers to a carbon at a point of attachment to the main chain, which is attached to two other carbons.
- *tert–* refers to a carbon that at a point of attachment to the main chain is attached to three other carbons.

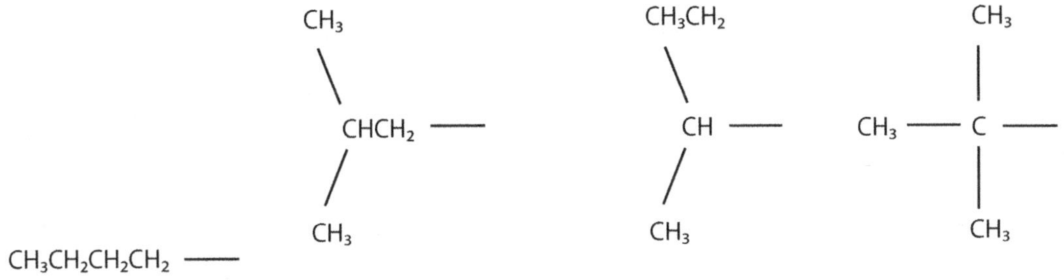

$CH_3CH_2CH_2CH_2$ —

n-butyl

CH_3 \ $CHCH_2$ — / CH_3

isobutyl

CH_3CH_2 \ CH — / CH_3

sec-butyl

CH_3 | CH_3 — C — | CH_3

tertbutyl

Figure 4.3. Branched Alkanes

The first step in naming a compound is to identify the longest carbon chain. Numbers are used to denote the position on the long chain where the groups are attached. Numbering starts at the end that produces lower numbers. If several of the same group are attached, the Greek prefixes *di–*, *tri–*, *tetra–*, etc, are used. If there are several different groups attached, they are named in order of increasing size or alphabetically.

In addition to forming single bonds, carbon atoms can form double and triple bonds. Compounds with double bonds between carbon atoms are called **alkenes** and those with triple bonds are called **alkynes**.

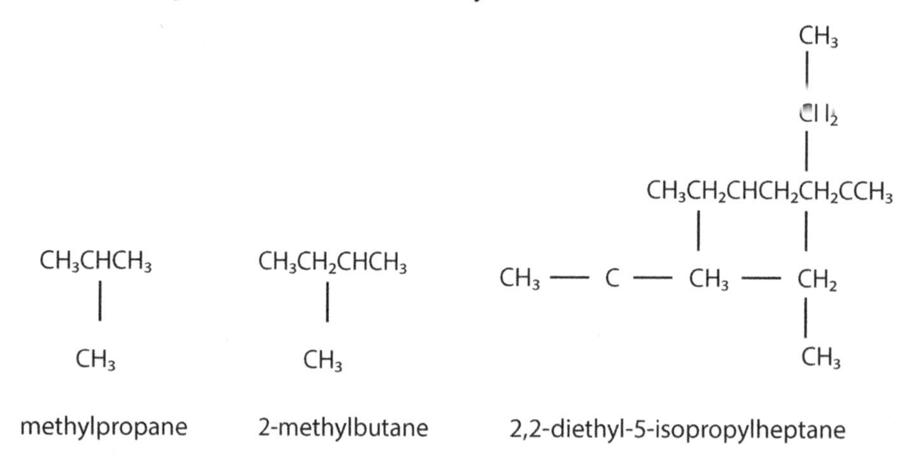

Figure 4.4. Naming Alkanes with Attached Groups

For **alkenes**, roots are the same as alkanes but with a suffix of *–ene* instead of *–ane*. The location of the double bond is denoted by a number corresponding to the position in the chain of the first carbon in the double bond. Counting starts from the end closest to the double bond. The same names and numbers denote alkyl groups and their positions as for alkanes.

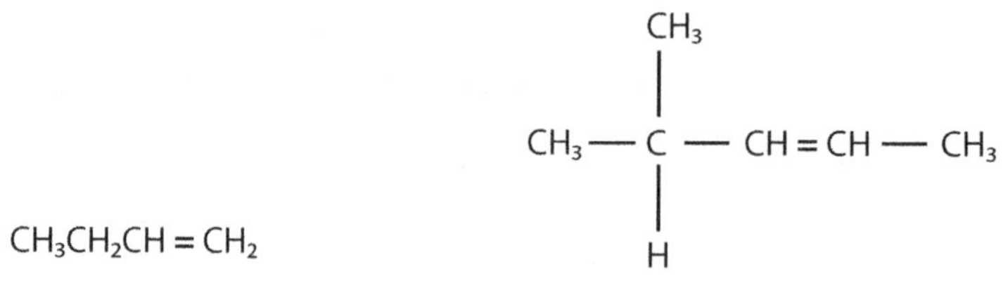

$CH_3CH_2CH=CH_2$

1-butene

$$CH_3-\overset{\displaystyle CH_3}{\underset{\displaystyle H}{C}}-CH=CH-CH_3$$

4-methyl-2-pentene

Figure 4.5. Alkenes

Alkynes have a triple bond between carbons. The nomenclature is the same as for alkenes, except the names end in *–yne* instead of *–ene*. The smallest alkyne, $HC\equiv CH$, has the common name *acetylene* and the IUPAC name *ethyne*.

Organic compounds can also have functional groups that give them specific chemical properties. Some of the most common groups contain oxygen or nitrogen. These include alcohols, ethers, aldehydes, ketones, and amines.

Alcohols contain an —OH group. The smaller alcohols have frequently used common names that consist of the name of the alkyl groups followed by *alcohol.* The *iso–*, *sec–*, and *tert–* prefixes are used to indicate the alkyl groups bonded to —OH. For example, isopropyl alcohol is $(CH_3)_2CHOH$.

Alcohols have similar IUPAC names as alkanes, except they end in *–ol.* A number is used to designate the position of the —OH group, starting from the closest end of the chain.

DID YOU KNOW?

Ethanol, CH_3CH_2OH, an alcohol that is commonly called "alcohol," is a polar molecule and can therefore dissolve easily in water, a requirement for its use in drinks

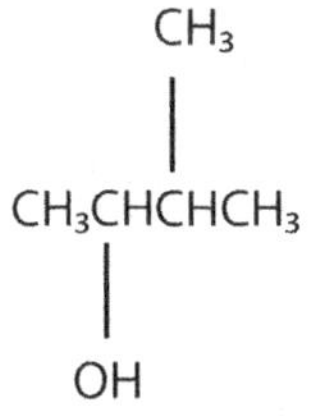

CH_3 (on C3)
$CH_3CHCHCH_3$
OH (on C2)

3-methyl-2-butanol

$CH_3—CH—CH_2—OH$
CH_3 (on CH)

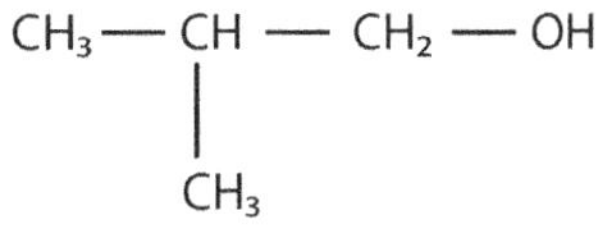

2-methyl-1-propanol

Figure 4.6. Alcohols

Another class of organic molecule with single C—O bonds are ethers. **Ethers** have the general structure R—O—R, where R is an alkyl or aromatic group. There are two common ways of naming ethers. The first is to name the alkyl/aromatic groups followed by the word ether. If the two R groups are the same, the alkyl group is named just once.

The second way of naming ethers is used most often when one group is large and doesn't have a common alkyl name. The larger group is named following alkane naming rules. A number denotes where on the main chain the oxygen is attached, and the smaller group containing the oxygen is named by its common root followed by *–oxy.*

CH_3OCH_3

methyl ether

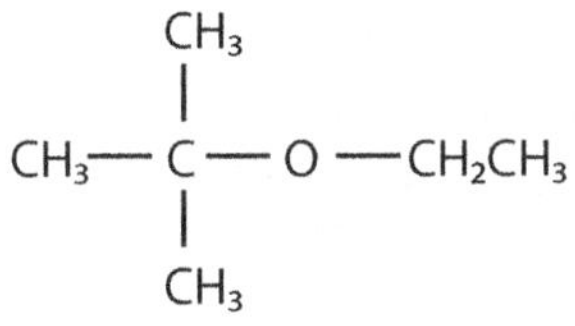

CH_3 (above C)
$CH_3—C—O—CH_2CH_3$
CH_3 (below C)

ethyl *tert*-butyl ether

$CH_3CH_2CH_2CH_2CHCH_3$
OCH_3 (on CH)

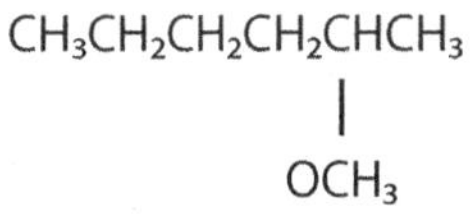

2-methoxyhexane

Figure 4.7. Ethers

The two types of organic compounds that contain carbon-oxygen double bonds are the aldehydes and ketones.

Not surprisingly, the smaller **aldehydes** have common names. Those names are derived from the names of the corresponding carboxylic acids—of the form RCOOH—which in turn get their names from where they naturally occur. The general structures and names are given in the table below.

Table 4.3. Naming Aldehydes

Chemical Formula	Common Name	IUPAC name
H_2CO	formaldehyde	methanal
CH_3CHO	acetaldehyde	ethanal
CH_3CH_2CHO	propionaldehyde	propanal
$CH_3(CH_2)_2CHO$	n-butyraldehyde	butanal
$CH_3(CH_2)_3CHO$	n-valeraldehyde	pentanal
$CH_3(CH_2)_4CHO$	n-caproaldehyde	hexanal

In conjunction with the common names, the Greek letters α, β, δ, and γ designate distance from the carbonyl carbon—CHO—with α being next to the carbonyl and β, δ, and γ getting progressively farther away.

The IUPAC system takes the alkane name of the longest chain containing the CHO group and replaces *-ane* with *-al*. Numbers denote the position of the substituents, with the carbonyl carbon being number one. H_2CO is *methanal*. CH_3CHO is *ethanal* and so on.

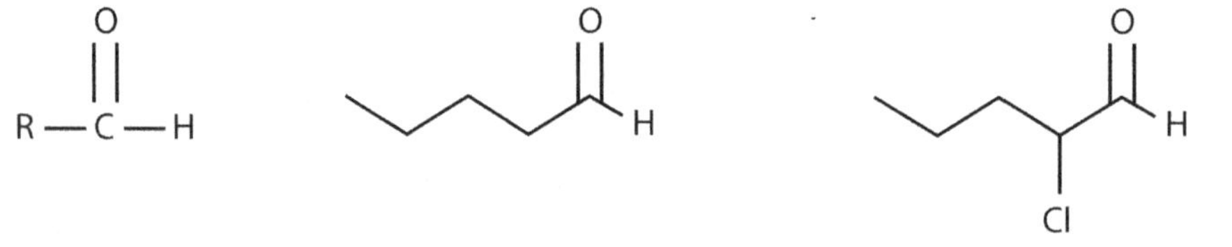

R—C(=O)—H
aldehyde

pentanal
(valeraldehyde)

2-chloropentanal
(α-chlorovaleraldehyde)

Figure 4.8. Aldehydes

As with aldehydes, there are two naming systems for **ketones**. In the common system, the smallest ketone CH_3COCH_3 is called acetone. Larger ketones are named with the names of the alkyl groups attached to the carbonyl and the word *ketone*. For instance, $CH_3CH_2COCH_3$ is methyl ethyl ketone. When the carbonyl is attached to a benzene ring, it is called a *phenone*.

The IUPAC system takes the alkane name of the longest straight chain containing the carbonyl and replaces the end *-e* with *-one*. Substituent positions and the position of the carbonyl are denoted by numbers, starting from the end of the chain closest to the carbonyl. $(CH_3)_2CHCOCH_3$ is called *3-methyl-2-butanone*.

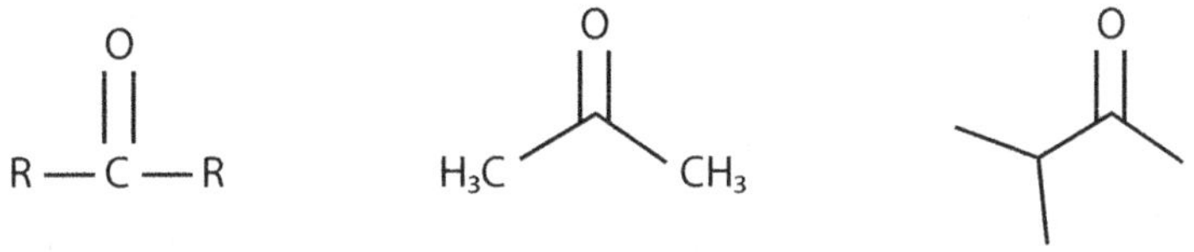

ketone	propanone (acetone)	3-methyl-2-butanone (methyl isopropyl ketone)
R—C(=O)—R	H_3C—C(=O)—CH_3	

Figure 4.9. Ketones

Amines are a class of organic compounds containing nitrogen. They are described as primary (RNH_2), secondary (R_2NH), or tertiary (R_3N). Smaller amines often have common names corresponding to the alkyl group(s) attached followed by amine. For instance, $CH_3NHCH_2CH_3$ is called *methylethylamine*.

IUPAC names are based on the alkane name of the longest straight chain attached to nitrogen, where the suffix *-amine* replaces *-e*. A number denotes the position of the amine group. For secondary and tertiary amines, the shorter chains attached are treated as alkyl groups and given the label *N-* to denote they are attached to nitrogen. For example, $CH_3CH_2CH_2N(CH_3)_2$ is called *N,N-dimethyl-1-propanamine*.

QUICK REVIEW

What are the similarities and differences between the names for functional groups? What patterns can you see that would help students learn the rules for naming organic compounds?

When amines are found in most oxygen-containing organic molecules, the amine is treated as a substituent attached to the main chain containing the oxygen group. The amine group is given the name *amino* preceded by *N-alkyl* describing any other alkyl group(s) attached to N.

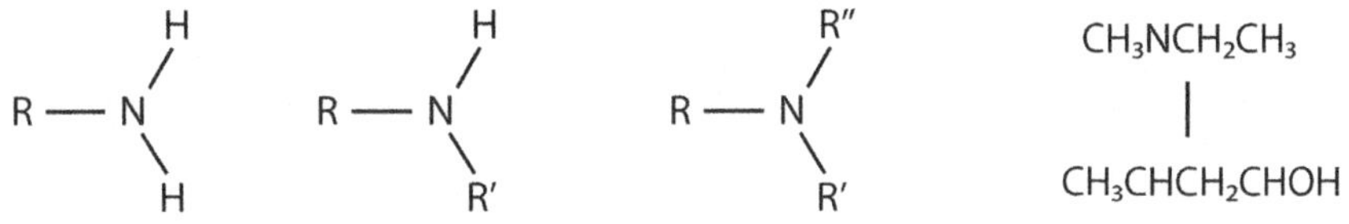

primary amine	secondary amine	tertiary amine	3-(N-methyl-N-ethylamino)-1-butanol
R—N(H)(H)	R—N(H)(R′)	R—N(R″)(R′)	$CH_3NCH_2CH_3$ attached to CH_3CHCH_2CHOH

Figure 4.10. Amines

Go on

SAMPLE QUESTIONS

3) **What is the name of the following molecule?**

CH_3
|
$CHCH_2CH_2CHCH_2CHCH_3$
| | |
CH_2 CH_3 CH_2
| |
CH_3 CH_3

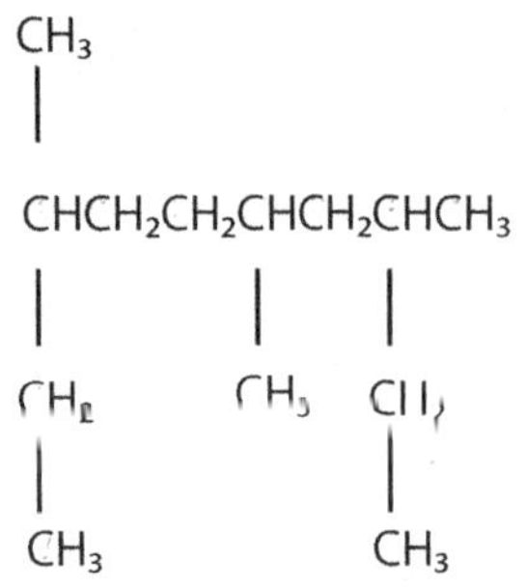

A. 1-methyl-1-ethyl-4-methyl-6-ethylheptane

B. dimethyl-diethyl-heptane

C. 1,4-dimethyl-1,6-diethylheptane

D. 3,5,8-trimethyldecane

Answers:

A. Incorrect. Identical groups should be combined with a Greek prefix for the number of like groups, as in *dimethyl* and *diethyl*. Also, the longest chain is longer than seven carbons.

B. Incorrect. Numbers are used to denote the position on the longest straight chain of the alkyl groups. Also, the longest chain is longer than seven carbons.

C. Incorrect. This would be correct if the longest chain was as drawn with seven carbons. Numbers denote the position of the groups on the main chain. Identical alkyl groups are denoted together with the Greek prefix *di–* for the number of them: two each of methyl and ethyl. However, the two ethyl groups can be considered part of a ten-carbon straight chain.

D. **Correct.** The longest straight chain possible is ten carbons long with methyl groups attached at positions three, five, and eight.

4) **What are the common and IUPAC names for the following molecule?**

CH_3
|
CH_3CH_2 — C — CH_3
|
OH

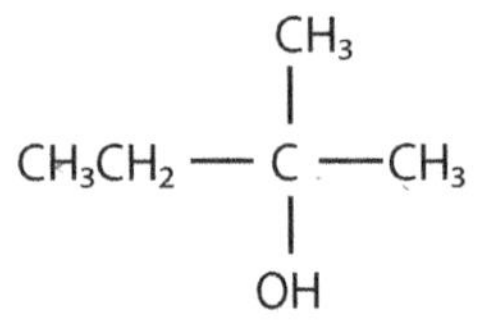

A. methylbutanol, 2-methyl-2-butanol

B. tert-pentyl alcohol, 3-methyl-3-butanol

C. isopentyl alcohol, 2-methyl-2-butanol

D. tert-pentyl alcohol, 2-methyl-2-butanol

Answers:

A. Incorrect. *Methylbutanol* is ambiguous. It doesn't designate where the methyl group is.

B. Incorrect. IUPAC numbering starts from the end closest to the hydroxyl group.

C. Incorrect. Isopentyl alcohol would have the methyl group attached to the next to last carbon on the chain, that is, the three position.

D. Correct. *tert–* indicates that the carbon bonded to —OH is bonded to three carbons; there are five carbons total, so by common naming conventions, this is a *pentyl alcohol*. IUPAC names the alcohol by the number of carbons in the main straight chain containing the —OH group: butanol. Counting starts from the end of the chain nearest the —OH, yielding 2-methyl-2-butanol.

5) **Give the common and IUPAC names of the following molecule.**

$CH_3CH_2CCH_2CH_2CH_3$

A. ethyl n-propyl ketone, 4-hexanone

B. ethyl propyl ketone, 3-hexanone

C. n-propyl ethyl ketone, 3-pentanone

D. ethyl n-propyl ketone, 3-hexanone

Answers:

A. Incorrect. IUPAC numbering starts at the end closest to the carbonyl.

B. Incorrect. Propyl is ambiguous. n-propyl should be used to denote a straight chain.

C. Incorrect. For common names, the name of the smaller alkyl group is generally listed first. For the IUPAC name, the main chain containing the carbonyl has a total of six carbons, so it is *hexanone*.

D. Correct. The smaller ethyl group is listed first, and n-propyl indicates a straight propyl chain. For the IUPAC name, the position of the carbonyl is counted from the closest end, and the six-carbon chain is called *hexanone*.

Chemical Reactions

ATOMIC MASS AND THE MOLE

Each element has a specific atomic mass, measured in atomic mass units (amu), that is the result of the number of protons, neutrons, and electrons in the atom. (The periodic table lists the atomic masses for all the elements.) For elements with isotopes, the atomic mass of each isotope is weighted based on its prevalence, and the resulting values are averaged. Carbon, for example, which exists mostly as ^{12}C (98.9 percent) but also as ^{13}C (1.1 percent) and ^{14}C (0.001 percent), has a mass of 12.01 amu.

Likewise, molecules and compounds have molecular mass or formula mass values that are equal to the sum of the masses of the atoms that compose them. CO_2, for example, has a molecular mass of $12.01 + (2 \times 16) = 44.01$ amu.

Avogadro's number, 6.02×10^{23}, is the number of atoms or molecules in a mole of any given element or compound. The number relates atomic or molecular mass to weight in grams, the unit typically used when working with chemical reactions. A mole of an element weighs the same in grams as the atomic weight. So, a mole of carbon, or 6.02×10^{23} atoms of carbon, weighs 12.01 g. The weight of a mole of an element or compound is called its **molar mass.**

DID YOU KNOW?

Tin (Sn), has ten stable isotopes, the most of any element on the periodic table. The most abundant in nature is ^{120}Sn, but large percentages of ^{118}Sn and ^{116}Sn, among others, result in an atomic mass for Tin of 118.71 amu.

The molar mass of an element or compound can be used as a conversion factor to convert between moles and grams:

$$\frac{3\text{ g C}}{} \times \frac{1\text{ mol}}{12.01\text{ g}} = 0.25\text{ mol C}$$

▶

5 mol O_2	32 g	= 160 g O_2
	1 mol	

Avogadro's number can be used as a conversion factor to convert between moles and number of atoms or molecules:

▶

3 mol CH_4	6.02×10^{23} molecules	= 1.8×10^{24} molecules CH_4
	1 mol	

Molar mass can be used to calculate the percent composition by mass of each element in a compound. The percent composition by mass is simply the percentage of a compound's mass contributed by each element.

$$\%\text{ mass of element} = \frac{\text{no. of atoms of element} \times \text{molar mass of element}}{\text{molar mass of compound}} \times 100$$

Percent composition can, in turn, be used to find the empirical formula for a given compound. The **molecular formula** of a compound is the number of each type of atom in the molecule, while the **empirical formula** gives the smallest whole number ratio of different atoms in a molecule. For example, the molecular formula of ethane is C_2H_6, and the empirical formula is CH_3.

An empirical formula can be determined from mass percent data using the following steps:

1. Starting with mass percentages for each element, find the mass of each element in a 100 g sample.
2. Convert the mass of elements to moles of elements.
3. Divide each number of moles by the smallest number of moles to determine the smallest whole number ratio of elements.
4. Write the empirical formula with elements and subscripts.

If the molar mass of the compound is known, the molecular formula can be determined from the empirical formula. The molar mass of the compound divided by the empirical molar mass yields the number that the empirical subscripts are multiplied by to get the molecular formula. If the molar mass of the compound equals the molar mass of the empirical formula, then the empirical formula is the molecular formula.

SAMPLE QUESTIONS

1) **How many moles of NaCl are in 5 g of NaCl?**

A. 0.09 mol

B. 11.69 mol

C. 3.01×10^{24} mol

D. 8.31×10^{-24} mol

Answer: A.

Find the molar mass of NaCl and use dimensional analysis.

Na: 22.99 g

Cl: 35.45 g

NaCl: 22.99 + 35.45 = 58.44 g

5 g	1 mol	= **0.09 mol**
1	58.44 g	

2) **What is the mass percent of O in $CaCO_3$?**

A. 12.00 percent

B. 15.99 percent

C. 40.04 percent

D. 47.96 percent

Answer: D.

$$\% \text{ mass of element} = \frac{\text{no.of atoms of element} \times \text{molar mass of element}}{\text{molar mass of compound}} \times 100$$

$$= \frac{\text{no.of atoms of O} \times \text{molar mass of O}}{\text{molar mass of } CaCO_3}$$

$$= \frac{3(16)}{40.08 + 12.01 + 3(16)} \times 100 = \mathbf{47.96\%}$$

3) **Find the empirical formula of a compound that is 68.54% carbon, 8.63% hydrogen, and 22.83% oxygen.**

A. C_2HO

B. C_4H_6O

C. CH_6O_4

D. CHO

Answer: B.

Convert percentages to masses assuming 100 grams of the substance is present.

68.54 g C

8.63 g H

22.83 g O

Convert mass to moles.

68.54 g C	1 mol C	= 5.70 mol C
1	12.01 g C	

8.63 g H	1 mol H	= 8.54 mol H
1	1.01 g H	

22.83 g O	1 mol O	= 1.42 mol O
1	16 g O	

Divide by the smallest value.

$C = \frac{5.70}{1.42} = 4$

$H = \frac{8.54}{1.42} = 6$

$O = \frac{1.42}{1.42} = 1$

The empirical formula for the compound is: $\mathbf{C_4H_6O}$

Chemical Reactions and Equations

Chemical reactions involve the conversion of reactants into products and are described by chemical equations. The left side of a chemical equation shows the **reactants**, those elements or compounds present at the beginning of a reaction. The right side of the equation shows the **products**, the elements and compounds that result from the reaction. In the chemical equation, chemical formulas are used to represent the reactants and products, and the arrow symbol indicates the direction of the reaction. A plus sign is used to show the relationship of multiple reactants and products (i.e., reactant A plus B yields product C plus D). All chemical reactions must obey the law of conservation of matter, which states that matter can neither be created nor destroyed (i.e., the mass of the reactants must be equal to the mass of the products).

A common chemical reaction is the reaction between baking soda and vinegar. Baking soda is a chemical compound called sodium bicarbonate ($NaHCO_3$), and vinegar is dilute acetic acid (CH_3COOH). Their reaction results in the formation of gas, water, and sodium acetate.

$$NaHCO_3\ (s) + CH_3COOH\ (l) \rightarrow CO_2\ (g) + H_2O\ (l) + NaC_2H_3O_2\ (aq)$$

In this equation, $NaHCO_3$ and CH_3COOH are the reactants and CO_2, H_2O, and $NaC_2H_3O_2$ are the products. The arrow in the equation indicates that the reaction will form or yield the products and moves in the forward direction. The physical state of the compounds is indicated in the parentheses next to them: *s* = solid, *l* = liquid, *g* = gas, and *aq* = aqueous.

Types of Chemical Reactions

There are several types of chemical reactions. One of the most common is a **combustion** reaction, which is when an element or compound burns in air or oxygen. This happens every time natural gas is used to produce heat and gasoline is used to power a vehicle. Combustion reactions are exothermic, meaning they give off heat. When elements are burned, the products are typically the most common oxide of the element; for example, sulfur produces sulfur dioxide and iron produces iron oxide. When an organic compound (a compound made of C, H, and O) combusts in oxygen, the reaction products are always carbon dioxide and water. The general chemical equation for this is:

$$C_xH_y + Z\,O_2 \rightarrow X\,CO_2 + \frac{Y}{2}\,H_2O$$

Neutralization reactions, also called acid-base reactions, occur when acids and bases react with each other. The reaction between strong acids and bases always produces salt and water, neutralizing their acidic and basic effects. This occurs because there are no longer excesses of hydrogen or hydroxide ions in the solution, resulting in a pH of 7 for strong acid-base neutralizations. For weak acids and bases, the pH of the solution will depend on the acid strength of the reactants.

It is easy to determine the products of a neutralization reaction since Acid + Base → Salt + Water. The salt will form from the anion of the acid and the cation of the base. The following is an example of a neutralization reaction involving a strong acid and base:

$$HCl\,(aq) + NaOH\,(aq) \rightarrow NaCl\,(aq) + H_2O\,(l)$$

In a **decomposition** reaction, one compound decomposes or breaks down into two or more products. The products can be elements or simpler compounds, and the number of products will be greater than the number of reactants. This is the opposite of a combination reaction or chemical synthesis. The general formula for a decomposition reaction is:

$$AB \rightarrow A + B$$

A decomposition reaction can occur spontaneously and may be an unwanted reaction. For example, hydrogen peroxide will decompose into water and oxygen over time. The decomposition of hydrogen peroxide is spontaneous, which is why bottles of hydrogen peroxide slowly lose their effectiveness over time. The equation for the decomposition of hydrogen peroxide is:

$$2\,H_2O_2\,(aq) \rightarrow 2\,H_2O\,(l) + O_2\,(g)$$

Some decomposition reactions occur so spontaneously, they are explosive. Nitroglycerine will violently decompose with very little provocation. Decomposition reactions that occur with the addition of heat are called *thermal decomposition reactions.* With the addition of heat, some metal oxides decompose into the component metal and oxygen.

In a **dehydration** reaction, the reacting molecules combine in such a way that a water molecule is lost from a reactant. Dehydration reactions are often used in organic synthesis. Two monosaccharides (sugars) can be joined together to form a disaccharide via the loss of water. The opposite of a dehydration reaction is a hydration or hydrolysis reaction in which water is a reactant. The conversion of alcohols to ethers is an example of a dehydration reaction:

$$2\,CH_3CH_2-OH \rightarrow CH_3CH_2-O-CH_2CH_3 + H_2O$$

In a **single-replacement** (or **displacement**) reaction, the reactant element replaces one of the elements in the reactant compound, releasing another element as a product. The general equation for this type of reaction is:

$$A + BC \rightarrow AC + B$$

For this reaction to occur, A and B must be different metals or halogens. The single replacement can be the replacement of one cation for another or one anion for another. An example of a cation single replacement reaction is:

$$3\ Na + AlCl_3 \rightarrow 3\ NaCl + Al$$

An example of an anion single replacement reaction is:

$$Br_2 + 2\ KI \rightarrow 2\ KBr + I_2$$

A **double-replacement** (or **displacement**) reaction is similar to a single replacement reaction but occurs between two compounds instead of a compound and an element. The two compounds react to form two new compounds. The general equation for a double-replacement reaction is:

$$AB + CD \rightarrow AD + CB$$

This can also be called an exchange reaction because the two compounds exchange partners. The neutralization reaction is a type of double-replacement reaction.

In some double composition reactions, one of the products will be a solid precipitate. In the reaction shown below, the aqueous reactants silver nitrate and sodium chloride react to form aqueous sodium nitrate and silver chloride, which is a solid:

$$AgNO_3\ (aq) + NaCl\ (aq) \rightarrow AgCl\ (s) + NaNO_3\ (aq)$$

SAMPLE QUESTION

4) **Identify the type of reaction shown below:**

$Pb(NO_3)_2\ (aq) + K_2CrO_4\ (aq) \rightarrow PbCrO_4\ (s) + 2\ KNO_3\ (aq)$

A. neutralization reaction

B. decomposition reaction

C. double-displacement reaction

D. single-replacement reaction

Answers:

A. Incorrect. A neutralization reaction includes an acid and a base as the reactants.

B. Incorrect. In a decomposition reaction, a reactant breaks down into multiple products.

C. **Correct.** In the reaction, the Pb and K exchange their anions in a double-displacement reaction.

D. Incorrect. In a single-replacement reaction, a single element reacts with a compound.

BALANCING CHEMICAL EQUATIONS

The law of conservation of mass states that matter can neither be created nor destroyed during a reaction. Accordingly, a chemical equation must be balanced to ensure that an equal number of each type of atom appears on both sides. This is not always the case when a chemical equation is initially written. Sometimes the coefficients, the numbers in front of the reactants and products, must be changed to balance the equation.

To balance a chemical reaction, use the following simple steps:

1. Write the chemical equation for the reaction. Determine if the equation needs to be balanced.
2. If the equation needs to be balanced, choose an element and balance it by adding the appropriate coefficient to the reactant or product as needed.
3. Balance the atoms of the remaining elements by adding coefficients. Only the coefficients can be changed, not the subscripts. Changing the subscripts would change the compound, not just the number of the compound.
4. Verify that the number of atoms of each element is balanced.

A simple combustion reaction of methane with oxygen results in carbon dioxide and water. With just the reactants and products, the chemical equation is:

$$CH_4\ (g) + O_2\ (g) \rightarrow CO_2\ (g) + H_2O\ (l)$$

However, this equation is not balanced. There are four reactant hydrogen atoms but only two hydrogen atoms in the product. Additionally, there are two reactant oxygen atoms but three product oxygen atoms. This equation can be balanced by adding more product or reactant molecules as needed.

The product side of the equation needs two additional hydrogen atoms, which must come from one of the two products. Since CO_2 does not have any hydrogen, H_2O is the only option for balancing hydrogen. Adding a two in front of the H_2O indicates that two molecules of water are produced in the reaction, resulting in a total of four hydrogen atoms.

This step balances the hydrogen atoms in the equation, but now there are four oxygen atoms on the product side and two on the reactant side. Since O_2 is the only reactant that contains oxygen, it is the only option for balancing the equation. By putting a 2 in front of the O_2, there will be a total of four oxygen atoms on both sides of the equation. The following is the balanced equation:

$$CH_4\ (g) + 2\ O_2\ (g) \rightarrow CO_2\ (g) + 2\ H_2O\ (l)$$

This combustion reaction requires two molecules of diatomic oxygen to move forward and results in two molecules of water being formed.

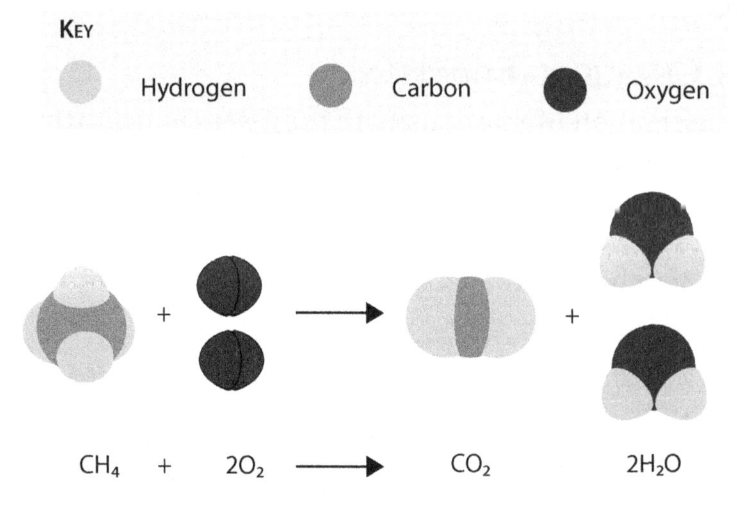

Figure 5.1. Combustion Reaction

SAMPLE QUESTIONS

5) **Balance the following combustion equation: $C_8H_{18} + O_2 \rightarrow CO_2 + H_2O$**

A. $C_8H_{18} + O_2 \rightarrow CO_2 + H_2O$

B. $C_8H_{18} + 6\,O_2 \rightarrow 8\,CO_2 + H_2O$

C. $4\,C_8H_{18} + 48\,O_2 \rightarrow 32\,CO_2 + 16\,H_2O$

D. $2\,C_8H_{18} + 25\,O_2 \rightarrow 16\,CO_2 + 18\,H_2O$

Answer: D.

$C_8H_{18} + O_2 \rightarrow 8\,CO_2 + H_2O$	Start by balancing the carbon atoms on each side of the equation.
$C_8H_{18} + O_2 \rightarrow 8\,CO_2 + 9\,H_2O$	Next, balance the hydrogen atoms on each side of the equation.
$C_8H_{18} + 12.5\,O_2 \rightarrow 8\,CO_2 + 9\,H_2O$	Then, balance the oxygen on each side of the equation.
$\mathbf{2\,C_8H_{18} + 25\,O_2 \rightarrow 16\,CO_2 + 18\,H_2O}$	Finally, remove the decimal by multiplying each coefficient by 2.

6) **Predict the missing product for the following reaction:**
$CuCO_3 \rightarrow CuO +$ ___

A. CuO_2

B. CO_2

C. CO

D. C_2

Answers:

A. Incorrect. This product would leave the right side with no C atoms.

B. Correct. The reaction is the decomposition of $CuCO_3$ into CuO and CO_2.

C. Incorrect. This reaction could not be balanced.

D. Incorrect. This reaction could not be balanced.

OXIDATION AND REDUCTION REACTIONS

Both single- and double-replacement reactions are types of **oxidation-reduction** reactions, also known as redox reactions. These reactions involve the exchange of electrons; one species is reduced while the other is oxidized. The reactant that is **oxidized** (that undergoes oxidation) loses electrons. The reactant that is **reduced** (that undergoes reduction) has gained electrons. In the reaction, the oxidizing agent accepts electrons, causing the oxidation of another species. The reducing agent donates electrons, causing the reduction of another species.

Both oxidation and reduction must occur together and in equal proportion, and the number of electrons lost and gained must be the same. Because of this, individual oxidation and reduction reactions are referred to as half reactions since they are only half of the electron exchange process.

OXIDATION NUMBERS

The transfer of electrons in redox reactions also results in a change in the oxidation number of species involved in the reaction. The **oxidation number** is the charge of an atom in a compound compared with its charge as an uncombined atom. The oxidation number of an atom can be determined using the following set of rules and the periodic table.

> HELPFUL HINT
>
> Two mnemonic devices can help in remembering which species gain or lose electrons:
>
> LEO the lion says, "GER!" (Loss of Electrons is Oxidation. Gain of Electrons is Reduction.)
>
> OIL RIG (Oxidation Involves Loss of electrons. Reduction Involves Gain of electrons.)

Oxidation Number Rules:

1. The oxidation number of a pure element is always 0.
2. The sum of the oxidation numbers in a neutral species is 0, and in an ion it is equal to the charge of the ion.
3. The oxidation number of an ion is equal to its charge.
4. Some elements will always have the same oxidation number. These elements can be used to determine the oxidation number of other elements in a compound.

- Group 1 metals have an oxidation number of +1.
- Group 2 metals have an oxidation number of +2.
- Hydrogen has an oxidation number of +1 unless it is combined with a metal, in which case its number is –1.
- Fluorine has an oxidation number of –1.
- Oxygen usually has an oxidation number of –2. The exception is peroxides, in which oxygen has an oxidation number of –1
- In binary metal compounds, Group 17 elements have an oxidation number of –1, Group 16 an oxidation number of –2, and Group 15 an oxidation number of –3.

SAMPLE QUESTION

7) **Determine the oxidation numbers for the species in the following reaction.**

$Fe\ (s) + H_2SO_4\ (aq) \rightarrow FeSO_4\ (aq) + H_2\ (g)$

A. Fe (0), H (–1), S (+4), O (–2) → Fe (0), S (+4), O (–1), H (–1)
B. Fe (+1), H (+1), S (+6), O (–2) → Fe (0), S (+4), O (–1), H (0)
C. Fe (0), H (+1), S: (+6), O (–2) → Fe (+2), S (+6), O (–2), H (0)
D. Fe (0), H (–1), S (+4), O (–2) → Fe (+2), S (+4), O (–1), H (0)

Answer: C.

- The elemental reactant (Fe) and product (H) are assigned 0.
- H is assigned +1 and O is assigned –2.
- Use the oxidation numbers of H and O to find the oxidation number for S.

  H_2SO_4: $2(1) + S + 4(-2) = 0$

  $S - 6 = 0$

  $S = +6$

Reduction Potentials

To balance redox reactions, the reaction must be separated into two half reactions, the oxidation reaction and the reduction reaction. Most half reactions are well known and have a standard potential associated with them. These potentials are all written for the reduction reaction and, as such, are called **standard reduction potentials.** The value of the reduction potential, $E°_{red}$, indicates how strongly the reduced species on the right wants the electrons, and it is measured in volts, the SI unit for electrical potential. The values for E° are for a certain specific set of conditions (e.g., a 1 M solution of an aqueous ion at 1 atm and 25 °C) and are called the voltages for the half cell. The symbol ° indicates the conditions are standard.

$$Li^+\ (aq) + e^- \rightarrow Li\ (s) \qquad E°_{red} = -3.04\ V$$

All standard potentials are measured against the standard hydrogen electrode (SHE) reaction, which is assigned a potential of zero volts. When the E° value for the lithium reduction reaction is –3.04, this really means that it is –3.04 volts compared to the reduction of hydrogen by the SHE reaction.

The reduction potentials indicate the spontaneity of the half reactions. A positive potential indicates a spontaneous forward reaction. Fluorine has a high affinity for electrons and a standard reduction potential of +2.87 volts, which indicates that the reaction is spontaneous. The more positive the E°, the more easily the substance on the left side of the reaction can be reduced. The more negative the E°, the less likely the substance on the left side of the reaction will be reduced and more likely an oxidation will occur.

If the half reaction is written in the reverse direction, the sign of E° must be reversed (i.e., a positive value becomes negative, and a negative value becomes positive). It is important to remember that the half reactions can occur in either direction.

Standard reduction potentials are used to form the **electrochemical reactivity series**. This series can be used to determine which elements oxidize more easily than others by ranking the reducing and oxidizing agents. Hydrogen is used as the reference point. The strongest reducing agents are the most reactive metals and are at the top of the table (for instance, Li, Na, and Mg). The metals at the bottom of the table are relatively unreactive.

Table 5.1. The Electrochemical Activity Series

Metal	Oxidation Reaction	E°_{red}
Lithium	$Li\ (s) \rightarrow Li^+\ (aq) + e^-$	–3.05
Potassium	$K\ (s) \rightarrow K^+\ (aq) + e^-$	–2.92
Barium	$Ba\ (s) \rightarrow Ba^{2+}\ (aq) + 2e^-$	–2.90
Calcium	$Ca\ (s) \rightarrow Ca^{2+}\ (aq) + 2e^-$	–2.76
Sodium	$Na\ (s) \rightarrow Na^+\ (aq) + e^-$	–2.71
Magnesium	$Mg\ (s) \rightarrow Mg^{2+}\ (aq) + 2e^-$	–2.37
Aluminum	$Al\ (s) \rightarrow Al^{3+}\ (aq) + 3e^-$	–1.66
Manganese	$Mn\ (s) \rightarrow Mn^{2+}\ (aq) + 2e^-$	–1.18
Zinc	$Zn\ (s) \rightarrow Zn^{2+}\ (aq) + 2e^-$	–0.76
Chromium	$Cr\ (s) \rightarrow Cr^{3+}\ (aq) + 3e^-$	–0.73
Iron	$Fe\ (s) \rightarrow Fe^{2+}\ (aq) + 2e^-$	–0.44
Cobalt	$Co\ (s) \rightarrow Co^{2+}\ (aq) + 2e^-$	–0.28
Nickel	$Ni\ (s) \rightarrow Ni^{2+}\ (aq) + 2e^-$	–0.23
Tin	$Sn\ (s) \rightarrow Sn^{2+}\ (aq) + 2e^-$	–0.14
Lead	$Pb\ (s) \rightarrow Pb^{2+}\ (aq) + 2e^-$	–0.13

EASE OF OXIDATION INCREASES

Table 5.1. The Electrochemical Activity Series (continued)

Metal	Oxidation Reaction	E°_{red}
Hydrogen	H_2 (*g*) → $2H^+$ (*aq*) + $2e^-$	0.00
Copper	Cu (*s*) → Cu^{2+} (*aq*) + $2e^-$	0.16
Silver	Ag (*s*) → Ag^+ (*aq*) + e^-	0.80
Mercury	Hg (*l*) → Hg^{2+} (*aq*) + $2e^-$	[illegible]
Platinum	Pt (*s*) → Pt^{2+} (*aq*) + $2e^-$	1.23
Gold	Au (*s*) → Au^{3+} (*aq*) + $3e^-$	1.50

EASE OF OXIDATION INCREASES ↑

SAMPLE QUESTION

8) **Which of the following ions is the strongest reducing agent?**

A. Mg^{2+}

B. Ba^{2+}

C. Fe^{3+}

D. K^+

Answer: D.

D. Ions with negative reduction potentials will be oxidized, and so will act as reducing agents. According to Table 5.1, potassium has the most negative reduction potential ($E^\circ_{red} = -2.92$ V) among the four answer choices.

Balancing Redox Reactions

Balancing redox reactions is a bit more complicated than balancing other types of chemical equations because it involves changes in the oxidation states of elements.

To balance redox reactions, first, determine the oxidation state for each element in the reaction. If the oxidation states change, this is a redox reaction.

Once it has been established the reaction is a redox reaction, separate the reaction into its two half reactions, the oxidation and reduction reactions. Include only the reaction compounds that change oxidation states in these half reactions. The other ions that do not change oxidation states are referred to as spectator ions because they do not participate in the redox reaction.

When the half reactions have been identified, balance the atoms that are not oxygen or hydrogen. After all other atoms are balanced, balance the oxygen atoms by adding H_2O to one side of each half reaction, and balance the hydrogen atoms by adding H^+.

Once all the atoms are balanced, balance the charges in each half reaction by adding electrons. If the half reactions do not have the same number of electrons, multiply the half reactions by a coefficient so they do have the same number of electrons.

Finally, combine the half reactions and simplify by removing the compounds that appear on both the reactant side and product side.

Below is a step-by-step example showing how to balance a redox reaction.

$$HNO_3\ (aq) + Cu\ (s) \rightarrow Cu^{2+}\ (aq) + NO\ (g)$$

1. This is a redox reaction because the oxidation state of copper changes from 0 to +2 and the oxidation state of nitrogen changes from +5 to +2.
2. The two half reactions are:
   $Cu(s) \rightarrow Cu^{2+}\ (aq)$ and $HNO_3\ (aq) \rightarrow NO\ (g)$
3. None of the ions are spectator ions in this example, so none of the ions are left out.
4. Because the atoms of copper and nitrogen are equal, no balancing is needed for those elements. However, the oxygen and hydrogen atoms in the nitric acid half reaction must be balanced.
5. Adding two molecules of water to the right side of the equation balances the number of oxygen atoms:
   $HNO_3\ (aq) \rightarrow NO\ (g) + 2\ H_2O\ (l)$
6. Now, hydrogen atoms need to be added.
   $3\ H^+ + HNO_3\ (aq) \rightarrow NO\ (g) + 2\ H_2O\ (l)$
7. This step balances the atoms in the equations, but the charges still need to be balanced by adding electrons. The 2+ charge is balanced by adding 2 electrons, which have a negative charge.
   $Cu\ (s) \rightarrow Cu^{2+}\ (aq) + 2\ e^-$
8. The 3+ charge from the added hydrogen atoms must be balanced by adding 3 electrons.
   $3\ e^- + 3\ H^+ + HNO_3\ (aq) \rightarrow NO\ (g) + 2\ H_2O\ (l)$
9. Next, the number of electrons in both half reactions must be equal. This can be done by multiplying the equations by 3 and 2, respectively.
   $3\ [Cu\ (s) \rightarrow Cu^{2+}\ (aq) + 2\ e^-]$ and
   $2\ [3\ e^- + 3\ H^+ + HNO_3\ (aq) \rightarrow NO\ (g) + 2\ H_2O\ (l)]$
10. Now the reactions can be added back together to give the balanced redox reaction:
    $3\ Cu\ (s) + 6\ H^+(aq) + 2\ HNO_3\ (aq) \rightarrow 3\ Cu^{2+}\ (aq) + 2\ NO\ (g) + 4\ H_2O\ (l)$

SAMPLE QUESTIONS

9) **Find the coefficients for the following redox reaction:**
C_2H_6 (*g*) + O_2 (*g*) → CO_2 (*g*) + H_2O (*g*)

A. 1:4:2:2

B. 2:7:4:6

C. 2:6:4:2

D. 2:7:4:2

Answer: B.

C_2H_6 (*g*) + O_2 (*g*) → 2 CO_2 (*g*) + H_2O (*g*)	Start by balancing the carbon atoms on each side of the equation.
C_2H_6 (*g*) + O_2 (*g*) → 2 CO_2 (*g*) + 3 H_2O (*g*)	Next, balance the hydrogen atoms on each side of the equation.
C_2H_6 (*g*) + 3.5 O_2 (*g*) → 2 CO_2 (*g*) + 3 H_2O (*g*)	Then, balance the oxygen on each side of the equation.
2 C_2H_6 (*g*) + 7 O_2 (*g*) → 4 CO_2 (*g*) + 6 H_2O (*g*)	Finally, remove the decimal by multiplying each coefficient by 2.

10) **Find the coefficients for the following redox reaction:**
HNO_3 (*aq*) + H_3AsO_3 (*aq*) → NO (*g*) + H_3AsO_4 (*aq*) + H_2O (*l*)

A. 1:3:1:3:2

B. 2:3:2:3:2

C. 2:3:2:3:1

D. 4:2:2:4:1

Answer: C.

HNO_3 (*aq*) + 3 H_3AsO_3 (*aq*) → NO (*g*) + H_3AsO_4 (*aq*) + H_2O (*l*)	First, work to balance the hydrogen atoms on each side.
HNO_3 (*aq*) + 3 H_3AsO_3 (*aq*) → NO (*g*) + 3 H_3AsO_4 (*aq*) + H_2O (*l*)	Then, balance the arsenic atoms in the products.
2 HNO_3 (*aq*) + 3 H_3AsO_3 (*aq*) → NO (*g*) + 3 H_3AsO_4 (*aq*) + H_2O (*l*)	Next, continue to work to balance the hydrogen.
2 HNO_3 (*aq*) + 3 H_3AsO_3 (*aq*) → 2 NO (*g*) + 3 H_3AsO_4 (*aq*) + H_2O (*l*)	Finally, balance the nitrogen and oxygen atoms in the products.

ELECTROCHEMICAL CELLS

An **electrochemical cell** is set up so that a redox reaction takes place, but electrons move through an outside conductor. Electrochemical cells are batteries and can generate electrical energy from chemical reactions or introduce electrical energy to facilitate a chemical reaction.

Electrochemical cells are composed of electrodes and a salt bridge. A common electrochemical cell that will be used to illustrate the components of the cell consists of Zn and Cu. There are two half reactions that occur in the cell, but they are separated into half cells. Each half cell comprises an electrode and an electrolyte. An electrode moves electrons (conducts electrical current). In the following example, the electrodes are metal plates of Zn and Cu, but electrodes can also be other metals, graphite, or another conductor. There are two types of electrodes: the **cathode**, where reduction takes place, and the **anode**, where oxidation occurs. Zn is the anode and Cu is the cathode in this example:

$$Zn \rightarrow Zn^{2+} + 2e^-, \text{ oxidation (anode)}$$

$$Cu^{2+} + 2e^- \rightarrow Cu, \text{ reduction (cathode)}$$

$$\text{Net reaction: } Cu^{2+} + Zn\ (s) \rightarrow Cu\ (s) + Zn^{2+}$$

The electrons flow from the anode to the cathode via a filament. If the electrons flowed continually with no other reactions, the half cells would very quickly build up a positive charge in the anode and a less positive charge in the cathode (charge difference), stopping the flow of electrons. This buildup is avoided by using a salt bridge to connect the two half cells. The salt bridge is a solution of a salt that allows negative and positive ions to pass freely while keeping the contents otherwise separated, allowing a steady-state charge distribution. In this example, Na_2SO_4 is used as the salt bridge. As the electrons flow in the cell, the negative ions (SO_4^{2-}) move to the anode, and the positive ions (Na^+) move toward the cathode. In general, anions always flow to the anode and cations to the cathode. This flow allows the current to flow by preventing charge buildup.

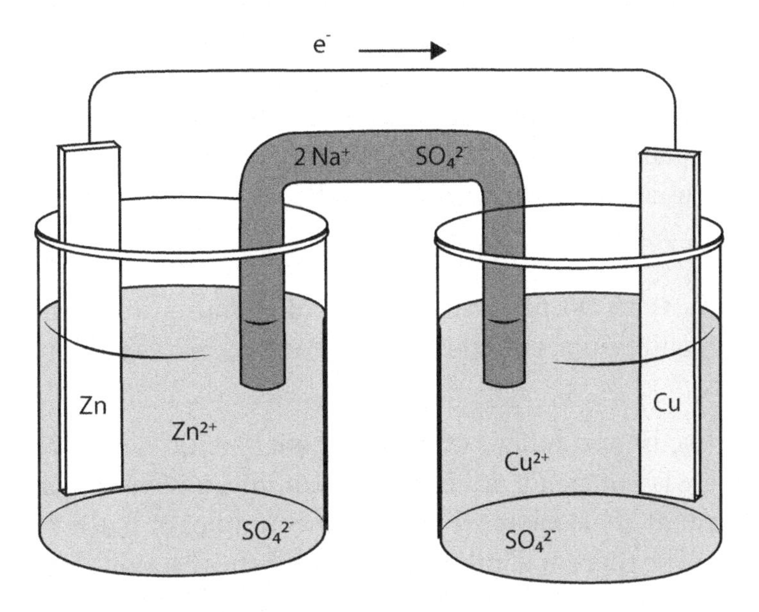

Figure 5.2. Electrochemical Cell

The following are rules for the operation of batteries (electrochemical cells):

- The redox reaction in the cell must favor the formation of products.
- There must be an external circuit for the electrons to flow through.
- All cells must have a salt bridge or some means of allowing ions to flow between the half cells.

SAMPLE QUESTION

11) In an electrochemical cell, oxidation occurs at the __________.

A. salt bridge

B. cathode

C. anode

D. ion channels

Answers:

A. Incorrect. The salt bridge is used as a barrier between the two parts of the cell to prevent a charge difference.

B. Incorrect. Reduction occurs at the cathode.

C. Correct. Oxidation reactions occur at the anode. In the example above, the anode contains Zn ions.

D. Incorrect. Ion channels are not associated with electrochemical cells.

Chemical Equilibrium

A **chemical equilibrium** occurs when the concentrations of reactants and products remain constant in a reaction system. This does not mean that the chemical reaction has stopped, just that the forward and backward reactions are occurring at equal rates. Because of this, chemical equilibria are often called *dynamic equilibria* and are represented in equations with a double arrow. An example of a system in chemical equilibrium is a weak acid, which only partially ionizes in water.

$$CH_3COOH\ (aq) + H_2O\ (l) \leftrightarrow CH_3COO^-\ (aq) + H_3O^+\ (aq)$$

While more than 90 percent of the acid remains in its molecular form (CH_3COOH) at equilibrium, both the forward and backward reactions are occurring at the same rates.

There are two important facts to know about chemical equilibrium. First, the equilibrium state is independent of how the equilibrium was reached if the temperature is constant. This means that the same number of moles of the reactants and products will be there at equilibrium whether the reaction starts with *x* moles of reactant or *x* moles of product. The Haber process for synthesizing ammonia is often used to illustrate this concept because the reaction does not go to completion, but instead reaches an equilibrium with all three components present.

$$N_2\,(g) + 3\,H_2\,(g) \leftrightarrow 2\,NH_3\,(g)$$

It does not matter whether N_2 and H_2 or NH_3 are added to the container; either situation will result in an equilibrium with the same concentrations of N_2, H_2, and NH_3.

Second, the equilibrium is not affected by catalysts. Catalysts can speed up the rate at which equilibrium is achieved, but they cannot change the equilibrium concentrations.

EQUILIBRIUM CONSTANTS

Each equilibrium has an equilibrium constant, *K*. This is a quotient of the equilibrium concentrations of reactants and products for a given reaction at a given temperature. *K* is independent of the initial concentrations of the reactants and products in a reaction, but is dependent on the temperature of the reaction system.

A mathematical expression, called the *equilibrium constant expression*, can be derived from the chemical equation for any equilibrium process. The equilibrium constant can reveal whether the reaction favors products or reactants, the direction the reaction will proceed in, and the concentration of products and reactants at equilibrium.

The equilibrium constant, K, is written with the concentrations of products in the numerator and the concentration of reactants in the denominator. The concentrations of both products and reactants are also raised to the power of their stoichiometric coefficients. However, only the concentrations of gases and dilute solutions should be included. The concentrations of pure solids and liquids do not appear in equilibrium constant expressions because their concentrations do not change as the reaction occurs.

The following general equilibrium reaction illustrates how the equilibrium constant is written:

$$aA + bB \leftrightarrow cC + dD$$

$$K = \frac{[C]^c[D]^d}{[A]^a[B]^b}$$

If $K > 1$: The reaction strongly favors products. The concentrations of products at equilibrium are much greater than those of the reactants.

If $K < 1$: The reaction strongly favors the reactants. The concentrations of the reactants at equilibrium are much greater than those of the products.

If $K \approx 1$: The reaction favors neither the reactants nor the products. The equilibrium mixture contains significant concentrations of reactants and products.

SAMPLE QUESTION

13) Write the equilibrium constant for the following reaction:

$Cl_2O_7\ (g) + 8\ H_2\ (g) \leftrightarrow 2\ HCl\ (g) + 7\ H_2O\ (g)$

A. $K = \frac{[H_2O]^1[HCl]^2}{[Cl_2O_7][H_2]^1}$

B. $K = \frac{[H_2O]^7[HCl]^2}{[Cl_2O_7][H_2]^8}$

C. $K = \frac{[H_2O]^2[HCl]^7}{[Cl_2O_7][H_2]^8}$

D. $K = \frac{[Cl_2O_7][H_2]^8}{[H_2O]^7[HCl]^2}$

Answer: B.

The products are always in the denominator and the reactants in the numerator. Additionally, the concentrations of both the products and reactants must be raised to the power of their coefficients from the equation.

Le Châtelier's Principle

Le Châtelier's principle states that if a chemical reaction system is at equilibrium, and the conditions are changed so it is no longer at equilibrium, the system will react to counteract the change and reach a new equilibrium. This applies to changes in the concentration of reactants or products, temperature, and to changes in pressure or volume in a gas-phase equilibrium.

Applying changes to a system in equilibrium is known as *shifting the equilibrium*. The equilibrium can shift to either the right (forward direction, products) or left (reverse direction, reactants). If reactants are added to a system in equilibrium, the equilibrium will shift to the right (forward direction), but if reactants are removed from the system, the equilibrium will shift to the left (reverse direction). If products are added to the system, the equilibrium will also shift to the left (reverse direction), but if products are removed from the system, the equilibrium will shift to the right (forward direction).

Changing the temperature, pressure, or volume of a chemical reaction will also result in a change in the equilibrium of the system. If the temperature of a system is increased, the heat of the reaction system increases, and if the temperature is lowered, the heat of the reaction system decreases.

QUICK REVIEW

Transferring gas into and out of the blood is an equilibrium process. For oxygen, it is represented by $Hb_4 + 4O_2 \leftrightarrow Hb_4O_8$, where Hb is hemoglobin. How would this reaction maintain equilibrium when it occurs (1) in the lungs with high oxygen concentration and (2) near tissues with low oxygen concentration?

The effect of changes in temperature depend on whether the reaction is endothermic or exothermic. If a reaction is endothermic, heat can be considered a reactant, and the addition of heat to the system will push the equilibrium in the forward direction. If a reaction is exothermic, heat is a product, and the addition of heat will push the equilibrium in the reverse direction.

Table 5.2. Le Châtelier's Principle

Change	Shift	Effect on K
Increase in reaction concentration	To products	No change
Increase in product concentration	To reactants	No change
Increase pressure Decrease volume	Toward fewer moles of gas	No change
Decrease pressure Increase volume	Toward more moles of gas	No change
Increase temperature	Toward endothermic direction	Increases if products are favored
Decrease temperature	Toward exothermic direction	Decreases if reactants are favored
Addition of catalyst	No shift	No change

If a system has an equal number of moles of gas on each side of the chemical reaction, a change in the volume and partial pressures will not have an effect. However, if the product and reactant sides have different numbers of moles, a change in the volume will affect the reaction. If the volume decreases, increasing the partial pressure, the reaction shifts to the side of the equilibrium with fewer moles in an attempt to decrease the pressure. If the volume increases, decreasing the partial pressure, the reverse is true, and the equilibrium side with more moles is favored.

SAMPLE QUESTION

13) **Consider that the following reaction is in equilibrium: $BaSO_4$ (*s*) ↔ Ba^{2+} (*aq*) + SO_4^{2-} (*aq*)**
What will happen to the concentration of Ba^{2+} if more $BaSO_4$ is added to the reaction?

A. It will increase.
B. It will decrease.
C. There is insufficient information to determine the effect.
D. There will be no change.

Answer:

A. **Correct.** Adding more reactants will push the reaction forward toward the products to reach a new equilibrium.

Stoichiometry

Stoichiometry uses the relative quantities of the molecules in a chemical equation to calculate the amount of reactants used or product is made in a reaction. Stoichiometry problems are worked using dimensional analysis (or railroad tracks), which requires three basic steps:

1. Identify the given or initial value.
2. Add conversion factors that will leave the desired units when cancelled.
3. Multiply across the top and across the bottom, and then divide.

Common conversion factors used in stoichiometry are shown in the table below.

Table 5.3. Common Conversion Factors in Stoichiometry

Use...	To go between...	Example
mole ratio	moles of different substances in a chemical reaction	$\frac{1\ \text{mol}\ O_2}{2\ \text{mol}\ CO_2}$
molar mass	moles and grams	$\frac{1\ \text{mol}\ O_2}{32\ \text{g}\ O_2}$
Avogadro's number	moles and molecules	$\frac{1\ \text{mol}\ O_2}{6.02 \times 10^{23}\ \text{molecules}\ O_2}$
molar volume	moles and volume of gas (at STP)	$\frac{1\ \text{mol}\ O_2}{22.4\ \text{L}}$

The Amount of Products and Reactants

The main tool of stoichiometry is the **mole ratio**, which is simply a ratio of the number of moles of two substances in the equation. For example, in the combustion of methane (shown below), 2 moles of O_2 produce 1 mole of CO_2.

$$CH_4 + 2\ O_2 \rightarrow CO_2 + 2\ H_2O,$$

The mole ratio of O_2 and CO_2 is written as $\frac{2\ \text{mol}\ O_2}{1\ \text{mol}\ CO_2}$ or $\frac{1\ \text{mol}\ CO_2}{2\ \text{mol}\ O_2}$. This ratio can be used to determine how many moles of a specific reactant or product are required for the given amount of a reactant or product.

- If 0.4 mol of CH_4 reacts completely with oxygen, how many moles of water are produced?

$$\frac{0.4\ \text{mol}\ CH_4}{1} \times \frac{2\ \text{mol}\ H_2O}{1\ \text{mol}\ CH_4} = 0.8\ \text{mol}\ H_2O$$

- How many moles of O_2 are needed to produce 5 moles of CO_2?

5 mol CO_2	2 mol O_2	= 10 mol O_2
1	1 mol CO_2	

Combining the mole ratio with molar mass allows for the calculation of the mass of the required reactant or product.

- How many moles of water are formed from the complete reaction of 4.32 g of methane with oxygen?

4.32 g mol CH_4	1 mol CH_4	2 mol H_2O	= 0.54 mol H_2O
1	16 g mol CH_4	1 mol CH_4	

SAMPLE QUESTION

14) Which statement is NOT true of the chemical reaction $2\ BiCl_3 + 3\ H_2S \rightarrow Bi_2S_3 + 6\ HCl$?

A. When 4 grams of $BiCl_3$ react, 12 grams of HCl are formed.

B. When 20 molecules of $BiCl_3$ react, 10 molecules of Bi_2S_3 are produced.

C. When 3 moles of H_2S react, 2 moles of $BiCl_3$ also react.

D. When 34.08 grams of H_2S react, 109.38 grams of HCl are produced.

Answers:

A. **Correct.** When 4 g of $BiCl_3$ react, 1.39 g of HCl is produced.

4g $BiCl_3$	1 mol BiCl	6 mol HCl	36.46 g HCl	= 1.39 g HCl
1	315.33 g BiCl	2 mol $BiCl_3$	1 mol HCl	

B. Incorrect. According the equation, for every 2 moles of $BiCl_3$, 1 mole of Bi_2S_3 is formed.

C. Incorrect. According the equation, 3 moles of H_2S react with 2 moles of $BiCl_2$.

D. Incorrect. When 34.08 g of H_2S react, 109.38g of HCl is produced.

34.08 g H_2S	1 mol H_2S	6 HCl	36.46 g HCl	= 109.38 g HCl
1	34.08 g H_2S	2 H_2S	1 mol HCl	

LIMITING REACTANTS

In a chemical reaction where both reactants are present, it is possible for one reactant to be used up before the other. Once this reactant is gone, the reaction ceases and no further product can be made. The reactant that is used up, stopping the reaction, is the **limiting**

CONSIDER THIS

Think of stoichiometry as cooking, and the chemical equation as the recipe. If there is not enough of one ingredient (the limiting reactant), the amount of the other ingredients and the amount of food the recipe produces will change.

reactant. When calculating the amount of product made, it's important to use the amount of the limiting reactant (not any other reactants) as the initial value.

There are several ways to find the limiting reactant, but simplest is to find the amount of product made by each reactant. The reactant that produces the smallest amount of product will be the limiting reactant.

In the reaction below, what is the limiting reactant if 5 g of SiO_2 and 5 g of C are used?

$SiO_2 (s) + 3 C (s) \rightarrow SiC (s) + 2 CO (g)$

5 g C	0.416 mol C	1 mol SiC	40.1 g SiC	= 2.32 g SiC
1	12 g C	3 mol C	1 mol SiC	

5 g SiO_2	0.0832 mol SiO_2	1 mol SiC	40.1 g SiC	= 0.28 g SiC
1	60.19 g SiO_2	1 mol SiO_2	1 mol SiC	

Since the amount of SiO_2 present can produce only 0.28 g of SiC, the reaction is limited by SiO_2.

SAMPLE QUESTION

15) Determine the limiting reactant and the mass of $C_9H_8O_4$ produced when 1 g of $C_7H_6O_3$ and 3 g of $C_4H_6O_3$ react.

$2 C_7H_6O_3 (s) + C_4H_6O_3 (l) \rightarrow 2 C_9H_8O_4 (s) + H_2O (l)$

A. $C_4H_6O_3$, 2 g of $C_9H_8O_4$

B. $C_7H_6O_3$, 2 g of $C_9H_8O_4$

C. $C_7H_6O_3$, 1.3 g of $C_9H_8O_4$

D. $C_4H_6O_3$, 1.3 g of $C_9H_8O_4$

Answer: C.

Find the number of moles of each reactant.

3 g $C_4H_6O_3$	1 mol	= 0.029 mol $C_4H_6O_3$
1	102.1 g	

1 g $C_7H_6O_3$	1 mol H	= 0.007 mol $C_7H_6O_3$
1	138.12 g	

Determine which is the limiting reactant.

0.029 mol $C_4H_6O_3$	2 mol $C_7H_6O_3$	= 0.058 mol $C_7H_6O_3$
1	1 mol $C_4H_6O_3$	

In this reaction, 0.058 moles of $C_7H_6O_3$ are required for every 0.029 mol $C_4H_6O_3$. Because only 0.007 moles of $C_7H_6O_3$ are available, it is the limiting reactant.

Use the limiting reactant to determine yield for $C_9H_8O_4$.

0.007 mol $C_7H_6O_3$	2 mol $C_9H_8O_4$	180.17 g	= **1.3 g $C_9H_8O_4$**
	2 mol $C_7H_6O_3$	1 mol	

PERCENT YIELD

When the maximum quantity of the product is formed in a reaction, the yield is 100%. This is the theoretical yield of a reaction, and it is often different from the **actual yield** of a reaction, which is the quantity of the product actually created from the chemical reaction. Dividing the actual yield by the theoretical yield gives the **percent yield**.

$$\text{percent yield} = \frac{\text{actual yield}}{\text{theoretical yield}} \times 100\%$$

The percent yield can differ from the theoretical yield for a number of reasons. For example, the product can be lost during purification or the reactants can be used in unwanted side reactions.

SAMPLE QUESTION

16) Consider the equation: CO (*g*) + 2 H_2 (*g*) → CH_3OH (*l*). If 100 g of CO reacts with excess H_2 and produces 100 g of CH_3OH, what is the percent yield?

A. 100%

B. 92%

C. 80%

D. 87.5%

Answer: D.

Find the theoretical yield.

100 g CO	1 mol CO	1 mol CH_3OH	32 g CH_3OH	114.24 g CH_3OH
	28.01 g CO	1 mol CO	1 mol CH_3OH	

Use the formula for percent yield.

$$\text{percent yield} = \frac{\text{actual yield}}{\text{theoretical yield}} \times 100\%$$

$$= \frac{100\text{ g}}{114.24\text{ g}} \times 100\% = \mathbf{87.5\%}$$

Chemical Kinetics

Rate Laws

Chemical kinetics, the study of rates and mechanisms of chemical reactions, can be used to determine how quickly chemical reactions will occur. The **rate** of a chemical reaction describes how fast the reaction is; it is written as a change in the concentration of reactants or products per unit of time. The reaction rate's relationship with the reactant concentration can be described by a mathematical equation known as a **rate law**. The rate law uses a proportionality constant, k, called the **rate constant**. The rate constant is specific to each reaction, applies at a specific temperature, and is independent of concentration.

> HELPFUL HINT
>
> An uppercase K represents the equilibrium constant of a reaction. A lowercase k represents the rate constant for a reaction.

The rate law must be determined experimentally. For most homogeneous reactions, the rate law has the following general form:

$$\text{Rate} = k\,[A]^m[B]^n$$

where A and B are the reactants, products, or catalysts, and the exponents define the order of reaction.

The **reaction order**, or order of reaction, is the exponent to which each concentration term in the rate equation is raised. For the generic equation given above, the reaction order for A is m and for B it is n. The overall reaction order is $m + n$.

- In zero-order reactions, the rate is independent of the reactant concentration. Rate $= k\,[A]^0 = k$

Most reactions occur in two or more steps during which intermediate substances are formed and then consumed. Each step in a reaction will have its own reaction rate, with the slowest step determining the overall rate of the reaction.

- First-order reactions are reactions in which the reaction rate depends only on a single reactant that has an exponent of one. All unimolecular elementary reactions are first order. Rate $= k\,[A]$
- Second-order reactions are reactions with an overall order of two. This can be because the reaction is proportional to one concentration squared or to the product of two concentrations. Rate $= k\,[A]^2$ or $k\,[A][B]$

SAMPLE QUESTION

17) For the following reaction, determine the order based on the given rate law.

$2\,NO_2\,(g) \rightarrow 2\,NO\,(g) + O_2\,(g)$, Rate $= k\,[NO_2]^2$

A. second order

B. first order

C. zero order

D. There is not enough information to determine the answer.

Answer:

A. The only exponent is a 2, so this rate law has an overall order of 2.

REACTION RATES

Various factors can affect the speed of a reaction or reaction rate. In homogeneous reactions, in which all the reactants and products are in one phase, there are four main factors:

- the properties of the reactants and products (i.e., molecular structure and bonding)
- the concentrations of the reactants and sometimes the products
- the reaction temperature
- the presence and concentration of a catalyst

Heterogeneous reaction rates depend on those factors, but because those reactions take place at the surface/interface (e.g., where a solid and gas meet), their rates also depend on the surface area and nature of the surface. A heterogeneous reaction with a larger surface area will proceed more quickly.

It is possible to predict how certain factors will change the reaction rate. For example, as the reactant concentration increases, the reaction rate will also increase. This is explained by collision theory: Reactants must collide (meet) to react. If there are more reactants (i.e., a higher concentration), there is a higher probability of collision. Pressure also influences the reaction rate of gaseous reactions. An increase in the pressure results in an increase in the reaction rate, because increasing the pressure of a gas is equivalent to increasing the concentration. Finally, temperature changes the reaction rate. An increase in temperature typically delivers more energy to a system, increasing the collision rate and thus the reaction rate.

SAMPLE QUESTION

18) How will an increase in the concentration of the reactants affect the reaction rate?

A. It will slow down the reaction rate.

B. It will increase the reaction rate.

C. It will not change the reaction rate.

D. The effect can't be determined without knowing the reaction's rate law.

Answer:

B. A higher concentration of reactants increases the rate of reaction by increasing the number of collisions between reactant molecules.

Activation Energy

All chemical reactions require some energy to change reactants into products. The amount of energy required to overcome the energy barrier for a reaction is the **activation energy, E_a**, which can vary greatly from reaction to reaction. A reaction profile diagram shows the activation energy required to turn reactants into products.

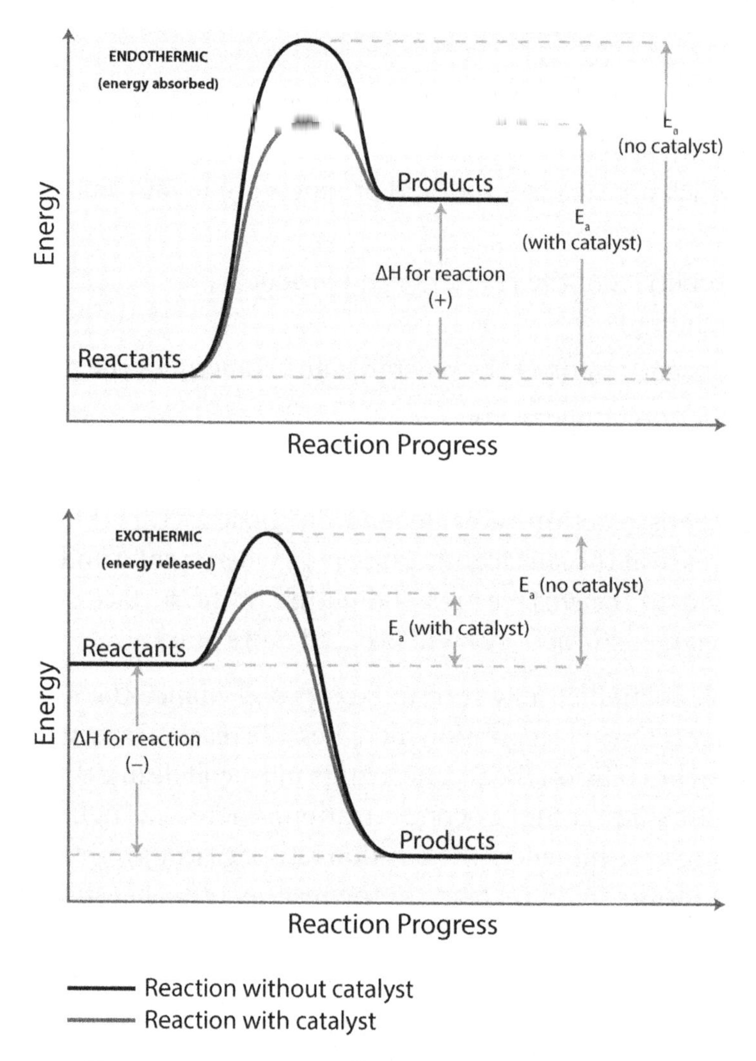

Figure 5.3. Reaction Profile Diagrams

> **DID YOU KNOW?**
>
> Catalytic converters in gasoline engines use a heterogeneous catalyst. A solid, metal is used to catalyze the reaction of harmful exhaust products, like carbon monoxide, nitrogen oxides, and unused fuel, into less harmful emissions, such as carbon dioxide, water, oxygen, and nitrogen.

If the activation energy is too high, a reaction may not proceed or may proceed only at a very slow rate. The activation energy can be modified by the addition of a **catalyst**. Overall, a catalyst is a compound that lowers the activation energy of a reaction by changing the mechanism to a new mechanism with a lower activation energy. By lowering the activation energy, a catalyst speeds up the rate of the reaction. Catalysts are not consumed by the chemical reaction and do not appear in the overall chemical equation. The presence of a catalyst is often indicated by placing the catalyst above or below the reaction arrow:

$$O_3 + O \underset{Cl}{\rightarrow} 2O_2$$

There are two types of catalysts: homogeneous and heterogeneous. **Homogeneous catalysts** are in the same phase as the reactants (dissolved in the solvent with the reactants). **Heterogeneous catalysts** are in a different phase from the reactants. These are usually solid catalysts used in a liquid- or gas phase reaction. Heterogeneous catalysts rely on their surface area to help speed up a reaction; a larger surface area results in a faster rate of reaction.

SAMPLE QUESTION

19) What is the role of a catalyst in a reaction?

A. to decrease the rate of the reaction

B. to increase the rate of the reaction

C. to change the chemical equilibrium

D. to increase the amount of product produced

Answers:

A. Incorrect. A catalyst is used to increase the rate of reaction, not to decrease it.

B. Correct. A catalyst increases the rate of reaction by changing the reaction mechanism.

C. Incorrect. Chemical equilibrium refers to a reaction where the forward and reverse reactions are occurring at the same rate. A catalyst is used to speed up a reaction, not to shift the equilibrium.

D. Incorrect. A catalyst does not influence the amount of product that results from a reaction.

6

Thermodynamics

Energy, work, and heat all play a crucial role in chemical reactions and changes of state. The study of the relationship between these three factors is called **thermodynamics.** By looking at the balance of energy gained and lost during chemical and physical changes, it is possible to determine whether these changes will occur spontaneously.

In thermodynamics, variables can be divided into two categories. **State functions** have a value that does not depend on the path taken by the process to reach its final state. Mass, volume, and pressure (along with many of the variables defined in this chapter) are state functions. A property that does depend on the path taken by the process is called **path function** or **process function**. Work and heat are both path functions.

To understand the laws of thermodynamics, it is necessary to understand systems and surroundings. A **system** is the part of the universe where an actual process takes place or where observations are made; the rest of the universe is the **surroundings**.

There are three types of systems:

- Open systems: Exchange of energy or matter between the system and its surroundings is possible.
- Closed systems: Only exchange of energy between the system and its surroundings is possible; exchange of matter is not possible.
- Isolated systems: No exchange of energy or matter between the system and its surroundings is possible.

HELPFUL HINT

The laws of thermodynamics govern the initial and the final states of the system—not the rate at which a reaction or a process occurs.

The Basics of Chemical Thermodynamics

Types of Energy

Energy (measured in Joules, J) is a property needed to perform work on or to heat an object. There are two kinds of energy: kinetic and potential. **Kinetic energy** is the energy possessed by objects in motion, and **potential energy** is possessed by objects that have the potential to be in motion due to their position. Potential energy is defined in relation to a specific point. For example, a book held 10 feet off the ground has more potential energy than a book held 5 feet off the ground, because it has the potential to fall farther (i.e., to do more work). Both kinetic and potential energy can be further broken down into other types of energy (shown in Table 6.1).

Table 6.1. Types of Energy

Kinetic	Thermal	Energy possessed by an object due to the movement and vibration of atoms or molecules, which generate heat.
	Sound	Energy associated with the vibration of an object because of a force and the subsequent transference of energy through the object in a wave.
	Motion	Energy associated with the motion of an object.
	Radiant	Energy from the sun, or the energy possessed by vibrating particles is electromagnetic energy.
Potential	Chemical	Energy that exists in the bonds between molecules and atoms.
	Elastic	Energy that is stored due to the deformation of an elastic object.
	Nuclear	Energy that is responsible for holding the nucleus of an atom together.
	Gravitational	Energy possessed by an object by the virtue of its height.
	Electrical	Energy that is stored in a battery.

The total amount of energy remains constant and can neither be created nor destroyed, a property known as the **law of conservation of energy**. Energy can, however, be transformed from one form into another. In the example above, dropping one of the books turns potential energy into kinetic energy. Conversely, picking up a book and placing it on a table turns kinetic energy into potential energy. Solar panels are another example of the law of conservation of energy: the panels transform solar energy into chemical energy, which is eventually transformed into mechanical energy.

SAMPLE QUESTION

1) **Compressing a spring increases the spring's**

   A. thermal kinetic energy.

   B. radiant kinetic energy.

   C. gravitational potential energy.

   D. elastic potential energy.

Answer:

D. **Correct.** A compressed spring has elastic potential energy, which can be turned into kinetic energy when the spring is released and begins to move.

THE LAWS OF THERMODYNAMICS

The **first law of thermodynamics** states that change in energy for a closed system is the difference between the heat supplied to the system and the work done by the system on its surroundings. It is essentially the law of conservation of energy extended to the principles of thermodynamics and heat. The law can be mathematically represented as

$$\Delta U = Q - W$$

where ΔU is the change in internal energy, Q is the heat added to the system, and W is the work done by the system.

In this equation, the signs of the variables depend on whether work is done on or by the system, and on whether heat is added to or lost from the system:

- When work is done on the system, W is positive.
- When work is done by the system, W is negative.
- When heat is added to the system, Q is positive.
- When heat is lost by the system, Q is negative.

The **second law of thermodynamics** states that, in an isolated system, the total entropy of the system always increases with time. This law is also called the *law of increased entropy.*

Entropy (S) is often described as a measure of randomness or chaos in a system. It can also be thought of as the number of possible configurations, or **microstates**, within a system. Increasing the number of possible microstates in a system will increase the chaos or randomness of a system: with increasing possible configurations, it is less likely that molecules will be in a particular microstate. This principle explains why gases spontaneously expand: molecules have more possible arrangements when they have more space to move around.

Systems will favor processes that create more possible configurations for the molecules in the system. Entropy will increase when:

- temperature increases
- volume increases
- the number of molecules in a system increases
- a solid or liquid changes to a gas
- a solid changes to a liquid
- a solution forms from a solid

In thermodynamics, change in entropy equals heat added to the system divided by the temperature at which the heat is added. It is important to note that entropy is a state function (it does not depend on the path of the process), and its value is always positive.

The **third law of thermodynamics** states that the entropy of a pure crystalline substance at absolute zero is 0. This is because all the molecules in a pure substance at 0 degrees K would have no energy and would be locked in place, meaning there is only one possible microstate.

According to the **zeroth law of thermodynamics**, two objects are said to be in thermal equilibrium when they have the same temperature. Similarly, if three or more substances are at the same temperature, all three of them will be in thermal equilibrium.

SAMPLE QUESTION

2) **Which of the following will increase the entropy of a system?**

A. 2 moles of liquid water are broken apart to form 2 moles of hydrogen gas and 2 moles of oxygen gas.

B. 2 moles of water vapor condense to form a liquid.

C. 2 moles of water are cooled from 25°C to 15°C.

D. 2 moles of water vapor are moved from a 1 L container to a 0.5 L container.

Answers:

A. **Correct.** Increases in the number of molecules in a system increases entropy.

B. Incorrect. The phase transition from gas (a high-energy state) to liquid (a low-energy state) decreases entropy.

C. Incorrect. Decreasing the temperature of a system decreases its entropy.

D. Incorrect. Decreasing the volume of a system decreases its entropy.

ENDOTHERMIC AND EXOTHERMIC REACTIONS

A chemical reaction always involves breaking the bonds of the reactants and forming the bonds of the products. Depending on whether the energy required to break the bonds is greater or smaller than the energy released when the products are formed, the reaction will either absorb or release energy. Based on whether energy is released or absorbed, a reaction can be called endothermic or exothermic.

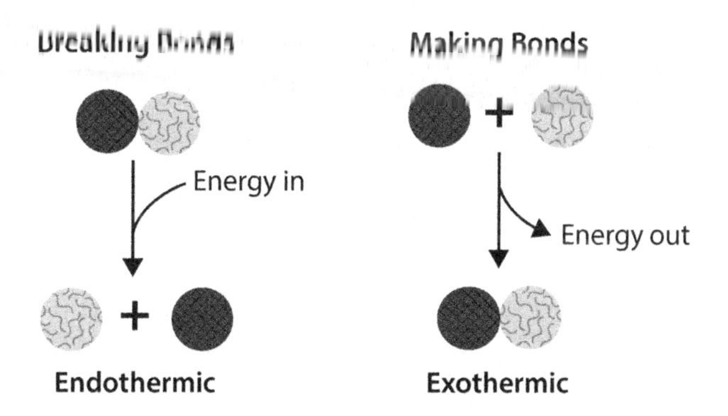

Figure 6.1. Endothermic and Exothermic Reactions

An **endothermic** process absorbs energy in the form of heat. In an endothermic reaction, the energy required to break the existing bonds is greater than the energy released when the new bonds form. These reactions have a positive change in enthalpy (ΔH) because the system is gaining heat. Examples of endothermic processes include:

- liquid water evaporation (an endothermic process)
- photosynthesis (an endothermic reaction)

> **HELPFUL HINT**
>
> Endothermic processes feel cold because they absorb heat from the environment.

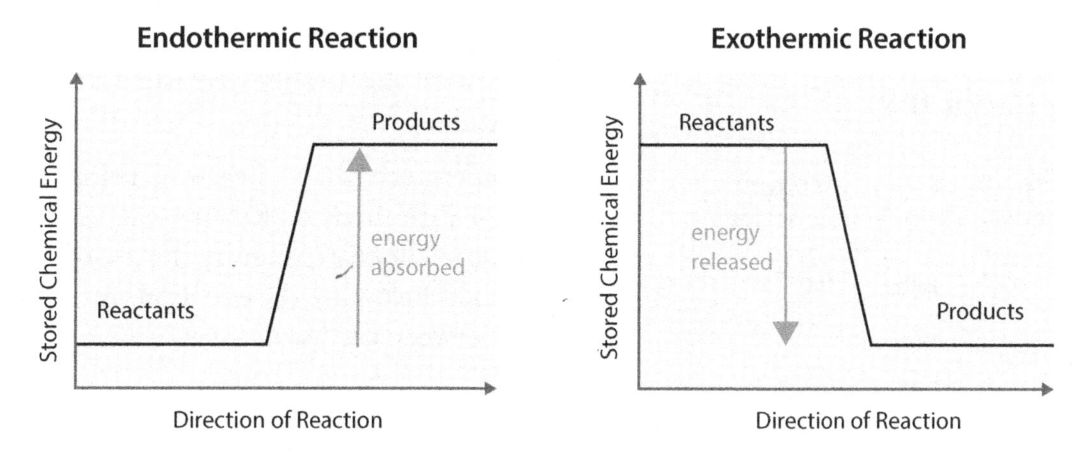

Figure 6.2. Stored Energy in Endothermic and Exothermic Reactions

An **exothermic** process releases energy from the system into the environment. This energy release is usually in the form of heat but can also be in the form of sound or light. An exothermic reaction occurs when the energy required to break bonds is less than the energy released when new bonds form. These reactions have a negative change in enthalpy ($-\Delta H$) because the system is losing heat. Examples of exothermic processes include:

- water vapor condensation (an exothermic process)
- hydrogen combustion (an exothermic reaction)

SAMPLE QUESTION

3) **Which of the following is an endothermic process?**

A. sublimation

B. freezing

C. deposition

D. condensation

Answer:

A. Correct. Energy is required to turn a solid into a gas, making the process endothermic. Energy is released during the processes of freezing, deposition, and condensation because they are transitions from high-energy states to low-energy states.

Temperature and Phase Transitions

Temperature and Heat

While it might look like a substance is not in motion, in fact, its atoms have kinetic energy and are constantly spinning and vibrating. **Temperature** is the name given to the kinetic energy of all the atoms or molecules in a substance. The more energy the atoms have (meaning the more they spin and vibrate) the higher the substance's temperature.

Temperature can be measured using the Celsius, Fahrenheit, or Kelvin scale. Most equations in chemistry require the use of the Kelvin scale. Below are the equations for converting between each scale:

- Celsius to Kelvin: $T_K = T_C + 273.15$
- Celsius to Fahrenheit: $T_F = \frac{9}{5}T_C + 32$
- Fahrenheit to Celsius: $T_C = \frac{5}{9}(T_F - 32)$

HELPFUL HINT

Use this equation to convert between temperature scales:

$$\frac{(F-32)}{180} = \frac{C}{100} = \frac{(K-273)}{100}$$

Table 6.2. The Three Temperature Scales

	Celsius Scale (°C)	Fahrenheit Scale (°F)	Kelvin Scale (K)
Boiling Point of Water	100	212	373.16
Melting Point of Ice	0	32	273.16
Absolute Zero	–273	–460	0

Heat is the movement of energy from one substance to another. Energy will spontaneously move from high-energy (high-temperature) substances to low energy (low-temperature) substances. This can be seen in phase changes. When an ice cube is put in water, energy moves from the water (which is warmer) to the ice (which is colder). The heat added to the ice will increase the kinetic energy of the molecules in the ice, causing them to move farther apart. With enough heat, the ice will melt and become water.

SAMPLE QUESTION

4) **Convert 89°F to °C.**

Answer:

Use the conversion formula where T_c = temperature in Celsius and T_F = temperature in Fahrenheit.

$$T_c = \frac{5}{9}(T_F - 32°)$$

$$= \frac{5 \times (89 - 32)}{9} = \mathbf{31.66}$$

Heat Capacity

Heat capacity (C) is the amount of energy required to raise the temperature of a substance by 1 K or 1°C. The unit for measuring specific heat is $J°C^{-1}$ or $J\ K^{-1}$. Heat capacity can be mathematically denoted as

$$C = \frac{Q}{\Delta T}$$

where C is heat capacity, Q is heat supplied to the substance, and ΔT is the difference between the final and initial temperatures.

Specific heat (c) is the amount of energy needed to increase the temperature of a unit mass of a sample by 1 K or 1°C. The unit for specific heat is $J\ kg^{-1}\ °C^{-1}$ or $J\ kg^{-1}\ K^{-1}$. It can be mathematically represented as

$$c = \frac{Q}{m\Delta T} \text{ or } Q = mc\Delta T$$

HELPFUL HINT

Heat capacity is an *extensive* property that depends on the mass of the substance. More mass requires more energy to raise its temperature. Specific heat is an *intensive* property because it does not depend on the mass of any specific sample.

where c is specific heat, Q is heat supplied to the substance, m is the mass of the substance, and ΔT is the difference between the final and initial temperatures.

HELPFUL HINT

Even though the numerical values for temperature in °C or K are different, DC and DK for two given temperatures will be same. This is NOT true when comparing the changes on the Fahrenheit scale.

Change in temperature of a substance is directly proportional to the heat supplied and inversely proportional to its mass (specific heat is a property of the substance and thus a constant). In other words, applying a certain amount of heat to a substance with a high specific heat will produce a smaller change in temperature than applying that same amount of heat to a substance with a low specific heat. Water, for example, has a relatively high specific heat and, therefore, is often used as a coolant in industrial applications because it can absorb more thermal energy.

SAMPLE QUESTIONS

5) **What is the specific heat for a 5 g metal block that experiences a rise in temperature of 27°C after 1,019 J of heat is added?**

Answer:

Use the formula for specific heat.

$$c = \frac{Q}{m\Delta T}$$

$$c = \frac{1019}{5(27)}$$

= **7.54 J/g°C**

6) **How much heat is required to raise the temperature of 250 g of water from 15°C to 65°C? (The specific heat of water is 4.18 J/g°C.)**

Answer:

Use the formula for specific heat.

$$Q = mc\Delta T$$

= (250 g)(4.18 J/g°C)(65°C – 15°C)

= **52,250 J**

Phase Transitions

A **phase transition** in a substance happens when it changes from a solid, liquid, or gas phase to a different phase. Temperature and pressure play an important role in the phase transitions because for any substance, change in phase takes place at a set temperature-pressure combination.

Table 6.3. Phase Transitions

Name	Process	Sign of Enthalpy Change
Condensing	gas to liquid	heat of vaporization (–)
Evaporating	liquid to gas	heat of vaporization (+)
Freezing	liquid to solid	heat of fusion (–)
Melting	solid to liquid	heat of fusion (+)
Deposition	gas to solid	heat of sublimation (–)
Sublimation	solid to gas	heat of sublimation (+)

The effect of temperature and pressure on the state of a substance is shown in a **phase diagram**. Every element and compound has a unique phase diagram that depends on that substance's chemical properties. The diagram shows temperature on the *x*-axis and pressure on the *y*-axis. Lines on the diagram show where the substance is a solid, liquid, and gas, and also where transitions between states occur. The diagram also shows when a substance becomes a **supercritical fluid**, a state that has the properties of both gas and liquid. Notable points on the diagram include:

DID YOU KNOW?

It is possible for two phases of a substance to coexist at the same time; this is called a *two-phase state*. A common example of a two-phase state is melting ice, where both solid and liquid water exist at the same time.

- melting point (T_m): temperature and pressure at which the solid melts to liquid
- boiling point (T_b): temperature and pressure at which liquid evaporates to gas

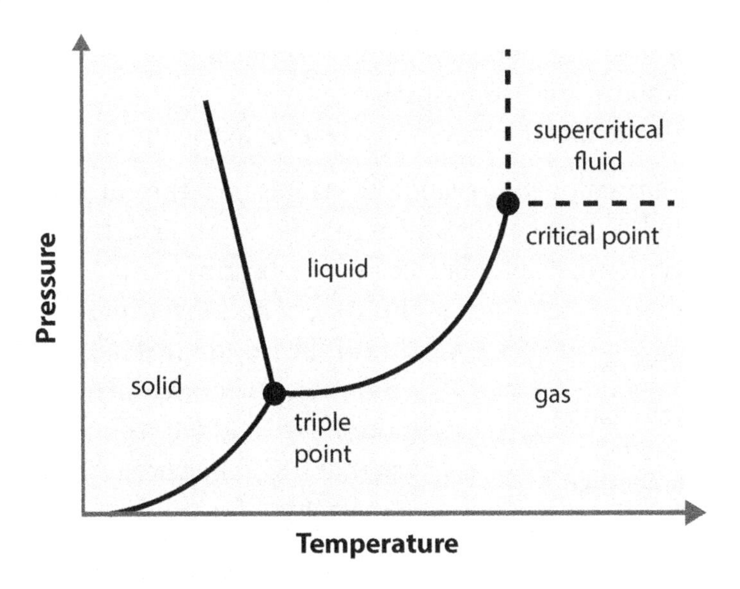

Figure 6.3. Phase Diagram

- triple point (T): temperature and pressure at which the solid, liquid, and gas states are in equilibrium
- critical point (C): temperature and pressure at which the substance becomes supercritical fluid

DID YOU KNOW?

Supercritical fluids have many household and industrial applications. For example, supercritical carbon dioxide is used in dry cleaning and is being introduced as a refrigerant in some parts of the world.

Every phase transition is accompanied by a change in enthalpy. The **heat of vaporization** (ΔH_{vap}) is the energy needed to transform a liquid to a gas at constant pressure. **Heat of fusion** (ΔH_{fus}) is the energy needed to change a substance from solid to liquid at constant pressure. Lastly, **heat of sublimation** (ΔH_{subl}) is the amount of energy needed to change a solid to gas without going through the liquid phase (again at constant pressure). The **molar heat** of vaporization, fusion, and sublimation is the amount of energy needed to change the substance between the relevant states.

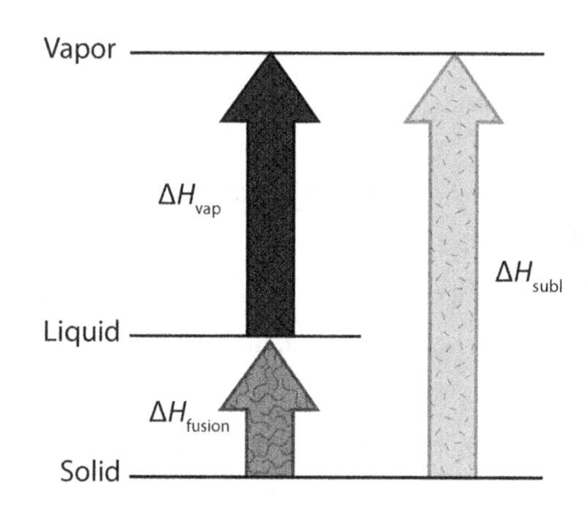

Figure 6.4. Changes in Enthalpies in Phase Transition

The heat of vaporization, fusion, and sublimation for a substance depend on the chemical properties of that substance. More energy is required to separate molecules within a substance that has strong intermolecular forces, so the heat of vaporization, fusion, and sublimation will be high. Conversely, substances with weak intermolecular forces will have lower heat values. For example, the molar heat of vaporization for water is 40.56 kJ/mol, while the molar heat of vaporization for helium is only 0.0845 kJ/mol.

The process of turning ice to vapor illustrates how the enthalpy of phase transitions is calculated. When heat is added to solid water (ice), the ice's temperature increases as molecules in the ice lattice begin vibrating. At 0°C, the heat added to the system no longer increases the temperature of the ice, but instead begins to break the ice's lattice structure, turning it into water. As more heat is added, the ice at 0°C becomes water at 0°C. The energy needed for this step is the heat of fusion.

HELPFUL HINT

The heat required to change between two phases will always be much larger than the heat required to raise the temperature of a substance in either phase.

Similarly, heat can be added to increase the temperature of the water to 100°C. At this point, adding more heat will break the intermolecular forces holding molecules in a liquid state, forming a gas at 100°C. The energy needed for this step is the heat of vaporization. Adding more heat to the gas past this point will increase the temperature of the gas. This process is shown in a **heating curve**.

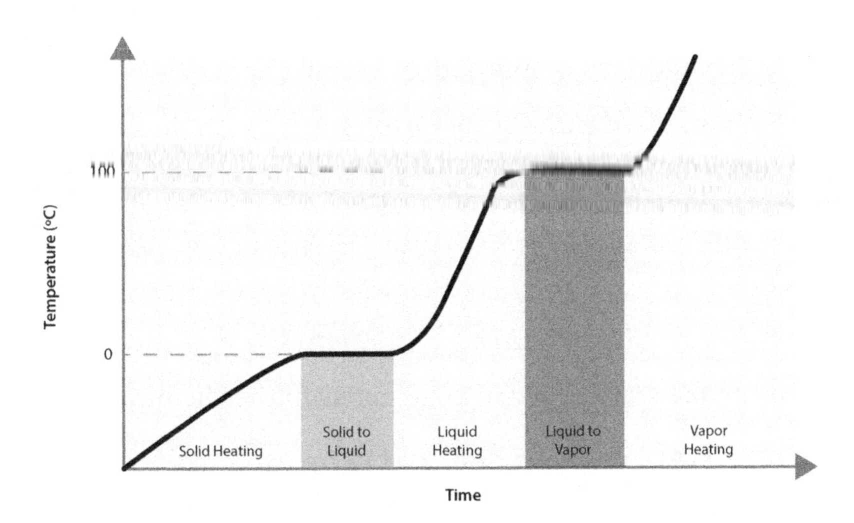

Figure 6.5. Heating Curve of Water

SAMPLE QUESTION

7) **How much energy is needed to turn 100 g of ice at −15°C to water at 45°C? (The specific heat of water is 4.18 J/g°C and the heat of fusion for water is 333.55 J/g.)**

Answer:

$Q = mc\Delta T$ $= (100\text{ g})(4.18\text{ J/g°C})(0°\text{C} - (-15\text{ °C}))$ $= 6{,}270\text{ J}$	Find the energy required to raise the temperature of the ice to 0°C.
$\Delta H_{fus} = (333.55\text{ J/g})(100\text{ g}) = 33{,}355\text{ J}$	Use the heat of fusion to find the energy required to turn the ice to water.
$Q = mc\Delta T$ $= (100\text{ g})(4.18\text{ J/g°C})(45°\text{C} - 0°\text{C})$ $= 18{,}810\text{ J}$	Find the energy required to increase the temperature of the water to 45°C.
6,270 J + 33,355 J + 18,810 J = **58,435 J**	Add the three values to find the total energy for the process.

ENTHALPY

Enthalpy (H) is the heat content of a system at constant pressure. The sign of ΔH describes whether the system has gained or lost heat. When ΔH is positive, the system has gained heat. When ΔH is negative, the system has lost heat. Like entropy, enthalpy is a state function. Enthalpy is given by the formula

$$\Delta H = \Delta U + P\Delta V$$

where ΔH is the change in enthalpy, ΔU is the change in the total internal energy of the system, P is pressure, and ΔV is the change in volume. ($P\Delta V$ is the work done when gases are expanded or compressed.)

A substance's **standard enthalpy of formation** ($\Delta H_f°$) is the change in enthalpy when a substance is formed under standard conditions (0°C and 10^5 Pa, denoted °). In a chemical reaction, the **enthalpy of reaction** (ΔH_{rxn}) is the sum of the enthalpy of formation of the reactants subtracted from the sum of the enthalpy of formation of the products:

$$\Delta H_{rxn} = \Sigma n\Delta H_{f\,\text{products}} - \Sigma m\Delta H_{f\,\text{reactants}}$$

where n and m are the stoichiometric coefficients in the chemical equation.

Table 6.4. Enthalpies of Formation

Substance	(kJ/mol)
Benzene	49.0
Carbon dioxide	–393.5
Carbon monoxide CO (*g*)	–110.5
Glucose	–1273
Hydrogen chloride HCl (*g*)	–92.30
Water	–285.8
Water vapor	–241.8

Because enthalpy is a state function, the ΔH of a chemical reaction depends only on the amount of matter in the reaction, and not on the path taken to reach the final state. Accordingly, **Hess's law** states that the ΔH for a reaction that occurs in a series of steps can be found by adding the enthalpy changes for each individual step. To use Hess's law, line up the equations for each step and reverse and/or multiply equations (and ΔH values) as necessary so that the intermediate products cancel. Then, add the ΔH values.

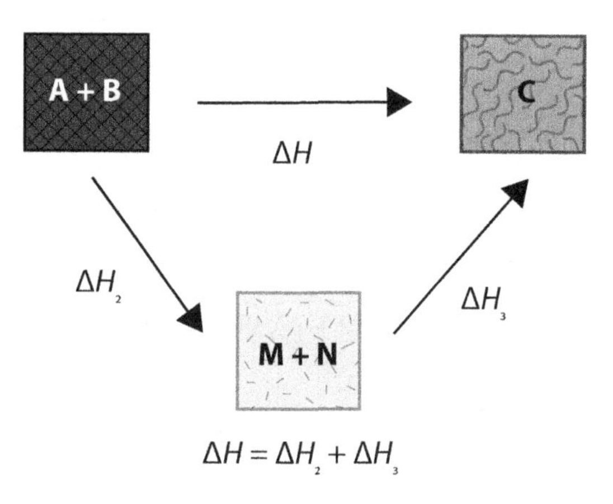

Figure 6.6. Hess's Law

$$A + B \xrightarrow{\Delta H_1} C$$

$$A + B \xrightarrow{\Delta H_2} M + N \xrightarrow{\Delta H_3} C$$

$$\Delta H_1 = \Delta H_2 + \Delta H_3$$

Enthalpies of reactions can also be found by looking at the enthalpy changes that result from the individual bonds that are broken and formed during the reaction. **Bond enthalpy** (D) is the ΔH for breaking a bond in one mole of a gaseous substance. The enthalpy of reaction can be estimated by subtracting the enthalpy of the bonds formed from the enthalpy of the bonds broken:

HELPFUL HINT

When reversing a reaction, change the sign of the corresponding ΔH value.

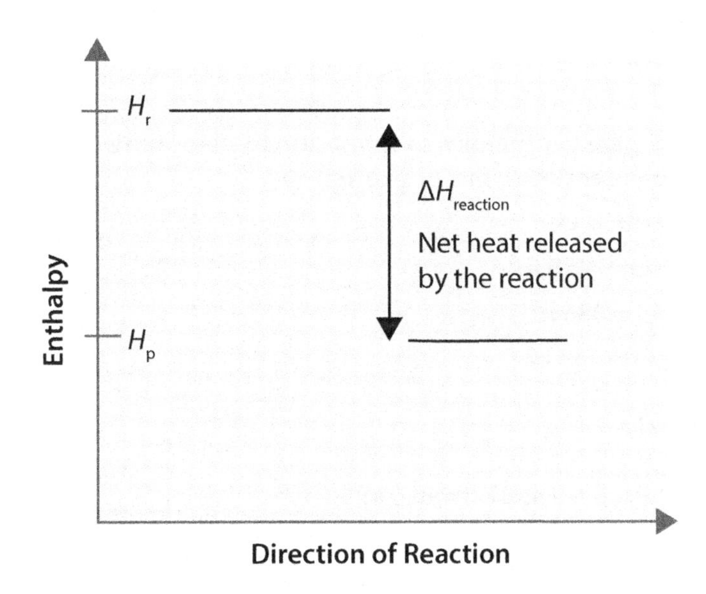

Figure 6.7. Enthalpy for Endothermic Reactions

$$\Delta H_{rxn} = \sum(\text{bond enthalpies of bonds broken}) - \sum(\text{bond enthalpies of bonds formed})$$

If ΔH is positive, meaning more energy was needed to break bonds than was released when new bonds formed, the reaction is endothermic. Conversely, when more energy is released by the formation of new bonds than was used to break bonds, ΔH is negative and the reaction is exothermic.

HELPFUL HINT

Bond enthalpy is always positive because breaking bonds always requires energy.

Go on

SAMPLE QUESTIONS

8) **Find the enthalpy of reaction for the reaction 4 NH_3 (*g*) + 5 O_2 (*g*) → 4 NO (*g*) + 6 H_2O (*g*) given the following enthalpies of reaction:**

N_2 (*g*) + O_2 (*g*) → 2 NO (*g*) ΔH = –180.5 kJ

N_2 (*g*) + 3 H_2 (*g*) → 2 NH_3 (*g*) ΔH = –91.8 kJ

2 H_2 (*g*) + O_2 (*g*) → 2 H_2O (*g*) ΔH = –483.6 kJ

Answer:

	2[N_2 (*g*) + O_2 (*g*) → 2 NO (*g*)]	ΔH = 2(–180.5 kJ) Multiply by 2.
	2[2 NH_3 (*g*) → N_2 (*g*) + 3 H_2 (*g*)]	ΔH = 2(91.8 kJ) Multiply by 2 & reverse.
+	3[2 H_2 (*g*) + O_2 (*g*) → 2 H_2O (*g*)]	ΔH= 3(–483.6 kJ) Multiply by 3.
4 NH_3 (*g*) +5 O_2 (*g*) → 4 NO (*g*) + 6 H_2O (*g*)		ΔH = **–1,628 kJ**

9) **Use the given enthalpies of formation to determine whether the following reaction is endothermic or exothermic.**

2 HCl → H_2 + Cl_2

ΔH_f° [HCl] = 428 kJ

ΔH_f° [H_2] = 436 kJ

ΔH_f° [Cl_2] = 239 kJ

Answer:

2 ΔH_f° [HCl] = 2(428 kJ) = 856 kJ	Calculate the total enthalpy of the reactants.
ΔH_f° [H_2] + ΔH_f° [Cl_2] = 436 + 239 = 675 kJ/mol	Calculate the total enthalpy of the products.
$\Delta H_{rxn} = \Sigma n\Delta H_{f\,reactants} - \Sigma m\Delta H_{f\,products}$ = 856 kJ – 675 kJ = 181 kJ/mol ΔH is positive, so the reaction is **endothermic.**	Find the difference between the products and reactants.

Gibbs Free Energy

Spontaneous processes are processes that are thermodynamically favorable, meaning that under a given set of conditions, these processes take place on their own. To determine whether a process will occur spontaneously, it is necessary to look at the resulting changes in both enthalpy and entropy. The difference between the process's enthalpy and entropy is called the **Gibbs free energy** (G), which is represented as

> **HELPFUL HINT**
>
> Spontaneity of a process describes the direction of a reaction, not the reaction's speed.

$$\Delta G = \Delta H - T\Delta S$$

where ΔG is the change in Gibbs free energy, ΔH is the change in enthalpy, T is the absolute temperature, and ΔS is the change in entropy.

The sign of ΔG for a process determines whether that process occurs spontaneously:

- $\Delta G < 0$: Process is spontaneous in the forward direction.
- $\Delta G > 0$: Process is nonspontaneous (but is spontaneous in the reverse direction).
- $\Delta G = 0$: Process is at equilibrium.

As with enthalpy, the **standard free energy of formation** ($\Delta G_f°$) describes the free energy change that results when a substance is formed. The **standard free energy change** for a process is the difference between the sum of the standard free energies of formation of the products and the reactants:

$$\Delta G_{\text{reaction}} = \Sigma n \Delta G_{\text{f products}} - \Delta m \Sigma G_{\text{f reactants}}$$

Table 6.5. Effects of Enthalpy and Entropy on Spontaneity

$\Delta G = \Delta H - T\Delta S$

ΔH	ΔS	ΔG	Spontaneous?
+	–	+	No
–	+	–	Yes
+	+	+ or –	At high temperatures
–	–	+ or –	At low temperatures

SAMPLE QUESTION

10) Calculate the Gibbs free energy change at 25°C for a reaction where ΔH is – 750 kJ and ΔS is 0.5 kJ/K, and determine whether the reaction is spontaneous.

Answer:

$\Delta G = \Delta H - T\Delta S$ $\Delta H = -750$ kJ $\Delta S = 0.5$ kJ/K	Identify the appropriate equation and variables.
$T = 25 + 273 = 298$ K	Find temperature in Kelvins.
$\Delta G = -750 - (298 \times 0.5)$ **$\Delta G = -899$ kJ** **ΔG is negative, so the reaction is spontaneous.**	Plug in the values and solve.

Solutions and Acid-Base Chemistry

Solutions and Solubility

A solution consists of a solute and a solvent. The **solute** is the substance that is dissolved, and the **solvent** is the substance that dissolves the solute. For example, when making a salt water solution, the salt (NaCl) is the solute and water (H_2O) is the solvent. The concentration of a solution is the amount of solute dissolved in the solvent.

The **solubility** of a solution is the maximum amount of solute that will dissolve in a specific quantity of solvent at a specified temperature. A concentrated solution contains an amount of solute near the solubility limit (i.e., a large amount of dissolved solute). A dilute solution contains less solute and more solvent than a concentrated solution.

Solutions can be saturated, unsaturated, or supersaturated based on the amount of solute dissolved in the solution. A **saturated solution** has the maximum amount of solute (i.e., the solute concentration equals the solute solubility in the solvent). There is a dynamic equilibrium in a saturated solution between the undissolved and dissolved solute, and the solution is in equilibrium with its solute and solvent. If the solute is a solid, the solid is observed in the solution.

An **unsaturated solution** contains the solute at a concentration less than the solubility of the solute. Therefore, an unsaturated solution can dissolve more solute without additional solvent. As solute is added to an unsaturated solution, it can become a saturated solution.

A **supersaturated solution** is a solution that contains more than the solubility (equilibrium concentration) of the solute at a specified temperature. A supersaturated solution can be made by heating the solution to dissolve additional solute and then slowly cooling it down to a specified temperature. For example, a saturated solution of ammonia chloride can be made at 80°C and cooled to 25°C, at which point it becomes a supersaturated solution. If the solution is cooled slowly, none of the ammonia chloride will precipitate out immediately. Eventually, the excess solute will slowly precipitate, or crystallize, out of the solution, but this may take days or months.

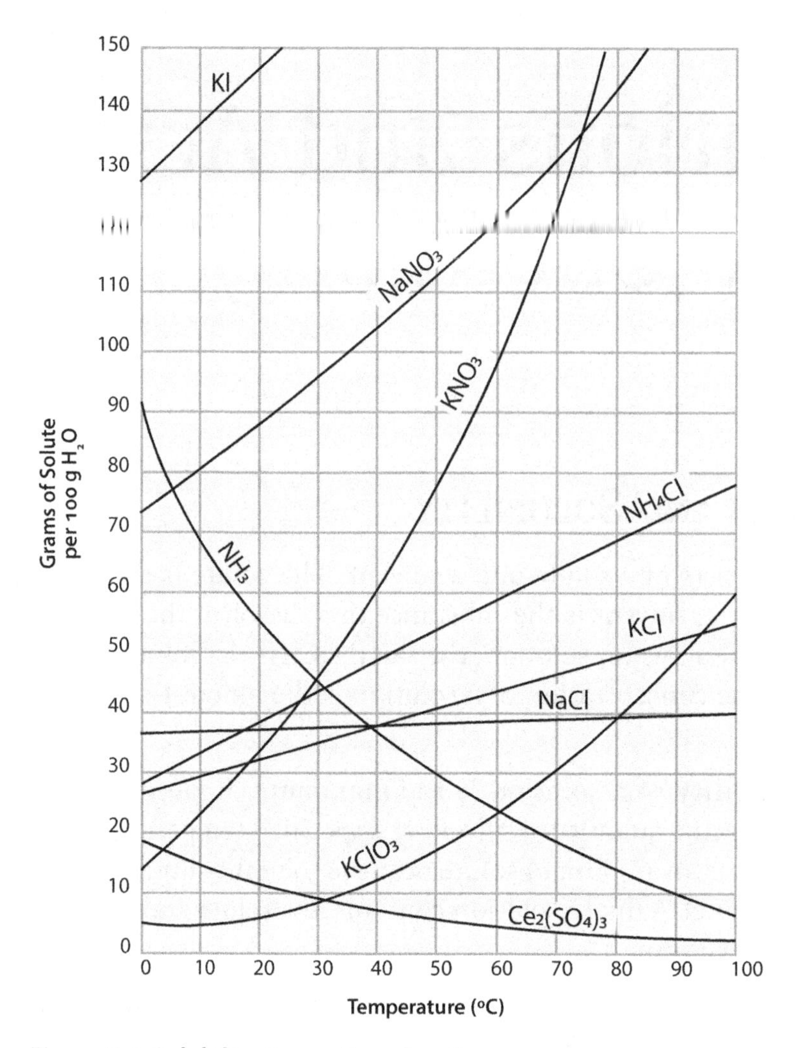

Figure 7.1. Solubility Curves Based on Temperature

A solubility curve (see Figure 7.1) can be used to determine the solubility of a solute at a particular temperature. These diagrams are specific for each compound/ molecule and indicate the number of grams of the solute that can be dissolved in *X* grams or milliliters of a solvent at specific temperatures. The curve in the diagram represents the solubility and indicates the concentration required for a saturated solution at each temperature. The area above the curve represents supersaturated solutions, and the area below the curve represents unsaturated solutions.

Temperature-based solubility diagrams and curves can be used to describe the solubility of solids, liquids, and gases. Typically, the solubility of a solute in a solvent increases with an increase in temperature, but this is not always true. When a solute is dissolved in a solution, the process is analogous to melting, and heat or energy is required to break the bonds holding the solute together. Heat is also given off by the formation of new solvation/solvent bonds. In the uncommon event that the heat given off by the formation of the solvent bonds is greater than that needed to break the solute bonds, an increase in temperature will decrease the solubility. However, in most cases, an increase in temperature will increase the solubility by providing additional energy to break apart (dissolve) the solute. The solubility of gases in solution typically decreases with an increase in temperature because of an increase in the energy in the solution, allowing the gas molecules to "escape" the solution.

A pressure-dependent solubility curve is often used to describe the solubility of gases. As the pressure increases, the solubility of a gas increases. The increased pressure "forces" the gas molecules into solution. The pressure does not have an impact on the solubility of liquids and solids.

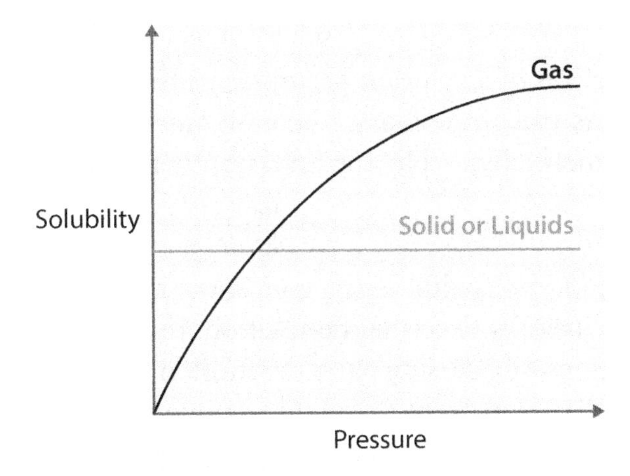

Figure 7.2. Solubility Curves Based on Pressure

There are many different ways to describe the concentration of a solution. **Molarity** (molar concentration) is commonly used in chemistry to describe the concentration of a solution. The molarity of a solution is the number of moles of solute per liter (volume) of the solution and is abbreviated as M (mol/L).

$$\text{Molarity} = \frac{\text{moles of solute}}{\text{liters of solution}}$$

Because molarity is based on volume and volume is temperature dependent, molarity is temperature dependent. A temperature-independent unit to define concentration is molality. **Molality** (*b*) is the concentration of a solute (in moles) in a given mass of the solvent and is abbreviated m (mol/kg).

> **DID YOU KNOW?**
>
> Decompression sickness, also called the bends, is an ailment that afflicts divers who come to the surface too quickly. The high pressure deep in the ocean allows more gas to be dissolved in the fluid inside the diver's body. A quick drop in pressure (rising to the surface quickly) will lower the solubility of the gas, causing the gas to come out of solution and form bubbles inside the diver's body.

$$\text{Molality} = \frac{\text{moles of solute}}{\text{kilograms of solvent}}$$

The **mass fraction** of a solute is the fraction of the solution's total mass that the solute contributes. This is commonly expressed as the **weight percent**, which is calculated by multiplying the mass fraction by 100%. To calculate the weight percent of sucrose in a solution, the masses of the sucrose and total solution are needed:

$$\text{mass fraction of sucrose} = \frac{\text{mass of sucrose}}{\text{mass of the solution}} = \frac{25\text{ g}}{100\text{ g}} = 0.25$$

$$\text{weight percent} = 0.25 \times 100\% = 25\%\text{ wt. solution of sucrose}$$

The weight percent can be converted to molarity if the density of the solution is known.

In addition to weight percent, **volume percent** can be used. In volume percent, the amount of solute and solution are both measured in volume.

$$\text{volume percent} = \frac{\text{volume of solute}}{\text{volume of solution}} \times 100$$

The **mole fraction** of a solution is similar to the mass fraction, but uses the number of moles instead of the mass. The mole fraction is the moles of the solute (or solution component) divided by the total number of moles in the solution.

$$\text{mole fraction} = \frac{\text{moles of solute}}{\text{moles of the solution}}$$

When a solution is very dilute, the concentration units previously described can be too large to usefully describe the solution. In this case the mass fraction of the solution can be described using parts per million or per billion. *Parts per million* (ppm) is equivalent to one gram of solute per one million grams of solution or 1 milligram of solute per 1 kilogram of solution. *Parts per billion* (ppb) is equivalent to one gram of solute in one billion grams of solution or 1 microgram of solute per 1 kilogram of solution.

Frequently, a series of solutions that vary in concentration is needed for experiments. To come up with a series of solutions, a concentrated solution of known concentration is used and diluted to the needed concentrations. During dilution, the number of moles of the solute remains constant, but the volume changes, which changes the molarity of the solution. A simple relationship can be used to determine how much solution and solvent are needed for the dilutions:

$$M_sV_s = M_dV_d$$

The **dissolution rate** of a solution is the rate at which the solute is dissolved in the solvent to form a solution. The dissolution rate can be affected by a number of factors such as the temperature, pressure, surface area, and solution agitation (stirring). Changes in the solubility change the dissolution rate, and an increase in the solubility will increase the dissolution rate. Because of this, an increase in temperature for solids and liquids will likely increase the dissolution rate, and an increase in the pressure for gases will increase the dissolution rate. An increase in the surface area of a solid will increase the dissolution rate by providing more surface for the solvent to solvate, and stirring or agitating a solution will increase the dissolution rate by providing more energy to break the solute bonds.

SAMPLE QUESTIONS

1) **What is the molarity of a solution if 12 grams of NaCl are added to 100 mL of water?**

A. 1.2 M

B. 2.05 M

C. 4 M

D. 12 M

Answer: B.

Convert the grams of NaCl into moles to calculate the molarity.

$12\text{ g NaCl} \times \frac{1\text{ mole of NaCl}}{58.44\text{ grams}} =$

0.205 moles of NaCl

Divide the moles of the solute by the liters of solution to find the molarity.

$\text{Molarity} = \frac{0.205\text{ moles of NaCl}}{0.1\text{ L}}$

= 2.05 M NaCl

2) **What is the molality of a 100 mL solution of water with 20 g of $NaNO_3$?**

A. 1 m

B. 2.35 m

C. 20.1 m

D. 3.33 m

Answer: B.

Convert grams of $NaNO_3$ into moles.

$20\text{ g } NaNO_3 \times \frac{1\text{ mole } NaNO_3}{84.995\text{ g } NaNO_3} = 0.235\text{ moles } NaNO_3$

Use the formula for molality. Assume a density of 1 g/mL for water.

$\text{Molality} = \frac{0.235\text{ moles NaNO3}}{0.1\text{ kg solvent}}$

= 2.35 m $NaNO_3$

3) **To make 100 mL of 1 M HCl from a 6 M HCl solution, how many mL of a 6 M solution are needed?**

A. 6 mL

B. 7.6 mL

C. 12.2 mL

D. 16.7 mL

Answer: D.

Use the formula for finding the volume of a diluted solution.

$M_sV_s = M_dV_d$

$(6\text{ M})(V_s) = (0.1\text{ L})(1\text{ M})$

$V_s = \frac{0.1\text{ L} \times 1\text{ mol}}{6\text{ mol/L}} = 0.0167\text{ L}$

Colligative Properties of Solutions

A colligative property of a solution depends only on the concentration of the solute particles in the solution and not on the type of particles present. There are four colligative properties: vapor pressure, boiling point, freezing point, and osmotic pressure. All colligative properties can be understood by looking at the differences in entropy between the pure solvent and the solution.

Vapor Pressure

The liquid in a closed system is in equilibrium with its vapor. In this equilibrium, the rate at which molecules escape the liquid is equal to the rate at which the vapor molecules return to the liquid. The pressure created by the vapor at equilibrium is that substance's **vapor pressure.** Liquids that have a vapor pressure are described as **volatile**; those that have no vapor pressure (meaning the liquid does not vaporize), are **non-volatile**.

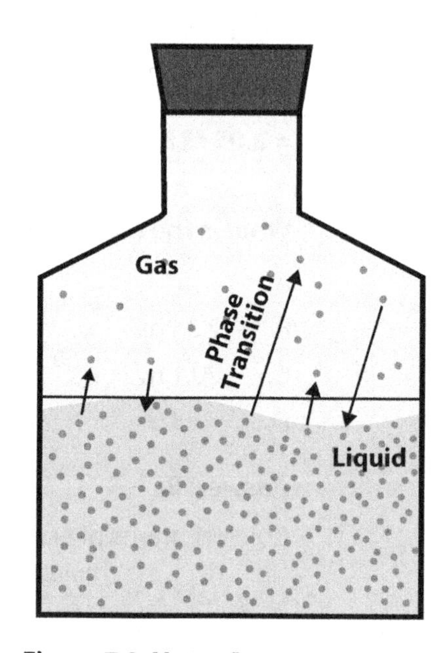

Figure 7.3. Vapor Pressure

A substance's vapor pressure increases with temperature, as molecules have more energy to escape the liquid. The addition of a nonvolatile solute to a volatile substance will lower that substance's vapor pressure. The amount that the vapor pressure decreases depends on the solute concentration, and can be described by Raoult's law:

$$P_1 = X_1 P_1^{\circ}$$

where P_1 is the vapor pressure of the solvent over the solution, P_1° is the vapor pressure of the pure solvent, and X_1 is the mole fraction of the solvent in the solution.

SAMPLE QUESTION

4) **Calculate the vapor pressure of water for a solution containing 0.5 moles of sucrose and 10 moles of water at 25°C. The vapor pressure of pure water at 25°C is 23.76 mm Hg.**

A. 22.63 mm Hg
B. 24 mm Hg
C. 23.76 mm Hg
D. 21 mm Hg

Answer: A.

$\frac{10 \text{ mol water}}{10.5 \text{ mol}} = 0.952$	Calculate the mole fraction of water.
$P_1 = 0.952 \times 23.76$ mm Hg = **22.63 mm Hg**	Use Raoult's law.

BOILING POINT AND FREEZING POINT

The boiling point of a solvent or solution is the temperature at which the vapor pressure of the solution is equal to 1 atm. Because a solution has a lower vapor pressure than the solvent, the solution must now reach a higher temperature to have a vapor pressure equal to the atmospheric pressure. The difference between the normal boiling point of a solvent and the higher boiling point of a solution is referred to as boiling point elevation. The increase in the boiling point is related to the concentration of the solute. In this case, the concentration of the solute needs to be expressed in molality because molality is independent of temperature. The increase in the boiling point can be calculated by:

$$\Delta Tb = T_{B\,(solution)} - T_{B\,(solvent)} = K_b m$$

where K_b is the molal boiling point elevation constant of the solvent and m is the molality of the solute.

The freezing point of a liquid is the temperature at which the first molecules begin to cluster together into a crystal lattice to form a solid. At the freezing point, there is a dynamic equilibrium between crystallization and melting. When a solution freezes, the pure solvent clusters together to form solid solvent, and an equilibrium between the solution and solid solvent is established. In a solution, all of the molecules in contact with the frozen solvent are not solvent molecules, causing a slower dynamic equilibrium between crystallization and melting. The slower rate also correlates to a lower freezing point, meaning the freezing temperature for a solution is lower than that of the pure solvent. The lowering of the freezing point, called freezing point depression, can be calculated in the same way as the boiling point elevation:

> QUICK REVIEW
>
> Why is salt used to keep water from freezing on the roads in the winter?

$$\Delta T_f = K_f m$$

where K_f is a constant that depends only on the solvent and m is the molality of the solute.

SAMPLE QUESTION

5) **Calculate the boiling and freezing points of an aqueous solution containing 39.5 g of ethylene glycol (MW 62.07 g) dissolved in 750 mL of water. The K_b for water is 0.52 °C kg mol^{-1} and the K_f is 1.86 °C kg mol^{-1}.**

A. Boiling: 101 °C
Freezing: 0 °C

B. Boiling: 100.75 °C
Freezing: −1.8 °C

C. Boiling: 110 °C
Freezing: −5 °C

D. Boiling: 100.44 °C
Freezing: −1.58 °C

Answer: D.

Determine the molality of the solution (moles of solute per kilogram of solvent).

$$39.5 \text{ g ethylene glycol} \times \frac{1 \text{ mol ethylene glycol}}{62.07 \text{ g}}$$

$= 0.636$ mol ethylene glycol

Find the molality of the solution. The density of water is 1 g/mL, so 750 mL is equal to 750 g or 0.75 kg

$$b = \frac{0.636 \text{ mol}}{0.75 \text{ kg}} = 0.848 \text{ m}$$

Determine boiling point elevation.

$\Delta T_b = (0.52°\text{C kg mol}^{-1})(0.848 \text{ mol/kg}) = 0.44\ °\text{C}$, which gives a boiling point of **100.44 °C**.

Determine freezing point depression.

$\Delta T_f = (1.86°\text{C kg mol}^{-1})(0.848 \text{ mol/kg}) = 1.58°\text{C}$, which gives a freezing point of **−1.58 °C**.

Osmotic Pressure

Osmosis is the movement of a solvent through a semipermeable membrane from a region with a lower solute concentration to a region with a higher solute concentration (i.e., the solvent moves from a higher solvent concentration to a lower solvent concentration region). When a solution is separated from pure water by a semipermeable membrane, water (the solvent) will move from across the membrane into the solution. The pressure required to prevent this osmosis is a solution's **osmotic pressure** (Π).

As with other colligative properties, osmotic pressure depends on the concentration of the solution: a higher concentration in the solute increases the pressure required to prevent mixing. The osmotic pressure can be calculated using the following equation:

$$\pi = \left(\frac{n}{V}\right)RT = MRT$$

where n is the number of particles per formula unit of solute, V is the volume of solution, R is the gas constant, T is the absolute temperature (in Kelvin), and M is the molarity of the solution.

SAMPLE QUESTION

6) **What is the osmotic pressure of a 1.50 M solution of sucrose at 25°C?**

A. 3.08 atm

B. 36.7 atm

C. 37.5 atm

D. 447.225 atm

Answer: B.

Use the equation for osmotic pressure.

$\pi = (1.50\ \text{M})\left(0.08206\ \frac{\text{L} \times \text{atm}}{\text{mol} \times \text{K}}\right)(298.15\ \text{K}) = \mathbf{36.7\ atm}$

SOLUBILITY EQUILIBRIA

Most ionic compounds are completely soluble in water, meaning they dissociate into their component ions. However, some ionic compounds are only slightly soluble and partially dissociate, while others are insoluble in water. The solubility of ionic compounds in water is determined by two competing forces: the force of attraction between the ions and water, and the force of attraction between the ions. It is not easy to predict which of these forces will prevail in ionic compounds, but there are rules to help determine solubility.

Solubility Rules:

- All ammonium and alkali metal salts are soluble.
- All nitrates are soluble.
- All chlorides, bromides, and iodides are soluble except for: AgCl, Hg_2Cl_2, $PbCl_2$, AgBr, Hg_2Br_2, $PbBr_2$, AgI, Hg_2I_2, PbI_2.
- Most sulfates are soluble except for: $CaSO_4$, $SrSO_4$, $BaSO_4$, $PbSO_4$.
- All chlorates are soluble.
- All perchlorates are soluble.
- All acetates are soluble.
- All phosphates are insoluble except for: NH_4^+ and alkali metal phosphates.

- All carbonates are insoluble except for: NH_4^+ and alkali metal carbonates.
- All hydroxides are insoluble except for: NH_4^+ and alkali metal hydroxides; $Sr(OH)_2$, $Ba(OH)_2$, and $Ca(OH)_2$ are slightly soluble.
- All oxides are insoluble except for alkali metal oxides.
- All oxalates are insoluble except for: NH_4^+ and alkali metal oxalates.
- All sulfides are insoluble except for: NH_4^+ and alkali metal sulfides; MgS, CaS, and BaS are sparingly soluble.

HELPFUL HINT

If a compound contains at least one of the ions listed for soluble compounds in the solubility rules, the compound is at least partially soluble.

In the case of saturated solutions of ionic compounds, a solubility equilibrium is established between the dissolved and undissolved ions. The equilibrium constant that describes this relationship is called the **solubility product constant**, K_{sp}. The value of K_{sp} indicates the extent to which a solid will dissolve into its component ions in solution. A general equilibrium expression for the dissolution of a slightly soluble salt is:

$$A_xB_y(s) \leftrightarrow x\,A^{n+}\,(aq) + y\,B^{m-}\,(aq); \qquad K_{sp} = [A^{n+}]^x\,[B^{m-}]^y$$

Note that the K_{sp} is related only to the concentration of the ions in solution.

When a reaction between two aqueous solutions results in an insoluble product, a solid will form. This solid is called a precipitate, and the process is called **precipitation**. For example, when two soluble compounds, $BaCl_2$ and Na_2SO_4, react, they form $BaSO_4$ and NaCl. NaCl is soluble, but a check of the solubility rules shows that $BaSO_4$ is not soluble and will precipitate from the solution.

Additional factors that can influence the solubility of ionic compounds include temperature, pressure, formation of ion pairs, competing equilibria, pH, the formation of complex ions, and the presence of common ions. The **common ion effect** occurs when the presence of a second solute with a common ion decreases the solubility of an ionic compound. The common ion shifts the equilibrium in the solution to the left, based on Le Châtelier's principle, making the compound less soluble. For example, the solubility of $BaSO_4$ can be reduced by adding $NaSO_4$ to the solution. The increased concentration of the SO_4^{2-} ions decreases the solubility of $BaSO_4$ by shifting the equilibrium to offset the additional sulfate ions by forming solid $BaSO_4$.

DID YOU KNOW?

Precipitation can be used to make water drinkable by turning dissolved contaminants into solids that can be removed.

Table 7.1. Effects of Temperature and Pressure on Solubility

Factor	Solute State	Effect
Temperature	Solid	In an endothermic reaction, an increase in temperature increases solubility.
		In an exothermic reaction, an increase in temperature reduces solubility.
	Gas	An increase in temperature reduces solubility.
Pressure	Gas	An increase in the pressure above a solution increases solubility.

SAMPLE QUESTIONS

7) **Predict the solubility of the following compounds:**

1. **NH_4Cl**
2. **$Mg_3(PO_4)_2$**
3. **$Ba(OH)_2$**
4. **$Ca(NO_3)_2$**

A. Soluble: 1, 3, and 4
   Insoluble: 2

B. Soluble: 1, 2, and 4
   Insoluble: 3

C. Soluble: 2 and 4
   Insoluble: 1, 3

D. Soluble: 1, 2, 3, and 4

Answer: A.

All common chlorides are soluble. All phosphates are insoluble. $Ba(OH)_2$ is an exception to the rule that all hydroxides are insoluble; and all nitrates are soluble.

8) **In a saturated CaF_2 solution, the calcium concentration is 9.1 mg/L. Calculate the K_{sp} for CaF_2 assuming the compound dissociates completely into Ca^{2+} and F^-.**

A. 4.9×10^{-11}

B. 6×10^{-8}

C. 9.1×10^{-4}

D. 7.6×10^{-13}

Answer: A.

$CaF_2\ (s) \leftrightarrow Ca^{2+}\ (aq) + 2\ F^-\ (aq)$	Write the chemical equilibrium equation.
$K_{sp} = [Ca^{2+}]\ [F^-]^2$	Write the equilibrium constant expression, K_{sp}.
$\frac{9.1\text{ mg }Ca^{2+}}{1\text{ L}} \times \frac{1\text{ g }Ca^{2+}}{1000\text{ mg }Ca^{2+}} \times \frac{1\text{ mol }Ca^{2+}}{40\text{ g }Ca^{2+}}$ $= 2.3 \times 10^{-4}\text{ M }Ca^{2+}$ Based on the balanced equation, 2 moles of F ions are produced for every mole of Ca ions, so the F ion concentration must be 4.6×10^{-4} M.	Determine the molar concentrations of the Ca and F ions.
$K_{sp} = (2.3 \times 10^{-4})(4.6 \times 10^{-4})^2$ **$= 4.9 \times 10^{-11}$**	Determine the K_{sp} using these concentrations.

Introduction to Acid–Base Chemistry

Definitions of Acids and Bases

There are three main definitions for acids and bases. The first is the Arrhenius definition. An **Arrhenius acid** is a substance that dissociates in water to form hydrogen ions, and an **Arrhenius base** is a substance that dissociates in water to form hydroxide ions. The Arrhenius definition is restricted to aqueous solutions and refers to the concentration of the solvent ions. An Arrhenius acid must increase the hydrogen ion concentration or decrease the hydroxide concentration in an aqueous solution; an Arrhenius base must increase the hydroxide ion concentration or decrease the hydrogen ion concentration in an aqueous solution.

The second definition is the Brønsted-Lowry definition. A **Brønsted-Lowry acid** is a hydrogen ion donor, and a **Brønsted-Lowry base** is a hydrogen ion acceptor. Under this definition, all acids donate hydrogen ions and all bases accept the hydrogen ions. Thus, the acid-base reaction is the removal of a hydrogen ion from the acid and its addition to the base.

A conjugate acid-base pair is a pair of molecules or ions that are related to each other via the loss or gain of a hydrogen ion. The removal of the hydrogen ion from the acid produces the conjugate base, and the addition of the hydrogen ion to the base results in the formation of the conjugate acid.

$$HA + B \rightarrow BH^+\ \text{(conjugate acid)} + A^-\ \text{(conjugate base)}$$

To act as a Brønsted-Lowry base, a molecule or ion must have an unshared pair of electrons so it can accept a hydrogen ion. According to the Brønsted-Lowry definition, water can act as either an acid or a base, depending on whether an acid or a base is present, since water can both donate and accept hydrogen ions to become either OH^- or H_3O^+. All hydrogen-containing substances are acids according to this definition.

The third and final definition is the Lewis definition. A **Lewis acid** is a compound that can receive an electron pair to form a new bond, and a **Lewis base** is a compound that can donate an electron pair to form a new bond. Based on this definition, an acid-base reaction occurs when there is a molecule with a lone pair of electrons and a molecule that can accept the lone pair. Lewis acids tend to be cations or neutral molecules with an empty orbital, and Lewis bases tend to be anions or neutral molecules with a lone pair of electrons. All metal cations are potential Lewis acids. Water acts as a Lewis base when it forms a coordinate covalent, both with metal ions.

An example of a typical Lewis acid-base reaction is the reaction of boron trifluoride with a flouride ion to produce the ion tetrafluoroborate: $BF_3 + F^- \rightarrow BF_4^-$

Table 7.2. The Three Definitions of Acids and Bases

	Arrhenius	Brønsted-Lowry	Lewis
Acid	provider of H^+ in HOH	proton donor	electron pair acceptor
Base	provider of OH^- in HOH	proton acceptor	electron pair donor
Neutralization	formation of water	proton transfer	coordinate covalent bond formation
Equation	$H^+ + OH^- \rightarrow HOH$	$HA + B \rightarrow BH^+ + A^-$	$A + B \rightarrow A{:}B$
Limitation	water solution only	proton transfer reactions only	generalized theory

SAMPLE QUESTION

9) **HBr (*aq*) + H_2O (*l*) → H_3O^+ (*aq*) + Br^- (*aq*)**

Which of the following is the conjugate base in the reaction shown above?

A. HBr

B. H_2O

C. H_3O^+

D. Br^-

Answer: D.

The acid HBr loses a proton, creating the conjugate base Br^-.

The pH Scale

The pH scale (see Figure 7.5) is used to indicate how acidic or basic an aqueous solution is. **pH** is the negative of the base 10 logarithm (log) of the hydronium ion concentration (H_3O^+).

$$pH = -\log[H_3O^+] \text{ or } -\log[H^+]$$

HELPFUL HINT

The hydronium ion and hydrogen ion are often used interchangeably when talking about acid-base reactions. It was initially thought that hydrogen ions existed in solution, but it was later shown that they exist as the hydronium ions in water.

The concentrations of H_3O^+ and OH^- vary widely in aqueous solutions, from 10 M to 10^{-15} M, depending on the acid and base present. The pH scale ranges from 0 to 14 with 7 representing a neutral solution (pure water). pH values less than 7 are acidic and pH values greater than 7 are basic.

The pOH of a solution can also be calculated based on the hydroxide ion concentration.

$$pOH = -\log[OH^-]$$

pH and pOH are related by the following expression:

$$pH + pOH = 14$$

When one value is known, the other value can be determined. For example, a 0.1 M solution of a strong base, such as NaOH, has an $[OH^-]$ of 0.1 M and a pOH of 1, which gives a pH of 13.

Water undergoes self-ionization to form a hydroxide ion and a hydronium ion. This equilibrium applies to pure water and any aqueous solution. The ionization constant for water at 25°C is:

$$K_w = [H_3O^+]\,[OH^-] = 1.0 \times 10^{-14}$$

The K_w is related to pH and pOH via the equation:

$$-\log K_w = pK_w = pH + pOH = 14$$

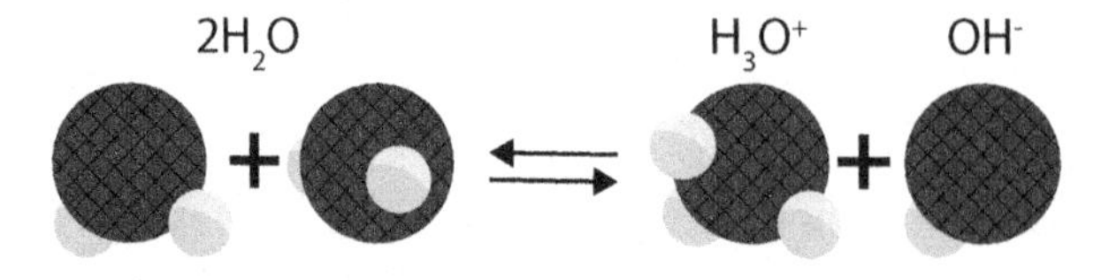

Figure 7.4. Self-Ionization of Water

The ionization constant decreases as the temperature and pressure increase, and it changes with the electrolyte concentration.

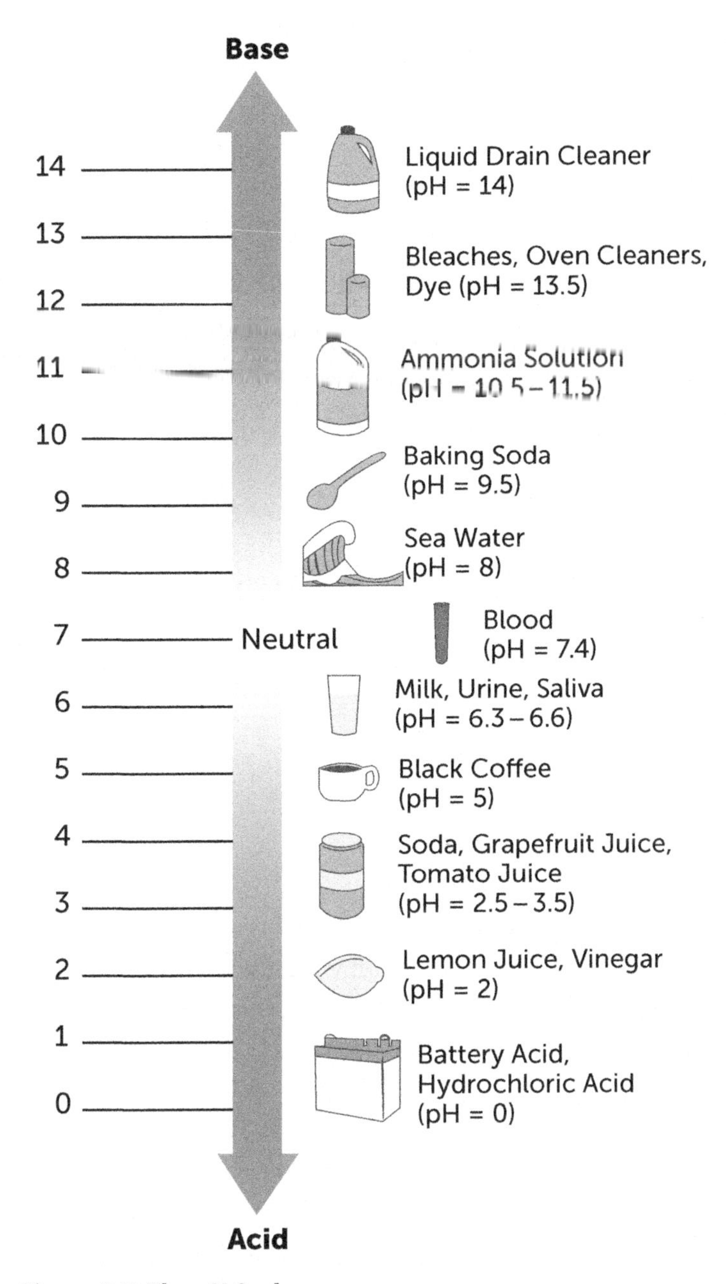

Figure 7.5. The pH Scale

SAMPLE QUESTIONS

10) What is the pH of a 500 mL solution containing 1.25 g of HCl?

A. 1

B. 0.5

C. 1.16

D. 2.25

Answer: C.

$1.25 \text{ g HCl} \times \frac{1 \text{ mol HCl}}{36.46 \text{ g HCl}} = 0.034 \text{ mol HCl}$	Determine the number of moles of HCl.

$[H_3O^+] = \frac{0.034 \text{ mol HCl}}{0.5 \text{ L}} = 0.069 \text{ M} = 0.069 \text{ M}$ $pH = -\log(0.069)$ **= 1.16**	Because HCl is a strong acid, the moles of H_3O^+ are equal to the moles of the acid.

11) What is the $[H_3O^+]$ for a solution with a pH of 8.3?

A. 5×10^{-7} M

B. 5×10^{-9} M

C. 8.3×10^{-5} M

D. 8.3×10^{-9} M

Answer: B.

To determine the $[H_3O^+]$, use the equation for pH.

$pH = -\log[H_3O^+]$

$8.30 = -\log[H_3O^+]$

$10^{-8.3} = [H_3O^+]$

$\mathbf{[H_3O^+] = 5 \times 10^{-9} M}$

Neutralization and Titration

When acids and bases react quantitatively with each other, the hydrogen and hydroxide ions react with each other to form water, neutralizing the solution. Water is neutral and the remaining ions form a salt in the solution. For example, when HCl (a strong acid) and NaOH (a strong base) react, they create water and NaCl.

The general neutralization reaction is:

$$HX\ (aq) + MOH\ (aq) \rightarrow H_2O\ (l) + MX\ (aq)$$

To neutralize an acid an equivalent quantity of base must be added, and vice versa, to ensure that the concentrations of hydrogen and hydroxide ions are zero. The point of neutralization, the **equivalence point**, is the point in an acid-base reaction at which chemically equivalent quantities of the acid and base have been mixed. For strong acids and bases the neutralization endpoint results in a neutral pH of 7.

QUICK REVIEW

What acidic and basic solutions do you use on a daily basis?

An acid-base **titration** is a method to determine the concentration of an acid or base in an aqueous solution by adding known amounts of an acid or base. A standard solution of an acid or base (a titrant) is prepared and placed in a burette, which accurately measures the volume of the solution as it is added to the unknown solution. An indicator is also added to the unknown solution that will show when the unknown solution has been neutralized.

During the titration, small amounts of the titrate are added to the unknown solution. When the moles of acid and base are equal (at the equivalence point), the indicator will change color. The volume of titrant added can then be used to determine the initial concentration of the unknown acid or base. For strong acids and bases the equivalence point is at pH 7. For a strong acid titration with a weak base, the pH will be less than 7, and for a strong base titration with a weak acid, the pH will be greater than 7.

Titrations are typically plotted as titration curves (see Figure 7.6), with the volume of the added acid or base on the *x*-axis and the pH on the *y*-axis. Near the equivalence point the pH tends to change very quickly, so it is important to add small increments of the titrant as the equivalence point is approached to accurately determine the equivalent volume.

In a typical titration of HNO_3 with NaOH, a standardized solution of NaOH is placed in the burette, and a known amount of the HNO_3 solution is placed in an Erlenmeyer flask with phenolphthalein, a commonly used acid-base indicator. In its acidic form, phenolphthalein is colorless; in its basic form, it is red. NaOH is stirred into the HNO_3 solution until the solution turns pink, indicating the reaction is complete and the endpoint has been reached. The volume of NaOH added is measured and used to calculate the concentration of the HNO_3.

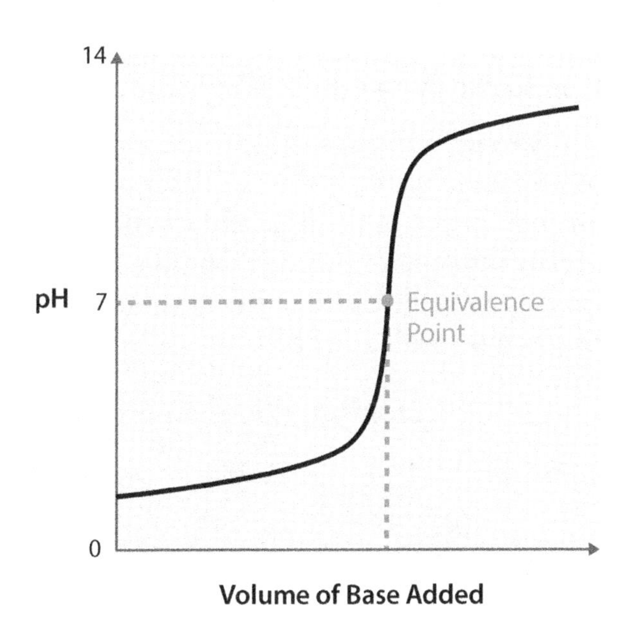

Figure 7.6. Titration Curve

SAMPLE QUESTION

12) If 20 mL of a 0.5 M NaOH solution is used to titrate a 50 mL solution of HNO_3, what is the concentration of the HNO_3?

A. 0.5 M

B. 0.25 M

C. 0.2 M

D. 0.35 M

Answer: C.

Use dimensional analysis to find the molarity of the HNO_3 solution.

20 mL NaOH	1000 mL	0.5 mol NaOH	1 mol HNO_3	**0.2 M HNO_3**
50 mL HNO_3	1 L	1000 mL	1 mol NaOH	

Acid–Base Equilibria

Strong Acids and Bases

Strong acids ionize completely in water while **weak acids** only partially ionize. The strength of an acid can depend on the electronegativity of the conjugate base, the atomic radius of the resultant anion, the charge of the species, and the equilibrium of the dissociation reaction. Because strong acids completely dissociate in aqueous solutions, the concentration of the hydronium ions in water is equal to the concentration of the acid added to the solution. The dissociation of weak acids must be represented by an equilibrium of the acid molecules and constituent ions.

Strong and weak bases are categorized in the same way. Strong bases completely dissociate in water, and weak bases only partially dissociate. Weak bases exist as an equilibrium of the base and its component ions. Strong bases completely dissociate into ions in aqueous solution. Weak bases do not completely dissociate and exist as an equilibrium of the base and its component ions. See Table 7.3 for a list of common acids and bases.

Table 7.3. Common Acids and Bases

Strong acids	HCl	Hydrochloric acid
	HNO_3	Nitric acid
	H_2SO_4	Sulfuric acid
	$HClO_4$	Perchloric acid
	HBr	Hydrobromic acid
	HI	Hydroiodic acid
Strong bases	LiOH	Lithium hydroxide
	NaOH	Sodium hydroxide
	KOH	Potassium hydroxide
	$Ca(OH)_2$	Calcium hydroxide
	$Ba(OH)_2$	Barium hydroxide
	$Sr(OH)_2$	Strontium hydroxide
Weak acids	H_3PO_4	Phosphoric acid
	CH_3COOH	Acetic acid
	H_2CO_3	Carbonic acid
	HCN	Hydrocyanic acid
	HCOOH	Formic acid
	C_6H_5COOH	Benzoic acid

Table 7.3. Common Acids and Bases (continued)

Weak bases	NH_3	Ammonia
	CH_3NH_2	Methylamine

SAMPLE QUESTION

13) **Which of the following is a strong acid?**

A. HClO

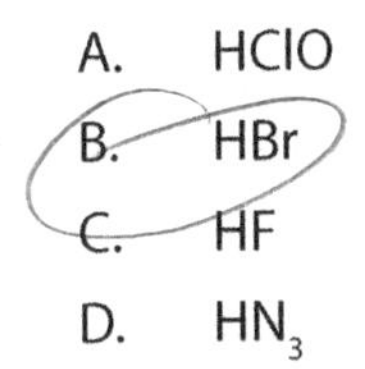

B. HBr

C. HF

D. HN_3

Answer: B.

HBr is one of the strong acids.

EQUILIBRIUM EQUATIONS FOR ACIDS AND BASES

The previous section introduced the pH calculations for strong acids and bases. Because strong acids and bases completely dissociate, the concentration of H^+ and/or OH^- is easily determined based on the concentration of the acid or base. This is not the case for weak acids and bases. Because weak acids only partially ionize in water, a different approach must be used to calculate the pH of a solution containing a weak acid.

The equilibrium equation for a weak acid is:

$$HA\ (aq) + H_2O\ (l) \rightarrow H_3O^+\ (aq) + A^-\ (aq)$$

or

$$HA\ (aq) \rightarrow H^+\ (aq) + A^-\ (aq)$$

The equilibrium constant expression, K_a, is the acid dissociation constant:

$$K_a = \frac{[H_3O^+][A^-]}{[HA]} \text{ or } \frac{[H^+][A^-]}{[HA]}$$

The larger the K_a value is, the stronger the acid is. The K_a value can also be used to calculate the pH of a solution if the initial concentration of the weak acid is known.

Weak bases react with water to form the conjugate acid of the base and hydroxide ions. The general equilibrium expression is:

$$B\ (aq) + H_2O\ (l) \leftrightarrow HB^+\ (aq) + OH^-\ (aq)$$

The equilibrium constant expression K_b is the base dissociation constant:

$$K_b = \frac{[HB^+][OH^-]}{[B]}$$

SAMPLE QUESTIONS

14) Calculate the pH of a 0.3 M solution of acetic acid (CH_3COOH), which has a K_a of 1.8 × 10–5.

A. 2.64

B. 1.3

C. 1.8

D. 3

Answer: A.

$CH_3COOH\ (aq) \leftrightarrow CH_3COO^-\ (aq) + H^+\ (aq)$	Write the ionization equilibrium for the acid.
$K_a = \frac{[H^+][CH_3COO^-]}{[CH_3COOH]} = 1.8 \times 10{-}5$	Write the equilibrium constant expression, K_a.
$K_a = \frac{(x)(x)}{0.3 - x} = 1.8 \times 10^{-5}$	Now determine the concentrations of the components. The concentration of H^+ can be assigned as x and will be equal to the concentration of CH_3COO^-. The concentration of CH_3COOH will be equal to 0.3 – x.
$\frac{x^2}{0.3} = 1.8 \times 10^{-5}$ $x = 2.3 \times 10^{-3}$ M pH = $-\log(2.3 \times 10^{-3})$ **= 2.64**	x is assumed to be negligible compared to 0.3 M so the equation can be simplified and solved.

15) Calculate the [OH^-] in a 0.15 M solution of NH_3, which has a K_b of 1.8 × 10^{-5}.

A. 0.1 M

B. 0.001 M

C. 0.0016 M

D. 0.016 M

Answer: C.

$NH_3\ (aq) + H_2O\ (l) \leftrightarrow NH_4^+\ (aq) + OH^-\ (aq)$	Write the ionization equilibrium equation.
$K_b = \frac{[NH_4^+][OH-]}{[NH_3]} = 1.8 \times 10^{-5}$	Write the expression for K_b.
$[NH_4^+] = [OH^-] = x$ and $[NH_3] = 0.15$ M – x $K_b = \frac{(x)(x)}{0.15 - x} = 1.8 \times 10^{-5}$	The concentration of NH_4^+ will equal the concentration of OH^-, so both can be assigned the variable x. The concentration of NH_3 will be equal to 0.15 – x.

$\frac{x^2}{0.15} = 1.8 \times 10^{-5}$

x = 0.0016 M = [OH⁻]

The concentration of x compared to 0.15 M can again be assumed to be negligible, so the equation can be simplified and solved.

MONOPROTIC AND POLYPROTIC ACIDS

Acids that have one ionizable proton are called **monoprotic acids**. These acids are described by the dissociation equation given earlier:

$$HA\ (aq) + H_2O\ (l) \leftrightarrow H_3O^+\ (aq) + A^-\ (aq)$$

Acids that have more than one ionizable proton are called **polyprotic acids**. These acids will lose protons in successive steps, each of which will have its own dissociation constant:

$$H_2A\ (aq) + H_2O\ (l) \leftrightarrow H_3O^+\ (aq) + HA^-\ (aq) \quad K_{a_1}$$

$$HA^-\ (aq) + H_2O\ (l) \leftrightarrow H_3O^+\ (aq) + A^{2-}\ (aq) \quad K_{a_2}$$

Sulfurous acid is a polyprotic acid that can ionize in successive steps:

$$H_2SO_3\ (aq) \leftrightarrow H^+\ (aq) + HSO_3^-\ (aq) \quad K_{a_1} = 1.7 \times 10^{-2}$$

$$HSO_3^-\ (aq) \leftrightarrow H^+\ (aq) + SO_3^{2-}\ (aq) \quad K_{a_2} = 6.4 \times 10^{-8}$$

For polyprotic acids, removing the first proton is always easier than removing the second. This is also true for acids with three protons. The K_a values become increasingly smaller as more protons are removed. Because the K_a values for the second and third proton removals are so small, it is typically possible to estimate the pH of a polyprotic acid by using only K_{a_1}.

SAMPLE QUESTION

16) In polyprotic acids, the K_a value is always __________ for the first dissociation compared to the K_a value for the second dissociation.

A. higher

B. lower

C. the same

D. halved

Answer: A.

The K_a value is always the highest for the first dissociation and decreases for each subsequent dissociation.

Ions in Solution

An **electrolyte** is a substance that dissolves into anions and cations in water to produce an electrically conducting solution. This occurs when a salt, acids, and bases are dissolved in water. The overall solution is still electrically neutral, but if an electrical potential is applied, the cations are drawn to the electrode with an abundance of electrons and the anions are drawn to the electrode with a deficit of electrons. The movement of the ions results in a current.

Electrolytes can be either strong or weak. A weak electrolyte does not completely dissociate in the solvent, while a strong electrolyte completely or nearly completely dissociates in the solvent.

Nonelectrolytes do not dissociate in solution nor do they produce ions. Because they do not form ions, nonelectrolytes are poor conductors of electricity. Polar covalent substances such as sugar and alcohols are examples of nonelectrolytes.

Almost all salts are strong electrolytes and completely dissociate in water. Many salts have acid-base properties that come from their component ions reacting with water. When ions react with water to generate H^+ or OH^-, a hydrolysis reaction occurs. The pH of an aqueous salt solution can be predicted by considering the ions of the salt.

Anions can be considered conjugate bases of acids. For example, Cl^- is the conjugate base of HCl and CH_3COO^- is the conjugate base of acetic acid. If an anion is a conjugate base of a strong acid, such as Cl^-, the anion will not have a tendency to take protons from water and will not affect the pH. However, if the anion is a conjugate base of a weak acid, it will react with water to produce the weak acid and hydroxide ions, affecting the pH.

$$X^- (aq) + H_2O\ (l) \leftrightarrow HX\ (aq) + OH^- (aq)$$

Polyatomic cations with one or more protons can be considered conjugate acids of weak bases. The cation NH_4^+ can donate protons to water to produce hydronium ions and decrease the pH.

$$NH_4^+ (aq) + H_2O\ (l) \leftrightarrow NH_3\ (aq) + H_3O^+ (aq)$$

Overall, if an aqueous salt solution contains anions and cations that do not react with water, the pH will be neutral.

To summarize the effects of cations and anions on an aqueous solution:

1. An anion that is a conjugate base of a strong acid will not change the pH.
2. An anion that is the conjugate base of a weak acid will increase the pH.
3. A cation that is the conjugate acid of a weak base will decrease the pH.
4. With the exception of Group 1 ions and Ca, Sr, and Ba, metal ions decrease the pH.
5. When a solution contains the conjugate base of a weak acid and the conjugate acid of a weak base, the ion with the larger ionization constant will influence the pH.

SAMPLE QUESTION

17) **Which of the following is the product of a reaction between a polyprotic acid and water?**

A. H_2O

B. OH^-

C. H_3O^+

D. H^+

Answer:

A. Incorrect. Water is one of the reactants in this example.

B. Incorrect. The hydroxide ion (OH^-) is increased when a base is added to water.

C. **Correct.** Adding an acid to water increases the concentration of the hydronium ion (H_3O^+) as the acid "donates" a proton to water to become H_3O^+.

D. Incorrect. Hydrogen ions (H^+) typically represent protons in acid/base reactions.

BUFFERS

A **buffer**, or buffer solution, is a chemical system that resists changes in pH when small quantities of acids or bases are added. A buffer can do this because it contains a weak acid to react with any added base and a weak base to react with any added acid. The acid and base components of the buffer must not react with each other. Typically, a weak acid and its conjugate base or a weak base with its conjugate acid are used to create buffers in a 1:1 ratio.

Human blood is an example of a buffer solution. Blood contains CO_2, which reacts in water to form H_2CO_3. This results in the following equilibria:

$$CO_2\,(aq) + H_2O\,(l) \leftrightarrow H_2CO_3\,(aq)$$

$$H_2CO_3\,(aq)\text{ (weak acid)} + H_2O\,(l) \leftrightarrow H_3O^+\,(aq) + HCO_3^-\,(aq)\text{ (conjugate base)}$$

If a strong acid is added to this solution, the conjugate base will react with the hydronium ions to form more of the weak acid. If a strong base is added to the solution, the weak acid will react with the hydroxide ions to form more of the conjugate base.

The pH of a buffer solution can be calculated based on the $[H_3O^+]$ in the K_a expression, if the K_a and concentration of the conjugate acid and base are known; it can also be calculated using the Henderson-Hasselbach equation:

$$pH = pK_a + \log\frac{[\text{conjugate base}]}{[\text{conjugate acid}]} = pK_a + \log\frac{[A^-]}{[HA]}$$

SAMPLE QUESTION

18) Which of the following statements about buffers are true?

I. A buffer solution could consist of equal concentrations of ammonia and ammonium bromide.

II. A buffer solution could consist of 1 mole of HF and 0.5 mole of NaOH in one liter of water.

III. A buffer solution will change only slightly in pH upon addition of acid or base.

A. I only

B. III only

C. II and III only

D. I, II, and III

Answer: D.

All three statements are true.

8

Scientific Inquiry and Procedures

The Nature of Scientific Inquiry

If science is defined as the study of the natural world, then **scientific inquiry** is defined as the myriad ways in which scientists examine and form explanations about the natural world. There is no one set path that all scientists must follow in order to conduct scientific inquiry, but observations, hypotheses, variables, controls, drawing conclusions, using sources, and communicating findings all play major roles in the process.

The Scientific Method

Observations, or the receipt of knowledge of the natural world using senses or technology, are considered the core element of scientific inquiry. Observations can be quantitative or qualitative in nature. **Quantitative observations** are ones which can be measured, such as number, length, mass, or volume. Conversely, **qualitative observations** cannot be measured and are general qualities, such as color, shape, or texture.

Scientists observe the natural world in order to collect data of **natural phenomena**, or any state or process that occurs in nature. These observations are used to propose scientific **explanations** that describe how and why these phenomena occur. A proposed explanation of natural phenomena is also known as a **hypothesis**. Once a testable hypothesis is formed, then a scientific investigation can begin.

> HELPFUL HINT
>
> A hypothesis consists of more than an educated guess. Instead, a hypothesis is a **testable proposition** that scientists can use as the basis for an investigation. If it is not capable of being tested scientifically, it is not a hypothesis.

The data produced by scientific investigation must be analyzed and interpreted. By contextualizing the data, scientists seek to incorporate new information into the existing body of knowledge within the field. Once many hypotheses have been substantiated by data, a **theory** is developed. A theory provides an explanatory framework for observations. Although a theory may be shown to be incorrect, a theory may never be fully proven to be true. A scientific **law** is more firmly established than a theory, as it is a well-substantiated statement about a fundamental aspect of the universe.

A law differs from a theory in that it does not include mechanistic propositions. In other words, laws are statements about *what* is observed and theories are statements about *why* that observation is made. For instance, Boyle's law states that, at constant pressure, the volume of a gas is inversely proportional to the pressure to which it is subjected. No proposition is included in this law regarding how this relationship is maintained; simply, the relationship is observed. The theories of acid–base reactivity, however, such as the Arrhenius theory and the Brønsted-Lowry theory, propose specific mechanisms for acid–base reactions. The Arrhenius theory states that an acid donates an H^+ and a base donates an OH^-. The Brønsted–Lowry theory presents a slightly different model, stating that an acid donates an H^+ and a base accepts an H^+.

SAMPLE QUESTION

1) **Which of the following best defines a hypothesis?**

   A. A hypothesis is a proposed explanation for an observed phenomenon.

   B. A hypothesis is a question that a scientist seeks to answer.

   C. A hypothesis is a widely accepted and substantiated theory that demonstrates applicability.

   D. A hypothesis is a simplified version of a concept or observed phenomenon.

Answers:

A. **Correct.** A hypothesis is stated with regard to an observed phenomenon that is not understood, and it provides a suggested explanation for that phenomenon.

B. Incorrect. The process of scientific inquiry seeks to answer questions about observed phenomenon, and a hypothesis is a suggested answer to such questions.

C. Incorrect. A widely accepted and substantiated theory that demonstrates applicability is considered a law.

D. Incorrect. A simplified version of a theory is considered to be a model.

Experimental Design

A key characteristic of a hypothesis is that it must be testable. An **experimental design** is then established, which is a set of experiments carefully and deliberately chosen for the purpose of testing the stated hypothesis. The successful adherence to the scientific method may result in either the support or rejection of the hypothesis. Rejection of the hypothesis does not imply poor scientific practice, but in fact it implies successful scientific inquiry. Scientists must approach inquiry with openness and honesty, allowing their findings to shape their formulation of hypotheses and theories.

One possible outcome of an experimental investigation is the formation of a **null hypothesis**. A null hypothesis is a statement that there is no relationship between two measured phenomena, or no association between groups under observation. The investigator must remain open to the possibility that no true relationship exists.

In the design of an experiment, factors that can be manipulated, changed, or measured in experiments are defined as **variables**. **Independent variables** are deliberately changed in the course of experimentation, and **dependent variables** are those variables that are measured or observed. Dependent variables rely on independent variables. For example, imagine that a chemist is conducting an experiment in which she is heating a liquid to the point of evaporation. As the reaction progresses, she measures the mass of the liquid remaining in the container, and also records the temperature of the solution at each of these points in time. Temperature is the independent variable because it is the parameter she is deliberately changing over the course of the reaction, whereas liquid mass is the dependent variable because it is the measured parameter whose value depends on the value of the independent variable.

TYPES OF VARIABLES

independent: the variable changed by the experimenter

dependent: the variable being measured or observed

control: variables that do not change

confounding: outside variables that influence the results of the experiment

To properly design an experiment, it is necessary to include a control in the experimental design. A scientific **control** is used to measure the effects of variables other than the independent variables. In the control, the samples are treated identically to those being tested but are not subject to the independent variable. For example, if an experiment is designed to determine the effects of a pharmaceutical agent on cellular growth, a control sample of cells of the same type would be grown in conditions identical to those of the experimental groups. At the time of treatment, the control experimental group would be left untreated with the pharmaceutical agent. Inclusion of an experimental control increases the reliability of experimental outcomes, and provides confirmation that the experimental design is successfully testing the targeted phenomenon.

When analyzing data collected in a scientific investigation, it is important to recognize the role of confounding variables. **Confounding variables** are factors that are not directly manipulated or measured in a scientific study, but may have an effect on the variables included in the study. To avoid being misled by confounding variables, experimental controls should be included in the experimental design. In this way, the scientist can distinguish between correlative and causal relationships among variables.

Reproducibility is an essential feature of a scientific finding. Under the same conditions and using the same experimental methods, multiple researchers should be able to produce identical results. If a result is irreproducible, it will not be trusted and accepted in the science community.

In the course of scientific inquiry, the scientist seeks to minimize sources of human error. Human error occurs when unintentional events obscure the accuracy of the findings in an experiment. Errors originate from a variety of sources. It is possible that the observed phenomenon may be disrupted in the process of making the measurements that are part of the experimental design. Familiarity with a specific subject matter allows scientists to carefully plan experiments in a way that allows for minimal disruption of the natural phenomena they are investigating. Human error is distinct from poor experimental design; human error is an unintended error, whereas poor experimental design is the outcome of oversight or misinformation in the experimental design process.

CONSIDER THIS...

Confounding variables are a significant challenge in the development of scientific understanding. Can you think of a historical scientific development in which confounding variables initially halted progress?

SAMPLE QUESTION

2) **A chemist is studying a chemical reaction and has hypothesized that increasing the amount of a copper catalyst will increase the reaction yield. She observes that the percent yield is unchanged by increasing the amount of copper. She does an additional series of experiments in which she decreases the amount of copper, and observes that the percent yield is unchanged in these conditions as well. What can she conclude about her hypothesis?**

A. The hypothesis is supported by the observations in the experimental design.

B. The null hypothesis is true in this situation.

C. Further experiments are needed to determine whether the hypothesis may be confirmed.

D. The opposite of the hypothesized relationship is supported by her observations.

Answers:

A. Incorrect. For the hypothesis to be supported, there would be an observed direct correlation between the increase in amount of copper and the percent yield.

B. Correct. The null hypothesis, which is a statement that there is no relationship between the independent variable (amount of copper) and the dependent variable (percent yield), is true in this case.

C. Incorrect. The experimental design has provided sufficient information to show that the independent and dependent variables are unrelated to one another.

D. Incorrect. If the opposite of the hypothesized relationship were correct, lowering the amount of copper would have decreased the percent yield.

SCIENTIFIC MODELS

A useful tool for the scientist is the **model**, which is a simplified version of an observed phenomenon or concept. The purpose of using a model is to make complex concepts easier to visualize, quantify, observe, or simulate. Models make abstract or complicated concepts more accessible, facilitating their further investigation. To produce useful theories, models, and laws, it is necessary to make some assumptions, given the limited nature of observational skills. It is the goal of the scientist, however, to minimize the assumptions as much as possible.

Different models are selected for different purposes of investigation. **Physical models** are physical copies of a phenomenon that are built to scale and are used to physically visualize processes and phenomena, such as solar system movement. **Conceptual models** are also used to provide a visual representation of abstract concepts while also describing behavior, such as the fluid mosaic model. Models can also be **mathematical** or **graphical**. Mathematical models are used to describe and predict behavior or phenomena, such as population growth, while graphical models are used in probability and statistics. Graphical models are also used prominently in disciplines such as genetics in order to analyze genetic links.

Scientific models are representations of natural phenomena and processes, but cannot be exact replicas. In order to provide simple, useful explanations, scientists must make trade-offs regarding details, approximations, and accuracy of information. All models must be evaluated for their potential **limitations**. For example, the Bohr atomic model is limited by the fact that it is only useful for describing hydrogen atoms. To

> **DID YOU KNOW?**
>
> Many models are used in the process of **simulation**, or imitating a natural phenomenon or process. Simulations play a major role in both scientific investigations as well as engineering, which applies information learned from simulations to design real-world technology.

compensate for model limitations, scientists will often use multiple models in their investigations as well as modify existing models to explain new observations.

SAMPLE QUESTION

3) **The Bohr model, which is an atomic model that describes the concept of how components of an atom behave, is an example of which of the following types of models?**

A. physical model

B. graphical model

C. mathematical model

D. conceptual model

Answers:

A. Incorrect. Physical models are physical representations; the Bohr model is a conceptual diagram.

B. Incorrect. The Bohr model is a conceptual diagram and does not factor in probability or statistics like a graphical model does.

C. Incorrect. Mathematical models represent phenomena by using equations, while the Bohr model is a conceptual diagram.

D. **Correct.** The Bohr model is an example of a conceptual model that describes and explains the behavior of atoms.

Data Collection and Interpretation

Working in the laboratory involves dealing with a lot of measurements, that is, dealing with a lot of numbers. Managing measurements can become overwhelming at times, so specific scientific techniques are used to organize data. Furthermore, that data needs to be presented properly. Without being able to present results with clarity, a scientist's research and time spent in the laboratory will have no impact.

Precision and Accuracy

In science, it is important to have precise and accurate results because the results of one finding may be used as a baseline for another finding, and if the results of the first finding are not accurate, it increases the inaccuracy of the second finding, which can lead to the propagation of inaccuracy if the same results are used in subsequent experiments.

- **Precision** refers to how close together a series of measurements of the same quantity are to each other. If several measurements of the same quantity exist, and all the measurements are very similar to one another, then that set of measurements is precise.

- **Accuracy** refers to how close a measured value is to an accepted value (true value).

So, most measurements can fall in one of the following categories:

1. neither precise nor accurate
2. precise but not accurate
3. precise and accurate

To better understand the preceding three scenarios, consider a bucket filled with dirty water; turbidity measurements are taken to estimate the quality of water. Three sets of measurements are taken, and each set includes five measured values with the help of a turbidimeter (a digital instrument that displays the turbidity value on the screen). The measurements are compared to each other and to the true value of turbidity, which is 100 NTUs (Nephelometric Turbidity Units). The results are displayed in Table 8.1.

HELPFUL HINT

Turbidity is the cloudiness of the water due to the presence of a large number of individual particles, suspended solids, or dirt.

Table 8.1. Precision versus Accuracy

Set 1 (NTU)	Set 2 (NTU)	Set 3 (NTU)
130	151	100
180	151	101
200	152	100
150	150	99
120	150	100
Set 1: The values are neither close to one another nor close to the correct value of turbidity (100 NTUs). Hence, the set of measured values is neither precise nor accurate.	Set 2: The values are close together, but they are way off the correct value of turbidity. Hence, the set of measured values is precise but not accurate.	Set 3: The values are close together as well as very close to/the same as the correct value of turbidity. Hence, the set of measured values is precise and accurate.

Go on

SAMPLE QUESTION

4) Which of the following targets shows accuracy, but not precision?

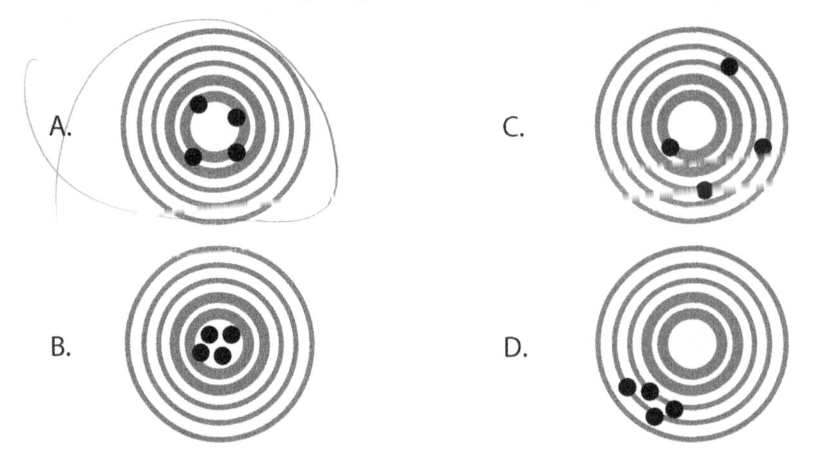

Answers:

A. **Correct.** This shows measurements that are accurate, but not precise.

B. Incorrect. This shows measurements that are both accurate and precise.

C. Incorrect. This shows measurements that are neither accurate nor precise.

D. Incorrect. This shows measurements that are precise, but not accurate.

SIGNIFICANT FIGURES

The concept of significant figures helps estimate uncertainty in the measured results; in other words, the uncertainty in an experimental result or a calculated value is indicated by the number of significant figures. **Significant figures** can be found by adding one uncertain digit to the number of certain digits in an experiment measurement. The rules for determining significant figures are as follows:

- All nonzero digits are significant; 15.36 has four significant figures.
- Zeros that are to the left of the first nonzero digit in the number are not considered significant; 023 has two significant figures, and 0.0673 has three significant figures.
- Zeros that are present between two nonzero digits are significant; 205 has three significant figures, and 0.7089 has four significant figures.
- Zeros that are present to the right of the decimal point are significant; 2.00 has three significant figures, and 0.3000 has four significant figures.

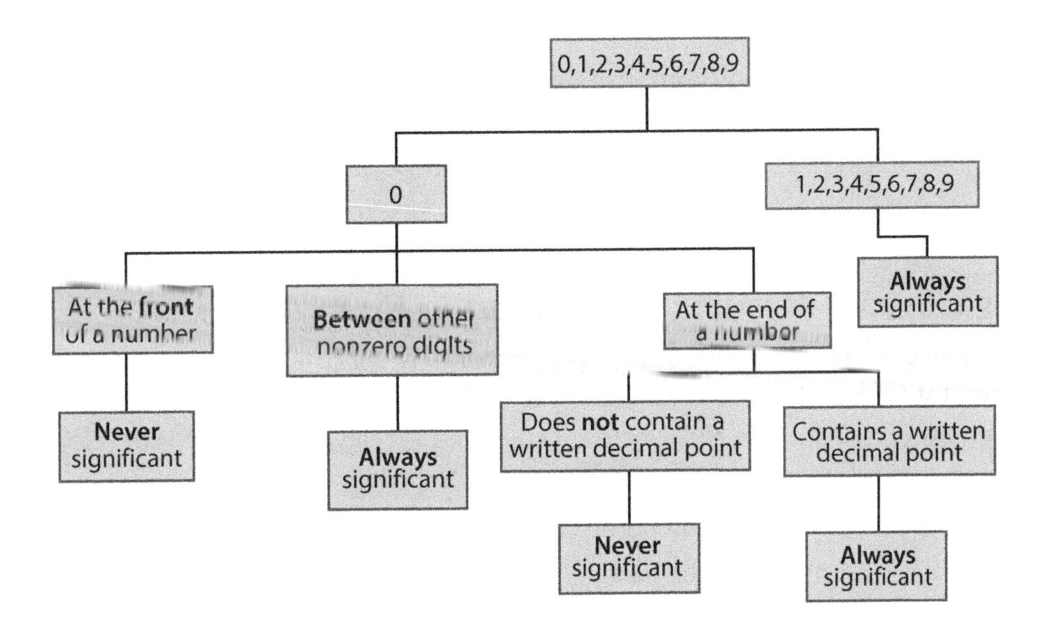

Figure 8.1. Significant Figures

The numbers involved in the addition and subtraction of significant figures can have different decimal places; however, the result should always be reported to the same number of decimal places as that of the number with the smallest number of decimal places.

For example, in the addition of 93.35, 2.1, and 28.013, the result will be reported with one decimal point because one of the numbers involved has just one decimal point (2.1). Hence, the result will be 123.4.

In multiplication and division of significant figures, the result should have as many significant figures as there are in the original number with the least significant figures. For example, the calculation $12.8 \times 5.678 = 72.6784$ would be reported as 72.7.

SAMPLE QUESTIONS

5) **How many significant figures are in the number 51800?** 3

Answer:

Determine if any nonzero digits exist and if there are any zeros between them. They are all significant: 5, 1, 8.

Trailing zeros are not significant because there is no decimal point.

Thus, total number of significant figures is three: 5, 1, 8.

6) **How many significant figures are in the number 78,340.00?**

7

Answer:

Determine if any nonzero digits exist and if there are any zeros between them. They are all significant: 7, 8, 3, 4.

Trailing zeros are significant because there is a decimal point. Thus, the total number of significant figures is seven: 7, 8, 3, 4, and the three trailing zeros.

Interpreting Results and Drawing Conclusions

Once collected, data must be analyzed in order to draw conclusions from it, and to interpret it so that the data can be used to make an impact on society or to support further studies. To make sure the data collected is relevant and helps develop the research, the following points should be kept in mind:

- making sure the data being collected is relevant to the research
- making sure that the pattern formed with the data is correct
- noting if the pattern formed by the collected data matches the expected pattern
- noting and analyzing the deviations from the expected pattern
- making sure to collect data that could explain the expected deviations
- making sure the data collected and the patterns formed answer the unanswered question
- making sure the results are worthy of further use

To further make sense of the data, descriptive analysis and inferential analysis are used. **Descriptive analysis** involves transforming raw data into a version that can be easily understood—for example, organizing data in tables and charts—whereas **inferential analysis** involves drawing conclusions from the results.

Data can be visually displayed with the help of graphs and charts. The types of graphs widely used to display data are the line graph, scatter graph, bar graph, histogram, and pie chart. It is important to know and identify the differences between these graphs because different graphs are used for displaying different kinds of data.

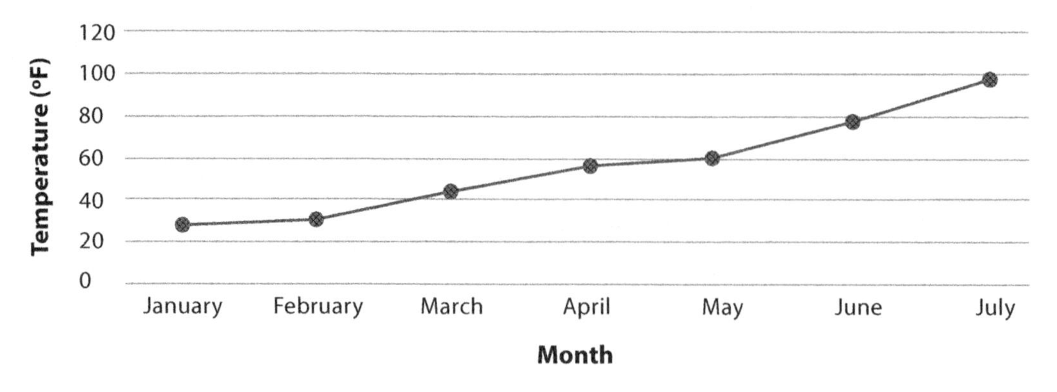

Figure 8.2. Line Graph

Line graphs show change over time. In chemistry experiments, line graphs are used extensively to show a trend in the collected data.

Scatter plots are used when correlating two sets of data. In cases where one variable is dependent on the other variable, the scatter plot shows the effect of the changes in one variable on the other variable. The scatter plot provides a way to analyze the nature of the data as quantitative changes are made to some parameters. A **line of best fit** is often included on scatter plots to show trends in the data.

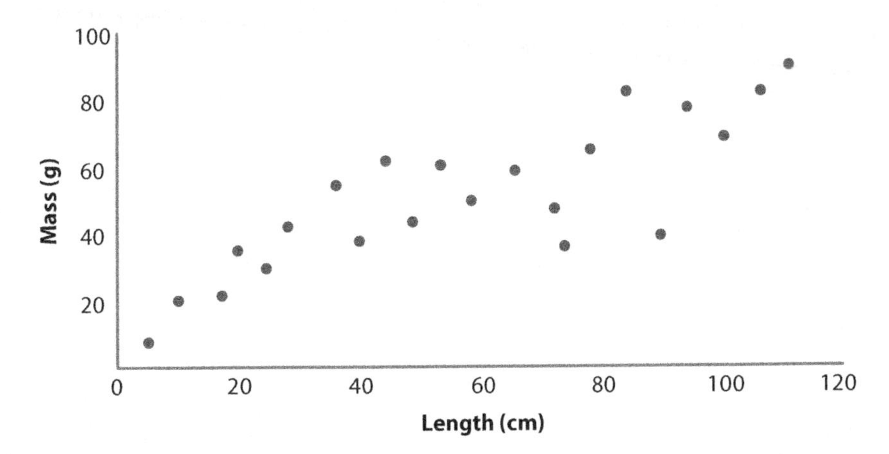

Figure 8.3. Scatter Plot

Bar graphs compare two or more groups. Most times the bar represents an average or mean of the data. In a bar graph, the length of the bar represents the magnitude of the quantity. Bar graphs are helpful in comparing qualitative data that exists in small numbers. In a bar graph, bars do not touch—in Figure 8.5 there is a small gap between the bars, which can make it difficult to differentiate between a bar graph and a histogram (explained next). However, if a gap exists between the bars, it implies it is a bar graph.

HELPFUL HINT

The base of the bars is the independent variable. The height or length of the bars shows the dependent variable.

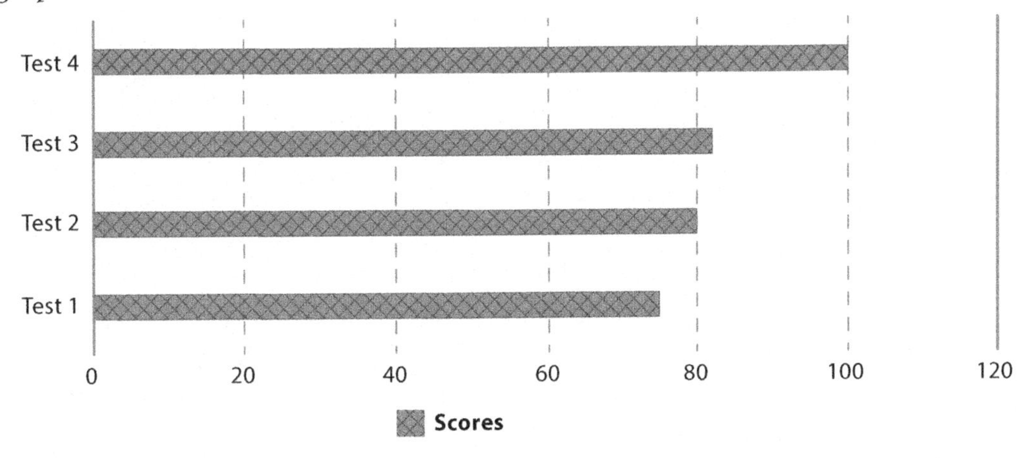

Figure 8.4. Bar Graph

Histograms are used to look at distribution of data. In a histogram, bars touch one another. A histogram might look like a bar graph, but it differs in a few ways. In a histogram, the length of the bars represents measurements that fall into a set of values, that is, along with the magnitude of an effect, a histogram gives a good idea about the spread of the measured values. Unlike bar graphs, which usually involve categories, histograms involve quantities.

Pie charts illustrate a part of the whole. A pie chart is a statistical graphic, circular in shape, and is divided to show different numerical proportions. There is a direct relation between the quantity represented and the arc length of each section in the pie chart.

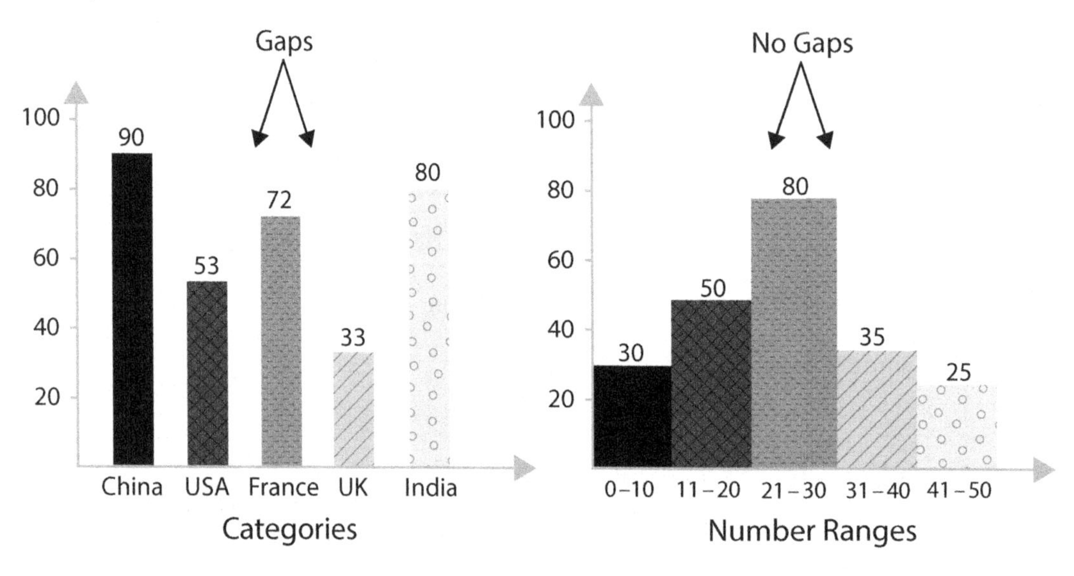

Figure 8.5. Bar Chart vs Histogram

No matter what kind of image is used, effective data presentation is impossible without considering the audience. The graphs or charts should be self-explanatory. The following steps will help ensure best representation of data:

- It is important to make sure the data is represented in the simplest way so that the audience is able to comprehend it. The best results are obtained when the most complicated data is broken down and represented in the simplest terms. Along with the use of basic Excel charts and graphs, many other options are available for the visual representation of the data.

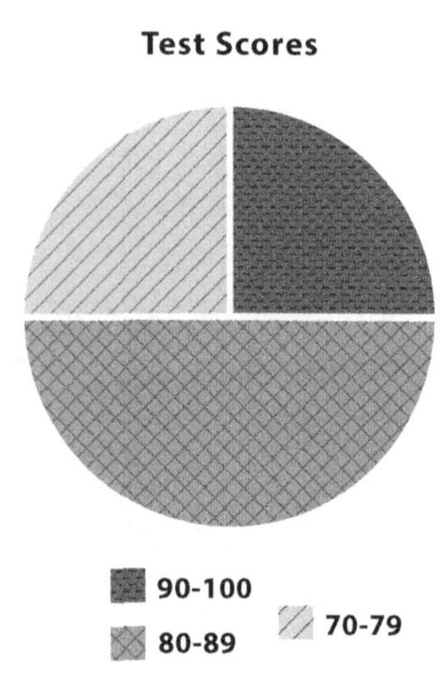

Figure 8.6. Pie Chart

- The data should be clear. Simple things should be kept in mind, like using bar graphs instead of histograms wherever it makes most sense. In addition to using different colors in the graph, different shapes can be used to make graphs clearer.
- Visual data must be labeled properly, and *everything* in the chart or graph should be labeled. Nothing should be left ambiguous; all the axes should be labeled. No matter how much effort went into the research, if the visual presentation is bad and fails to convey the message, the research is no good. Hence, to make the effort worthwhile, time and energy should be invested in the proper analysis and representation of the data.

SAMPLE QUESTION

7) **Which of the following types of graphs best shows the quantitative relationship between an independent and dependent variable over time?**

A. scatter plot

B. histogram

C. bar graph

D. pie chart

Answers:

A. Correct. Scatter plots show trends among quantitative independent and dependent variables.

B. Incorrect. Histograms show data in ranges of numbers.

C. Incorrect. Bar graphs show the relationship between categories of individual data, some of which may be qualitative.

D. Incorrect. Pie charts are best suited for showing data as a percentage compared to the entire data set.

UNITS AND NOTATION SYSTEMS

SCIENTIFIC NOTATION

In science, certain commonly used values are extremely big or extremely small, and writing such values again and again can become inconvenient. For example, the size of an electron is 0.00000000000000285 m. Writing this number multiple times in a calculation would be tedious. Writing it over and over also increases the possibility of error because there is a greater chance of leaving out one of the zeros. Scientific notation is important because it reduces the possibility of error and makes it easier to use these values multiple times.

When using scientific notation, there are two possible scenarios:

The number is *less* than 1: an extremely small number such as 0.00000000000000285 m

1. Place a decimal point after the first significant digit of the given number. In this example, this would result in 2.85.
2. Then, count the number of places that will be required to move the decimal point from where it currently exists to the right of the first significant figure. The number of places moved becomes the power of 10 and is multiplied by the number expressed as a decimal in step 1 (2.85). Because the shift of the decimal point was from left to right, the exponent is negative: 0.00000000000000285 m = 2.85×10^{-15} m

The number is *greater* than 1: an extremely large number such as 3,800,000,000,000 m

1. Place a decimal point after the first significant digit of the given number. In this example, this would result in 3.8.
2. Rewrite the number with a decimal place, which is usually placed at the end of the number. Here, this would result in 3,800,000,000,000.
3. Count the number of places that will be required to move decimal point from where it currently exists to the right of the first significant figure. The number of places moved becomes the power of 10 and is multiplied with the number expressed as a decimal in step 1 (3.8). Because the shift of the decimal point was from right to left, the exponent is positive: 3,800,000,000,000 m = 3.8×10^{12} m

SAMPLE QUESTION

8) Which of the following is the correct scientific notation for 844,000?

A. 84.4×10^4

B. 84.4×10^5

C. 8.44×10^6

D. 8.44×10^5

Answers:

A. Incorrect. The decimal is moved to the second significant figure, instead of the first. The power of 10 is also off by one digit.

B. Incorrect. The decimal is moved to the second significant figure, instead of the first.

C. Incorrect. The decimal is moved over 5 spots to the first significant figure, not 6 like this answer suggests.

D. **Correct.** The decimal is moved over 5 spots to the first significant figure.

STANDARD UNITS OF MEASUREMENT

The **metric system** is a decimal measurement system based on a consistent set of **metric units**, indicated by a prefix paired with a base unit. The metric system, which originated in the 1700s, was expanded upon and standardized in 1960 as the International System of Units, or **SI units**. SI units are used consistently across all disciplines in order to coordinate research efforts and reduce communication errors. There are seven base SI units (shown in Table 8.2).

Table 8.2. Standard Base Units

Physical Quantity	Name of Unit	Abbreviation
mass	kilogram	kg
length	meter	m
time	second	s
temperature	kelvin	K
electric current	ampere	A
amount of substance	mole	mol
luminous intensity	candela	cd

Derived units are made by combining one or more base units. Density, area, acceleration, and speed are all examples of derived units.

- area: $A = m \times m = m^2$
- speed: $\frac{distance}{time}$ (m/s)
- density; ρ: $\frac{mass}{volume}$ (kg/m^3)

Metric prefixes are placed in front of the base unit or the derived unit to indicate quantity. Since quantities can have a wide range of values, prefixes—like scientific notation—simplify expressing them. Each metric prefix is represented by a symbol and denotes what multiple of 10 it is. The detailed description of the metric prefixes can be found in Table 8.3.

Table 8.3. Metric Prefixes

Prefix	Symbol	Meaning	Exponential
exa	E	1,000,000,000,000,000,000	10^{18}
peta	P	1,000,000,000,000,000	10^{15}
tera	T	1,000,000,000,000	10^{12}
giga	G	1,000,000,000	10^{9}
mega	M	1,000,000	10^{6}
kilo	k	1,000	10^{3}
hecto	h	100	10^{2}
deka	da	10	10^{1}

Table 8.3. Metric Prefixes (continued)			
Prefix	**Symbol**	**Meaning**	**Exponential**
–	–	1	10^0
deci	d	0.1	10^{-1}
centi	c	0.01	10^{-2}
milli	m	0.001	[illegible]
micro	μ	0.000001	10^{-6}
nano	n	0.000000001	10^{-9}
pico	p	0.000000000001	10^{-12}
femto	f	0.000000000000001	10^{-15}
atto	a	0.000000000000000001	10^{-18}

Although the US Customary System is not commonly used in chemistry, it's helpful to be familiar with the common US units and the conversion factors needed to move between the US and SI systems.

Table 8.4. Commonly Used Measurements in the US Customary System		
Category	**Name of Unit**	**Conversion Factor**
Length	inch	1 in. = 1/12th ft.
	foot	1 ft.
	yard	1 yd. = 3 ft.
	mile	1 mi. = 5,280 ft.
	nautical mile	1 nautical mile = 6,076.12 ft.
Area	acre	1 ac. = 43,560 sq. ft.
Volume	fluid ounce	1 fl. oz. = 1/16th pt.
	pint	1 pt.
	quart	1 qt. = 2 pt.
	gallon	1 gal. = 8 pt.
Weight	ounce	1 oz. = 1/16th pt.
	pound	1 lb.
	stone	1 st. = 14 lb.
	ton	1 ton = 2,000 lb.

Table 8.5. US Customary to Metric Conversion Factors

1 in. = 2.54 cm	1 lb. = 0.454 kg
1 yd. = 0.914 m	1 cal = 4.19 J
1 mi. = 1.61 km	°F = $\frac{9}{5}$°C + 32
1 gal. = 3.785 L	1 cm^3 = 1 mL
1 oz. = 28.35 g	1 hr = 3600 s

SAMPLE QUESTION

9) **Which of the following is NOT a base SI unit?**

A. meter

B. gram

C. second

D. ampere

Answers:

A. Incorrect. The meter is the base SI unit for length.

B. Correct. The base SI unit for mass is the kilogram.

C. Incorrect. The second is the base SI unit for time.

D. Incorrect. The ampere is the base SI unit for electric current.

UNIT CONVERSION

The **factor-label method**, also known as dimensional analysis, is a **unit conversion** process to convert one set of units to another. It includes conversion factors, which are fractions where the numerator and denominator are given quantities expressed in different units. The numerator and denominator can also be reversed, that is, the reciprocal can be used as well.

HELPFUL HINT

The factor-label method is often referred to as **railroad tracks** because of the appearance of the lines on the page.

$$1000 \text{ m} = 1 \text{ km}$$

$$\frac{1 \text{ km}}{1000 \text{ m}} = \frac{1000 \text{ m}}{1 \text{ km}}$$

Conversion factors connect the new unit of measurement to the unit being converted. In this method, units are multiplied together, and the conversion factors are arranged in a manner where all units, except the required unit, cancel.

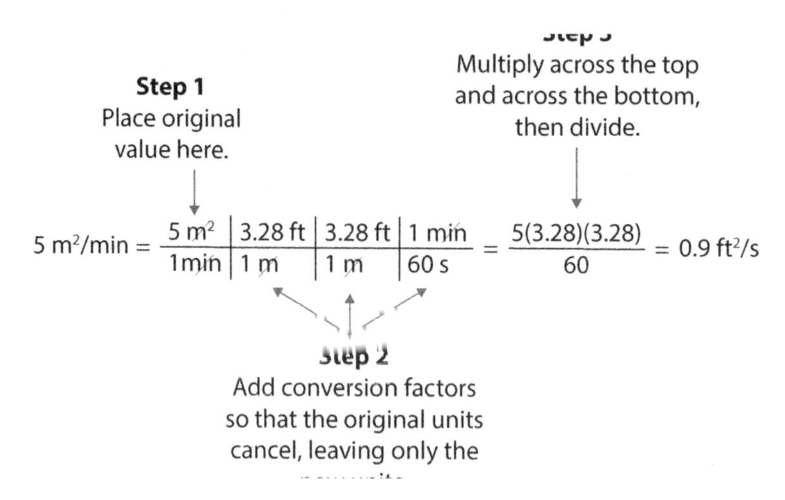

Figure 8.7. Dimensional Analysis

SAMPLE QUESTION

10) **Convert 8 miles/hour into metric units (meters/second).**

Answer:

Use dimensional analysis.

8 ~~miles~~	1.609 ~~km~~	1000 m	1 ~~hr.~~	1 ~~min.~~	**= 3.57 m/s**
~~hr.~~	1 ~~mile~~	1 ~~km~~	60 ~~min.~~	60 s	

Error Analysis

Performing a study or an experiment always involves noting measurements, and uncertainty in the measured results is always possible. There could be numerous reasons for the uncertainty—it could be a human error, machine error, lack of ideal conditions, or improper calibration. However, there are ways to minimize uncertainty in measurements to ensure precise and accurate results.

Because it is impossible to avoid uncertainty in measurements during experiments, focus should be on accurately reporting the uncertainties. It is important to highlight what the measurement errors are and how they propagate through the equation.

Errors in scientific experiments can be categorized as

1. systematic error or determinate error
2. random error or indeterminate error

Systematic error is a result of faulty experiment design or faulty equipment. This type of error can be reproduced if the experiment is carried out in the same way multiple times. The error values in such cases are either too high or too low. It is possible to eliminate systematic errors by making corrections to the equipment or the experiment design. In the case of uncertainties due to systematic errors, the resultant uncertainty is calculated by adding or subtracting uncertainty in each term.

Random error, on the other hand, is a result of uncontrollable factors. Random errors can be reduced but cannot be eliminated completely. It is usually difficult to identify the root cause for a random error because they may be due to environmental factors or human error.

The uncertainty calculation for random error can be figured using the following formulas:

- **Absolute uncertainty** is the margin of uncertainty associated with a measurement; for example, the absolute uncertainty of a measuring cylinder can be reported as 0.01 mL.
- **Relative uncertainty** is the ratio of the absolute uncertainty to the actual value of the measurement. For example, the relative uncertainty of a measuring cylinder reading of 8.47 mL with an absolute uncertainty of 0.01 is 0.001 (0.01 mL/8.47 mL).
- **Percent relative uncertainty** is the relative uncertainty expressed as a percentage. In the preceding example, the percent relative error would be 0.1 (0.01 mL/8.47 mL × 100).

Summing up uncertainties within an experiment can be complex. There may be numerous uncertainties involved in an experiment; some could be positive and the rest negative. They may even cancel each other out.

HELPFUL HINT

Overall uncertainty is the sum of absolute uncertainties.

SAMPLE QUESTION

11) Which of the following types of errors can alter the precision of a scientific investigation?

A. procedural flaws

B. systematic errors

C. analyzed error

D. random errors

Answers:

A. Incorrect. A procedural flaw is a root cause of a systematic error, which can alter the accuracy of an investigation.

B. Incorrect. Systematic errors impact the accuracy of an investigation, not the precision.

C. Incorrect. All error is analyzed error; only the random error impacts the precision of an investigation.

D. Correct. Random errors—or unpredictable changes—alter the precision of a measurement or how close measurements are to one another.

Laboratory Equipment

Although the subject matter and focus of investigations vary widely, there are many common pieces of equipment used across all disciplines. All equipment must be appropriately and safely used and maintained in order to preserve a safe laboratory space and ensure the accuracy, precision, validity, and reliability of the investigations taking place. Before using any equipment, all components must be checked for potential damage and all manufacturer instructions must be read and followed. Equipment and its components should also be used and stored in cool, dry laboratory spaces. If working with potentially hazardous equipment, such as powerful industrial magnets, warning signs need to be posted in the work area. Equipment components should be regularly cleaned, maintained, and replaced according to the manufacturer's instructions.

Optical Equipment

Optical lab equipment includes any equipment that disperses, concentrates, or redirects light using **lenses**, mirrors, or **prisms. Microscopes** and **telescopes** both commonly use an objective lens and eyepiece lens to magnify objects. Microscopes are used to magnify small objects at a short distance, while telescopes are used to magnify large objects from a great distance. Light Amplification by Stimulated Emission of Radiation, or **LASERs**, produce high-energy, narrow beams of concentrated, monochromatic light that can travel great distances and are used in a wide variety of applications, ranging from CD/DVD technology to anti-missile defense. **Spectrometers** are used to measure and record light properties and wave spectrums. Glass or plastic mirrors, prisms, and lenses used in any of these instruments must be cared for appropriately. Dust covers or lens caps should be placed over glass when the equipment is not in use, stored in a cool, dry area, and cleaned at appropriate intervals according to manufacturer instructions.

SAMPLE QUESTION

12) Which of the following is an example of safe, appropriate use of a piece of optical equipment?

A. leaving a spectrometer open and accessible for the next use

B. storing spectrometers in a humid storage space

C. cleaning glass lenses but not plastic lenses

D. placing a dust cover over a telescope after use is complete

Answers:

A. Incorrect. Optical equipment should be stored appropriately when not in use.

B. Incorrect. Optical equipment should be stored in a cool, dry place.

C. Incorrect. All lenses—both glass and plastic—must be cleaned at appropriate intervals.

D. Correct. Dust covers are an important piece of protective equipment that maintains the safety, cleanliness, and accuracy of the instrument.

SEPARATION EQUIPMENT

Separation lab equipment is used to **separate** a mixture into its distinct, separate components. There are several methods commonly used to complete this task. **Mechanical separation** is the separation of components using physical machines. This includes **filtration** via **funnels**, sieves, and other equipment to remove large particles from liquid and a **centrifuge** to separate a mixture by spinning it at high speeds. Centrifuges can be used to separate organelles or to isolate nucleic acid. The individual tubes must be balanced when placing in the equipment to avoid a large force unbalance as it spins at high speeds.

Chemical separation relies on chemically removing compounds through procedures such as **distillation**, which purifies and separates liquids through a heating and cooling process using burners, tubing, and flasks; and **chromatography**, which separates mixtures by allowing a gas or liquid to flow over a material, which causes the various components to separate as they flow at different rates. Chromatography systems typically involve the use of columns, detectors, and pumps.

Magnetic separation occurs when magnetic devices are used to attract and remove magnetic components out of the non-magnetic substance in the mixture. Scientific applications of this technology include magnetic-activated cell sorting (MACS), in which magnetic nanoparticles are used to separate cells based on their surface antigens. This equipment is highly specialized and includes separators and columns.

Separation on the cellular level can also be conducted using **electric separation**. A primary example of this is gel electrophoresis, which uses electrical pulses to separate DNA, RNA, and/or proteins. This process requires the use of a power supply, a series of chambers, and tables, trays, and combs for the gel.

SAMPLE QUESTION

13) Columns, pumps, and detectors are examples of primary equipment commonly used for which of the following methods of separation?

Go on

A. electric separation

B. chromatography

C. mechanical separation

D. filtration

Answers:

A. Incorrect. Electric separation also requires a power supply and separation chambers.

D. **Correct.** This is a basic list of equipment that is required to complete separation using chromatography.

C. Incorrect. Mechanical separation could use these components, but the primary definition of this type of equipment is that it relies on machines.

D. Incorrect. This is not the defining list of equipment for filtration methods, as it does not contain a sieve, mesh, or any filter.

Measurement, Mixing, and Heating Equipment

Measurement lab equipment includes **meter sticks** to measure lengths in meters, **graduated cylinders** to measure volume, **balances** to measure mass, and **thermometers** to measure temperature in Celsius or Kelvin. All measurement instruments must use **the metric system** and be able to read SI units in accordance with worldwide scientific standards. The **pH** of a substance is measured according to the 14-point pH scale using pH meters, which use probes. These devices should be carefully cleaned and calibrated before use. Precise, traceable **timers**—including decimal stopwatches and clocks—are used to measure and record time elapsed.

Mixing lab equipment includes any of the individual pieces of equipment used to move materials and mix together. **Pipettes** are used to transport precise amounts of liquids from one container to another. Containers include beakers, flasks, and test tubes. **Stirrers** are used to physically mix substances. These can be as simple as glass or plastic rods in small investigational settings, or as advanced as mechanical overhead stirrers, magnetic stirrers, or shakers in order to mix components at high speeds and/or at controlled temperatures.

There are multiple varieties of **heating lab equipment** that are used depending on the type and size of the laboratory investigation. When using any heating device, great care should be taken to remove all flammable materials from the work area. Plastic, closed or narrow-necked containers, such as flasks or reagent bottles, should be avoided. When heating things at very high temperatures, crucibles, which are resistant to high temperatures, should be used. Protective clothing should be worn and protective equipment, such as tongs or hot pads, should be used when transporting.

Some heating equipment uses open flames. **Alcohol burners** produce low, open flames at relatively low temperatures. **Bunsen burners** are similar in nature but produce higher, hotter flames. Both are used for heating and sterilizing non-flammable materials. When using any open flame heating equipment, all loose clothing or hair should be secured. Flames should never be leaned over or left unattended. Other heating equipment does not use open flames. This includes **hot plates**, which are used when controlled temperatures are required for heating substances, and **ovens**, which are used to uniformly heat and dry materials.

SAMPLE QUESTION

14) Which of the following extra care steps should be taken when using pH meters?

A. Calibrate the probe before use.

B. Remove flammable material from work area.

C. Attend to pH meters constantly, never leaving them unattended.

D. Inspect all parts before use.

Answers:

A. Correct. Due to the sensitive nature of the probe, pH meter probes should be cleaned and calibrated before each use.

B. Incorrect. This is a step necessary when using heating equipment.

C. Incorrect. This is a step necessary when using heating equipment that uses an open flame.

D. Incorrect. This is a step that is taken when using any piece of laboratory equipment.

STERILIZATION EQUIPMENT

Highly specialized **sterilization lab equipment** is used in laboratory settings to sterilize, effectively removing bacteria or any other microorganism that could present a hazard or manipulate the investigation. Quick, small scale sterilization can be completed by wiping materials with appropriate solvents or by heating in ovens or over burners. For larger scale sterilization, and in the case of potential biohazards, industrial **sterilizers** or **autoclaves** can be used. Autoclaves are strong vessels that use high pressure and temperatures, and autoclaving is considered the most reliable form of sterilization. Equipment and materials can be sterilized by placing in a high-pressure autoclave at a sustained temperature of 250 degrees for 15 minutes.

HELPFUL HINT

Autoclave machines have uses other than sterilization. The combination of pressure and heat applied appropriately can also inactivate potential biohazards, vulcanize rubber, and cure composites.

SAMPLE QUESTION

15) Which of the following correctly describes the definition of sterilization?

A. eliminating hazards from equipment

B. removing microorganisms from a surface

C. storing equipment at high pressures and temperatures

D. removing all sources of investigation manipulation

Answers:

A. Incorrect. Sterilization removes potential biohazards from equipment by removing microorganisms but does not eliminate all potential hazards.

B. Correct. Sterilization uses solvents and heat to denature and remove microorganisms.

C. Incorrect. This process can be used to sterilize but is not the definition of sterilization itself.

D. Incorrect. Sterilization removes potentially unintentional biological manipulations from equipment used in an investigation by removing microorganisms, but it does not eliminate sources of potential data manipulation.

Laboratory Safety

Working in a chemistry laboratory comes with a lot of personal responsibility. While most of the accidents that occur in the lab are minor and result from ignorance of safety procedures, serious or fatal accidents can occur. Hence, safety procedures are of utmost importance. Moreover, the instruments used for operations and experiments in laboratories are generally very expensive and require ongoing maintenance. Everyone working in the lab is responsible for the proper care of these instruments to prevent damage to them and ensure the most accurate results possible.

Safety Equipment and Guidelines

Accidents are always a risk in the lab. However, with proper implementation of safety guidelines and procedures, they can be avoided. Most accidents are minor, but major accidents can and do occur. Hence, it is the combined responsibility of the instructor and the students to make sure all the important precautions are taken while performing experiments.

In industrial settings, mandatory Occupational Safety and Health Administration (OSHA) training emphasizes how employees can protect themselves and their surroundings, making enforcement of safety procedures rigorous. However, such training in educational institutions has been slow to catch on. Students do not generally have hands-on training in laboratory experiments or handling chemicals.

It is important to ensure that students' enthusiasm about learning new concepts and conducting experiments does not override the need to understand the safety procedures. Students must understand the risks involved with the experiments, how to cope with an emergency, and how to protect themselves and their surroundings.

The first step to ensuring safety is to wear proper clothing. **Personal protective equipment (PPE)** and **proper clothing** can prevent serious injuries and ensures a safe working environment. The general laboratory PPE requirements are a lab coat, gloves, and safety glasses. While working with volatile or reactive chemicals, chemical aprons are required to protect the body from splash hazards. Special chemical-resistant safety glasses protect the eyes from splash hazards instead of the usual safety glasses; normal safety glasses only protect against flying debris. Respirators protect workers from harmful vapors (proper respirator training is required).

Safety gloves protect the hands; they must always be worn. Although safety gloves are nonabsorbent, chemicals can leach, so lab workers must change gloves frequently and wash their hands often. Thermal and puncture-resistant gloves are used for handling extremely hot or cold materials like dry ice, using an autoclave, or dealing with sharps. Gloves must be properly removed and discarded before leaving the laboratory and touching personal or public items.

In general, lab workers should cover the body properly by wearing long sleeves and pants and avoiding baggy clothes. In addition, instead of sandals, closed-toe shoes should be worn at all times. Anyone working in the lab should tie back long hair and remove jewelry before entering the lab. Lastly, all personal items should be kept outside the laboratory to prevent contamination.

A good knowledge of **safety equipment** found in the lab can help minimize the effects of an accident. When working in the laboratory for the first time, it is important to look around and identify the safety equipment.

A **safety shower** and an **eye wash station** are must-haves for every laboratory, and weekly testing is necessary to ensure they are always working and have clean water. In case of flame exposure, the safety shower should be immediately used on the affected area and 911 should be called. Similarly, if a worker's eyes are injured, he or she should use the eye wash, keeping the eyes open while rinsing them.

The fire extinguisher is another extremely important piece of safety equipment. There are four types of fires:

1. Class A fires involve ordinary combustible products like wood, cloth, paper.
2. Class B fires include organic solvents and flammable liquids.
3. Class C fires involve electrical equipment.
4. Class D fires involve combustible metals.

Class A fires can be extinguished using water and general purpose fire extinguishers. For Class B and Class C fires, chemical smoke extinguishers must be used because putting water on them can worsen the situation by increasing the chances of spreading the fire or electrocution. Dry chemical fire extinguishers are installed in most labs close to the exit in case Class A, Class B, or Class C fires occur. In large fires, the building should be evacuated immediately, 911 should be called, and no attempt should be made to extinguish the fire unless someone has been trained by a certified trainer.

All workers should know where fire blankets are located because these are used to douse small fires. If someone's clothing is on fire, the person should lie on the ground and others should roll him or her on a fire blanket until the flame is out. A fire blanket must not be used to douse the fire while the person is standing because the flame can travel upward toward the person's face.

Other pieces of safety equipment include a first aid kit and the chemical fume hood. The first aid kit can be used to treat minor injuries. The chemical fume hood is a closed ventilated area that helps a person escape toxic vapors. The exhaust must be switched on and chemicals should not be left in the hood after work is done. Also, evacuation routes must be posted near the exits and should be clear and easy to follow.

Everyone working in the lab should be aware of the locations of all safety equipment to take prompt action in case of emergency. In addition, safety equipment must be tested regularly to ensure proper working in case of an emergency.

SAMPLE QUESTIONS

16) Which of the following can NOT be considered PPE?

A. safety gloves

B. safety glasses

C. closed-toe boots

D. slippers

Answers:

A. Incorrect. Safety gloves protect lab workers from chemicals, sharps, and extreme temperatures.

B. Incorrect. Safety glasses protect the eyes from flying debris and splash hazards.

C. Incorrect. Closed-toe boots protect the feet from debris and splash hazards; their sturdiness also helps prevent trips and falls.

D. Correct. Slippers are not sturdy enough to protect the feet from debris or chemicals, and they may cause the wearer to slip and fall.

17) **During a college camping trip, the flame from the campfire grew unexpectedly and spread to the surrounding twigs and shrubs. This is an example of which of the following?**

A. Class A fire

B. Class B fire

C. Class C fire

D. Class D fire

Answers:

A. Correct. This is a Class A fire because it involves an ordinary combustible product (in this case, wood).

B. Incorrect. A Class B fire involves organic solvents and flammable liquids.

C. Incorrect. A Class C fire is an electrical fire.

D. Incorrect. A Class D fire involves combustible metals.

Preparation, Use, and Storage of Laboratory Materials

It is important to note the safe handling of the chemicals. One must take care to never leave the caps of the chemical bottles open and never remove chemicals from the lab. A secondary container should be used to transport chemicals between labs, and an acid/base should be added to the solvent, never vice versa. Care must be taken to wear appropriate PPE depending on the requirements of the chemical. In case of breaking a large chemical bottle, it is important to evacuate the lab, as the vapors could be potentially dangerous, and not reenter until advised. Special attention must be given to flammable and explosive chemicals by making sure they are always kept away from ignition sources. Flammable chemicals must be stored in dedicated cabinets, and when disposing of chemicals, chemical-resistant plastic containers must be used. Paper towels used to wipe chemicals are also considered hazardous and must be disposed of appropriately.

Thus, it is important to prepare for each laboratory activity and determine the possible risks, wear the appropriate PPE, and know what protective measures to take in case of emergency. Knowing the emergency procedures and exit procedures can help mitigate the effects of an accident.

Many chemicals used in the lab can be dangerous, so lab workers need all the information they can get. Each chemical has a technical document called the Material Safety Data Sheet (MSDS), which lists important information about the chemical's properties, hazards, and safety precautions. This information helps people prepare to use the chemicals in the lab. Anyone using the lab should know where these safety data sheets are stored. Furthermore, chemicals should be labeled according to the Globally Harmonized System of classification and labeling of chemicals (also called the GHS).

The MSDS is organized into sixteen sections:

1. **Identification**: chemical name, chemical description, and manufacturer's contact address.
2. **Hazard Identification**: safety symbols and warnings.
3. **Composition**: a list of ingredients.
4. **First Aid**: the treatment when a person is exposed to the chemical.
5. **Fire Fighting Measures**: instructions for taking correct measures depending on the type of fire caused by the chemical.
6. **Accidental Release**: instructions for cleanup and evacuation, if needed.
7. **Handling and Storage**: instructions listing the specific storage method for each type of chemical.
8. **Personal Protection and Exposure Control**: the type of PPE needed for each chemical and OSHA's exposure limit for each chemical.
9. **Physical and Chemical Properties**: physical and chemical characteristics of a chemical, such as color, odor, appearance, solubility, pH, evaporation rate, and other chemical properties.
10. **Stability and Reactivity**: ways to avoid hazardous reactions by detailing how reactive a chemical can be under various conditions.
11. **Toxicological Information**: long-term and short-term toxic effects of the chemical.
12. **Ecological**: information about how a chemical can affect the environment.
13. **Disposal**: instructions to safely dispose of a chemical based on its reactivity, flammability, and similar properties.
14. **Transport**: transportation methods for each chemical. Wrong decisions here can be disastrous.
15. **Regulatory Information**: legal requirements applicable to the chemical.
16. **Other Information**: when the Safety Data Sheet was last prepared or revised, other pertinent information.

The other way to obtain information about a chemical apart from the MSDS is the labels on the chemical bottles. The information lists the name of the product, signal word (indicates danger level), hazards, precautions, first aid instructions, supplier's contact information, and pictograms (represents specific hazards posed by the chemicals). It is important to understand if a chemical is flammable, is toxic, contains compressed gases or oxidizers, is explosive, poses skin and eye harm danger, is environmentally unsafe, or is acutely toxic.

Table 8.6. shows a list of pictograms along with the type of hazard they represent.

Table 8.6. Pictograms Depicting Hazards

PICTOGRAM	TYPE OF HAZARD
	Flammability
	Toxicity
	Health
	Compressed gases
	Oxidizers
	Unstable explosives
	Skin and eye exposure
	Environmental hazards
	Acute toxicity

Thus, it is clear how safety data sheets and the chemical labels provide important information regarding the safe use of chemicals in the laboratory.

The National Fire Protection Association (NFPA) has also developed widely used guidelines to identify safety hazards. The NFPA diamond uses colors to represent hazards.

The **blue diamond** represents a health hazard. Numbers indicate the extent of the hazardous effect:

- 4—deadly
- 3—extreme danger
- 2—hazardous
- 1—slightly hazardous
- 0—normal material

The **red diamond** represents a fire hazard. Numbers indicate flash point levels.

- 4—below 73°F
- 3—below 100°F
- 2—above 100°F, not exceeding 200°F
- 1—above 200°F
- 0—will not burn

The **yellow diamond** represents reactivity. Numbers indicate the extent of the hazardous effect.

- 4—may detonate
- 3—shock and heat may detonate
- 2—violent chemical change
- 1—unstable if heated
- 0—stable

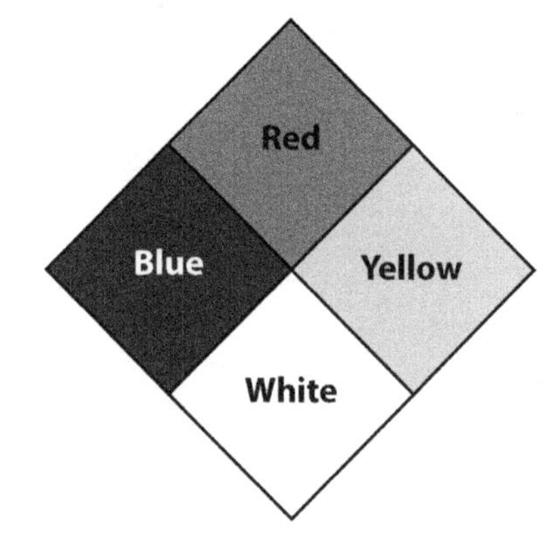

Figure 8.8. NFPA Diamond

The **white diamond** represents a specific hazard.

- ACID—acid
- ALK—shock and heat may detonate
- 2—alkali
- COR—corrosive
- OXY- oxidizer
- ☢—radioactive
- W—use no water

SAMPLE QUESTION

18) What hazards are represented by the two symbols below?

Answer:

The symbol on the left marks a flammable substance, and the symbol on the right marks oxidizers.

9

Practice Test

Read the question and choose the most correct answer.

1

Which ion has the greatest number of electrons?

A. Ca^{2+}

B. Cl^{-}

C. Ca^{+}

D. P^{3-}

2

Using the following equation, how many moles of P_4O_6 would be produced from 6 moles of O_2, assuming excess P_4 is present?

$P_4 + 3O_2 \rightarrow P_4O_6$

A. 1

B. 2

C. 3

D. 6

3

A student performed an experiment, forming a gas. When testing the gas with red litmus paper, the paper turned blue. What is the gas?

A. hydrogen chloride

B. methane

C. ammonia

D. helium

4

Which of the following should have the highest boiling point?

A. NH_3

B. H_2O

C. HF

D. H_2S

5

For which of the following elements is the aufbau principle NOT followed?

I. chromium
II. iron
III. copper

A. I only
B. II only
C. I and III only
D. I, II, and III

6

If the following reaction is at equilibrium, what would happen if the pressure of the reaction was decreased?

$N_2(g) + 3H_2(g) \leftrightarrows 2NH_3(g)$

A. There would be no effect on the equilibrium.
B. The reaction will shift toward the products.
C. The reactions will shift toward the reactants.
D. It cannot be determined which way the reaction will shift.

7

Which of the following solvents will have the greatest effect on the freezing point when 1.0 g of naphthalene is dissolved in 100 g of each solvent?

A. Benzene: K_f = 5.12°C/molal
B. Carbon disulfide: K_f = 3.83°C/molal
C. Chloroform: K_f = 4.70°C/molal
D. All will be equally affected.

8

Which of the following is NOT a typical property of metals?

A. Metals have low densities.
B. Metals are malleable.
C. Metals are good conductors of electricity and heat.
D. Metals in solid state consist of ordered structures with tightly packed atoms.

9

What is the oxidation number of P in $MgNaPO_4$?

A. −3
B. 0
C. +3
D. +5

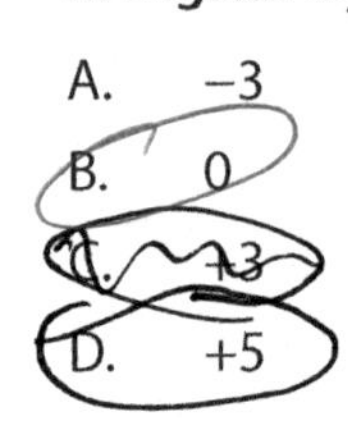

10

What is the formula for tin(IV) chloride pentahydrate?

A. $Sn_4Cl \cdot 5H_2O$
B. $SnCl_4 \cdot H_20$
C. $SnCl_4H_5$
D. $SnCl_4 \cdot 5H_20$

11

Which statement is true for ionization energy?

A. It increases moving left to right in a periodic table.
B. It remains constant moving left to right in a periodic table.
C. It decreases moving left to right in a periodic table.
D. It increases initially and then decreases moving left to right in a periodic table.

12

Which of the following is true of a solution?

A. It is a heterogeneous mixture.

B. It consists of only one kind of atom.

C. It is easy to separate using filtration.

D. It may be separated using distillation.

13

Sublimation is the change from

A. gas to solid

B. liquid to solid

C. gas to liquid

D. solid to gas

14

How many electrons can the *s* orbital hold?

A. two

B. three

C. eight

D. nine

15

A chemistry student is conducting an experiment in which she tests the relationship between reactant concentration and heat produced by a reaction. In her experiment, she alters the reactant concentration and measures heat produced. The independent variable in the experiment is the

A. reactant concentration.

B. reaction rate.

C. amount of heat produced by the reaction.

D. product concentration.

16

Which acids require the same number of moles of hydroxide to be titrated to the equivalence point?

I. hydrofluoric acid

II. nitric acid

III. phosphoric acid

A. I and II only

B. I and III only

C. II and III only

D. I, II, and III

17

Which of the following elements has chemical properties most similar to sulfur?

A. fluorine

B. argon

C. phosphorus

D. oxygen

18

Which of the following is a biological function of lipids?

A. genetic expression

B. energy storage

C. catalysis

D. molecule transportation

19

Which of the following actinides has the greatest number of *f* electrons?

A. actinium

B. thorium

C. uranium

D. plutonium

20

Isotones are

A. atoms that belong to different elements that have the same mass number but a different atomic number.

B. atoms that have the same number of neutrons.

C. atoms containing the same number of electrons or having the same electron configurations.

D. atoms belonging to the same element that have the same number of protons but a different number of neutrons.

21

Which of the following functional groups is found in the molecule below?

O

H_3C H

A. aldehyde

B. carboxylic acid

C. alcohol

D. ketone

22

How many neutrons are in an atom of the element $^{88}_{38}Sr$?

A. 38

B. 88

C. 50

D. 126

23

For a spontaneous process,

A. $\Delta G > 0$.

B. $\Delta S < 0$.

C. $\Delta G < 0$.

D. $\Delta S = \Delta G$.

24

What is the approximate mass percent of carbon in ethanol, CH_3CH_2OH?

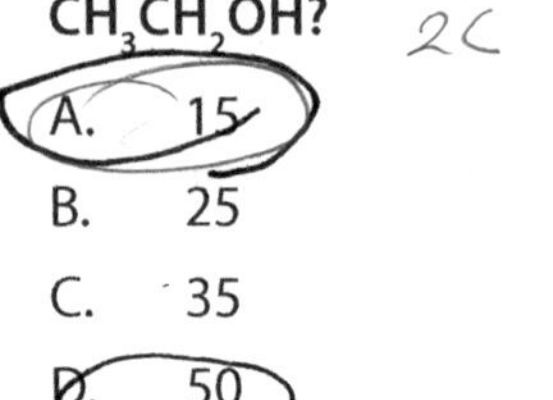

A. 15

B. 25

C. 35

D. 50

25

Acetic acid has a K_a of 1.8×10^{-5}. If equal concentrations of acetic acid (HOAc) and conjugate base acetate ion are present, the pH of the acid is between

A. 2 and 3.

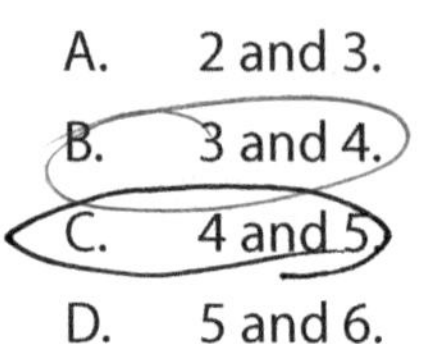

B. 3 and 4.

C. 4 and 5.

D. 5 and 6.

26

What is the specific chemical basis of magnetic resonance imaging (MRI) technology?

A. nuclear magnetic resonance

B. atomic theory

C. acid–base chemistry

D. thermodynamics

The graph below shows temperature versus heat added to water. Use the figure to answer questions 27 – 29.

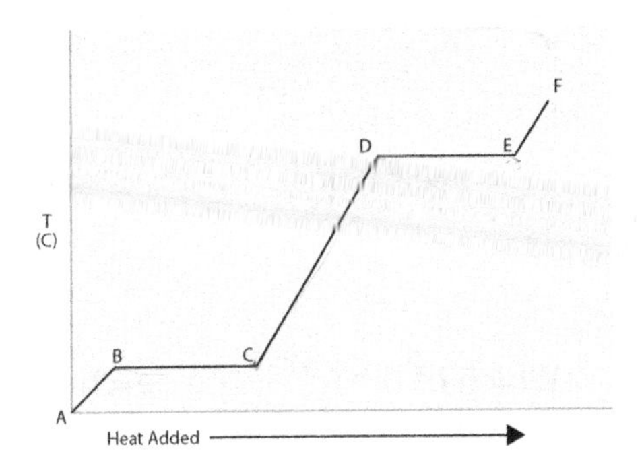

27

What does Point C represent?

A. boiling point

B. melting point

C. latent heat of vaporization

D. freezing point

28

Which of the following is NOT true about point E?

A. Molecules at point E have greater average kinetic energy than molecules at point C.

B. Evaporation occurs at point E.

C. Point E has higher entropy than point D.

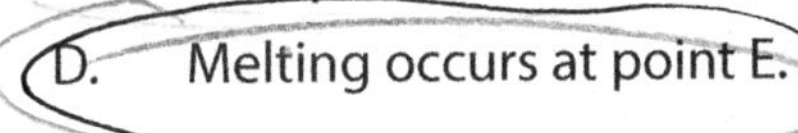

D. Melting occurs at point E.

29

Between points B and C the water is

A. boiling.

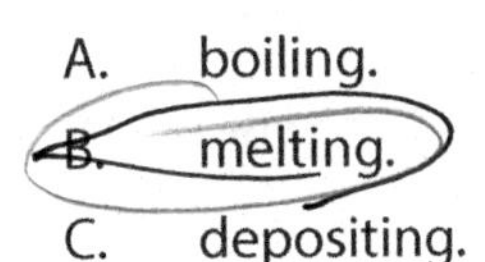

B. melting.

C. depositing.

D. sublimating.

30

Which of the following is NOT an organic compound?

A. C_3H_8

B. CH_3COOH

C. H_2CO_3

D. $HCOOH$

31

Which of the following elements has the lowest first ionization energy?

A. Ca

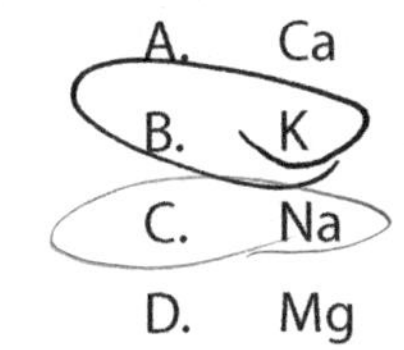

B. K

C. Na

D. Mg

32

Balance the following chemical equation:

$P_4 + O_2 + H_2O \rightarrow H_3PO_4$

A. 1:8:6:4

B. 1:2:2:4

C. 1:2:6:4

D. 1:5:6:4

33

The E° for the reduction of Cu^{2+} is +0.34 V. The E° of Zn^{2+} is −0.76 V. What is the emf of a galvanic cell where the concentration of Cu^{2+} and Zn^{2+} are the same?

A. −1.10 V

B. −0.42 V

C. 0.42 V

D. 1.10 V

34

Which statements are true of a buffer?

I. A buffer solution could consist of equal concentrations of ammonia and ammonium bromide.

II. A buffer solution could consist of one mole of HF and 0.5 mole of NaOH in one liter of water.

III. A buffer solution will change only slightly in pH upon addition of acid or base.

IV. In a buffer solution containing benzoic acid, C_6H_5COOH, and sodium benzoate, NaC_6H_5COO, the species that reacts with added $[OH^-]$ is the benzoate ion.

A. I and IV only

B. II and III only

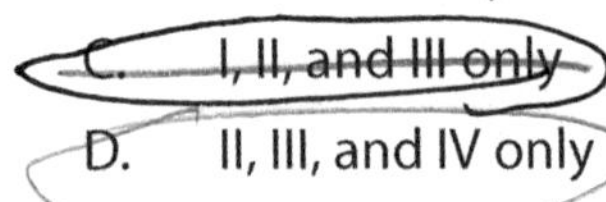

C. I, II, and III only

D. II, III, and IV only

35

A confounding variable is a variable that is

A. directly measured in an experiment.

B. deliberately changed over the course of an experiment.

C. not directly measured or manipulated, but has an effect on the experimental results.

D. has no direct relationship with the independent and dependent variables.

36

Electrons were discovered by

A. Ernest Rutherford.

B. J.J. Thomson.

C. John Dalton.

D. Niels Bohr.

37

Which of the following describes the temperatures reached by methane, ethane, propane, and n-butane at an equilibrium vapor pressure of 1 atm?

A. methane > ethane > propane > butane

B. methane = ethane = propane = butane

C. methane < ethane < propane < butane

D. methane < ethane = propane < butane

38

Which transition metal is the easiest to oxidize to the +2 cation?

A. copper

B. iron

C. zinc

D. cobalt

39

Which of the following is a decomposition reaction?

A. $2Na + Cl_2 \rightarrow 2NaCl$

B. $Zn + 2HCl \rightarrow ZnCl_2 + H_2$

C. $CH_4 + 2O_2 \rightarrow CO_2 + 2H_2O$

D. $H_2CO_3 \rightarrow H_2O + CO_2$

40

Use the bond energies given below to find the enthalpy for the reaction of carbon with oxygen to form carbon dioxide.

$C(s) + O_2(g) \rightarrow CO_2(g)$

Bond	Bond Energy
C=O	745 kg/mol
O=O	495 kg/mol

A. -9.95×10^2 kJ/mol

B. -2.56×10^2 kJ/mol

C. 2.56×10^2 kJ/mol

D. 9.95×10^2 kJ/mol

41

Which element is a metalloid?

A. rubidium

B. vanadium

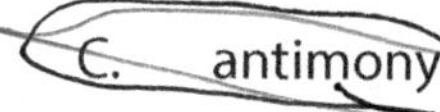

C. antimony

D. iodine

42

Which element is INCORRECTLY matched with its group name?

A. lithium – alkaline earth metal

B. iodine – halogen

C. argon – noble gas

D. iron – transition metal

43

How many significant figures are in the number 0.0200?

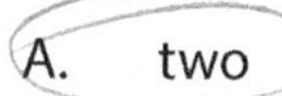

A. two

B. one

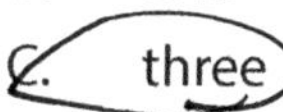

C. three

D. five

44

A student uses a scale to find the mass of a metal block and records the readings below.

8.114 kg

8.119 kg

8.111 kg

If the reported true value for the block is 6.115 kg, what can be said about the measured values?

A. The results are both accurate and precise.

B. The results are accurate but not precise.

C. The results are precise but not accurate.

D. They are neither accurate nor precise.

45

A 0.10 M solution of a weak acid has $[H_3O^+] = 7.08 \times 10^{-3}$ M. What is the percent dissociation of the acid?

A. 3.2%

B. 7.1%

C. 9.4%

D. 14%

46

Which of the following is true of an atom of Ar with a mass number of 40 and the ion S^{2-} with a mass number of 32?

A. They have the same number of protons.

B. They have the same number of electrons.

C. They have the same number of neutrons.

D. They have the same atomic radius.

47

Which statement about melting points is FALSE?

A. Diamond has a very high melting point since it is a network covalent solid.

B. Table salt has a high melting point because it is an ionic solid.

C. Tungsten carbide has a high melting point because it is an ionic solid.

D. Silicon carbide has a very high melting point because it is a network covalent solid.

48

A compound has an empirical formula of BH_3. If its molar mass is 27.67 g/mol, what is its molecular formula?

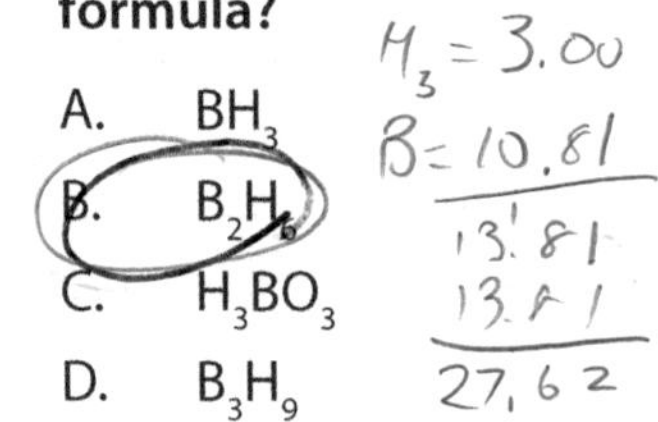

A. BH_3

B. B_2H_6

C. H_3BO_3

D. B_3H_9

49

Which of the following is a possible set of quantum numbers for an atom's electron configuration?

A. $n = 0, l = 0, ml = 0, ms = +1/2$

B. $n = 1, l = 0, ml = 0, ms = -1/2$

C. $n = 1, l = 1, ml = 0, ms = +1/2$

D. $n = 3, l = 3, ml = -3, ms = +1/2$

50

Which of the following is a chemical bond?

I. polar covalent bond

II. ionic bond

III. hydrogen bond

A. I only

B. I and II only

C. II and III only

D. I, II, and III

51

Which of the following is true when sodium acetate is added to acetic acid in solution?

A. The pH will go down.

B. The pH will stay the same.

C. The acetate ion will react with water to form hydronium ions.

D. The acetate ion will react with water to form hydroxide ions.

52

Which of the following is NOT a colligative property of a solution?

A. vapor pressure lowering

B. osmotic pressure

C. heat of solution

D. boiling point elevation

53

Which type of sensor can be used to detect colon cancer?

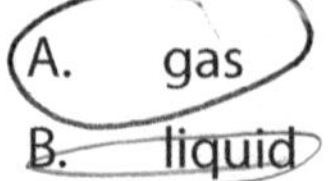

A. gas

B. liquid

C. solid

D. liquid crystal

54

The process that takes place when water reaches its boiling point is called

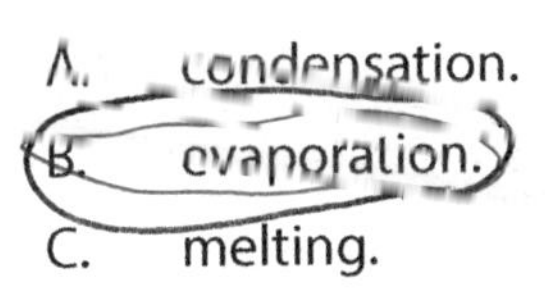

A. condensation.
B. evaporation.
C. melting.
D. sublimation.

55

Cathode rays are made of

A. positively charged particles.
B. neutral particles.
C. negatively charged particles.
D. X-rays.

56

Which statement about radioactive particles is true?

A. Alpha particles consist of two protons and two electrons.
B. Alpha particles are NOT deflected by electric and magnetic fields.
C. Beta particles are positively charged and are deflected by electric and magnetic fields.
D. Gamma rays are not deflected by the electric and magnetic fields because they do not possess any charge.

57

Which organic compound is INCORRECTLY matched with the functional group?

A. CH_3COOH—carboxyl
B. CH_3OH—hydroxyl
C. CH_3CN—carbonyl
D. CH_3COOCH_3—ester

58

Which of the following is amphoteric?

I. water
II. sodium hydrogen sulfate
III. sodium phosphate

A. I only
B. II only
C. I and II only
D. I, II, and III

59

Which of the following is NOT an example of a combustion reaction?

A. methane gas burning on a stove
B. hydrogen reacting with oxygen to give water
C. carbon reacting with oxygen to give carbon dioxide
D. an egg being boiled in water

60

Which of the following may NOT be determined by kinetics?

A. the mechanism of the reaction
B. the overall order of the reaction
C. how reaction concentrations will affect the rate
D. how product concentrations will affect the rate

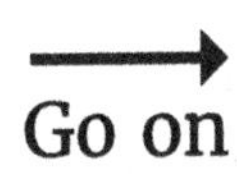

Go on

61

Which of the following elements is the most electronegative?

A. Mg

B. Si

C. S

D. Cl

62

Atomic number is defined as the number of

A. electrons in the nucleus.

B. protons in the nucleus.

C. protons and neutrons in the nucleus.

D. orbitals in an atom.

63

Which of the following bases has the highest pH if they all have the same molarity?

A. barium hydroxide

B. sodium hydroxide

C. potassium hydroxide

D. ammonium hydroxide

64

Which of the following is a double-replacement reaction?

I. Silver nitrate reacting with sodium chloride.

II. Hydrochloric acid reacting with sodium hydroxide.

III. Aluminum metal reacting with zinc chloride solution.

A. I only

B. II only

C. III only

D. I and II only

65

Which of the following is defined as the average kinetic energy of molecules?

A. pressure

B. mass

C. thermal energy

D. enthalpy

66

Which of the following is NOT a homogeneous mixture?

A. air

B. sandy water

C. brass

D. salt dissolved in water

67

What happens to the atomic radius when moving left to right on the periodic table?

A. It decreases.

B. It increases.

C. It stays constant.

D. It does not follow a set pattern.

68

Which of the following is a decomposition reaction?

A. $2HBr + Ba(OH)_2 \rightarrow BaBr_2 + 2H_2O$

B. $CH_4 + 2O_2 \rightarrow CO_2 + 2H_2O$

C. $MgSO_3 \rightarrow MgO + SO_2$

D. $Cu + 2AgNO_3 \rightarrow 2Ag + Cu(NO_3)_2$

69

When ordering different types of radiation in order of their frequency, which statement is true?

A. Microwave radiation has a higher frequency than radio waves.

B. Infrared radiation has a higher frequency than ultraviolet rays.

C. Gamma rays have a higher frequency than X-rays, but a lower frequency than ultraviolet rays.

D. Ultraviolet and X-ray radiations have a lower frequency than microwaves.

70

For a closed system, which of the following is true?

A. No exchange of matter is possible between a system and its surroundings, although exchange of energy is possible.

B. No exchange of energy is possible between a system and its surroundings, although exchange of matter is possible.

C. No exchange of energy or matter is possible between a system and its surroundings.

D. Exchange of energy and matter is possible between the system and its surroundings.

71

Which element will form a +2 ion?

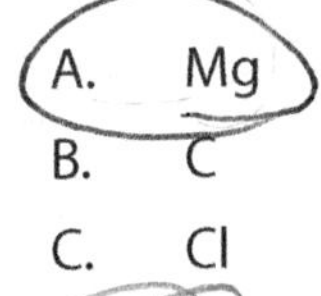

A. Mg

B. C

C. Cl

D. Na

72

What is the name of the compound $CaCl_2$?

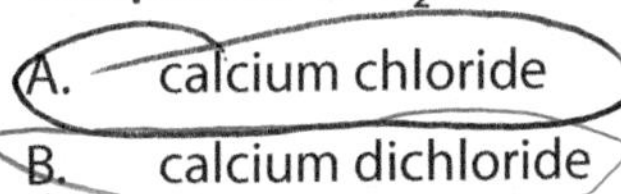

A. calcium chloride

B. calcium dichloride

C. chlorine calcide

D. calcium(II) chloride

73

What is the Lewis structure for Br_2O?

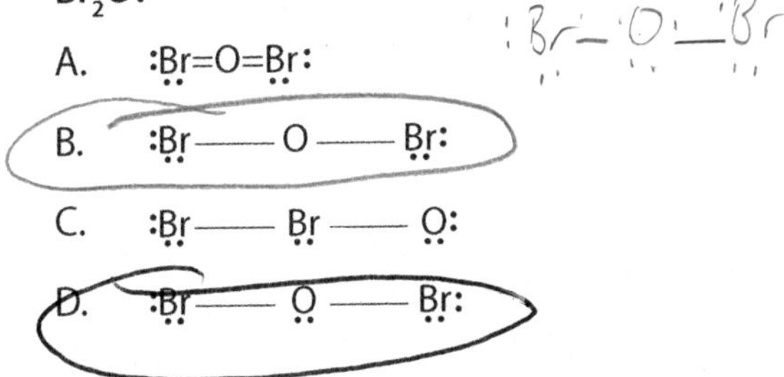

A. :Br=O=Br:

B. :Br —— O —— Br:

C. :Br —— Br —— O:

D. :Br —— O —— Br:

74

What is the equilibrium constant for $PCl_5(g) \leftrightarrows PCl_3(g) + Cl_2(g)$?

A. $K = \frac{[Cl_2][PCl_3]^2}{[PCl_5]}$

B. $K = \frac{[Cl_2][PCl_3]}{[PCl_5]}$

C. $K = \frac{[PCl_5]}{[Cl_2][PCl_3]}$

D. $K = \frac{[PCl_3]}{[PCl_5]}$

75

The vapor pressure lowering of a solution containing a nonvolatile solute is directly proportional to the

A. mole fraction of solute.
B. mole fraction of solvent.
C. molality of the solution.
D. osmotic pressure of the solute.

76

Which of the following is NOT true for systematic errors?

A. They are the result of faulty experimental design.
B. They are not reproducible.
C. It is not possible to eliminate these errors.
D. It is possible to eliminate these errors.

77

The heat energy required to change 1 g of a substance from a solid to a liquid state at the same temperature is

A. entropy.
B. specific latent heat of vaporization.
C. sensible heat.
D. specific latent heat of fusion.

78

What is the name of the compound $Cr(NO_3)_3$?

A. chromium trinitrate
B. chromium nitrate
C. chromium(III) nitrate
D. chromium(II) nitrate

79

Which of the following was NOT demonstrated by Niels Bohr with respect to the absorption and emission spectra?

A. When a heavy nucleus splits, the energy released is the calculated difference in the mass of products and reactants multiplied by velocity of light squared.
B. When an electron goes from a lower energy level to higher energy level, it absorbs some color of light.
C. When going from the fourth energy level to the second energy level, ultraviolet light is emitted.
D. When a beam of light passes through an atom, if the energy of this beam of light is sufficient, the electron moves from the ground state to a higher energy state.

80

Which of the following is NOT a Brønsted conjugate acid-base pair?

A. H_3O^+ and H_2O
B. Na_2S and NaS^-
C. HCl and Cl^-
D. H_2CO_3 and HCO_3^-

81

The entropy of the universe is

A. increasing.
B. decreasing.
C. constant.
D. zero.

Use the information below to answer questions 82 and 83.

An unknown liquid is experimentally determined to be 39.99 percent carbon, 6.73 percent hydrogen, and 53.28 percent oxygen. It also determined to have a formula mass of 60.06 amu.

82

What is the liquid's empirical formula?

A. CH_2O

B. $C_4H_7O_5$

C. CH_4O

D. $C_3H_6O_3$

83

What is the liquid's molecular formula?

A. $C_2H_4O_2$

B. CH_2O

C. $C_3H_6O_3$

D. $C_2H_3O_2$

84

Place these compounds in order of increasing bond strength: NaCl, $MgCl_2$, $MgBr_2$.

A. NaCl, $MgCl_2$, $MgBr_2$

B. $MgBr_2$, $MgCl_2$, NaCl

C. $MgCl_2$, NaCl, $MgBr_2$

D. NaCl, $MgBr_2$, $MgCl_2$

85

What is the mass number of ${}^{12}_{24}Mg$?

A. 2

B. 12

C. 24

D. 36

86

Determine the reaction type and the missing compound for the following reaction:

$BaCO_3$ (*s*) → BaO (*s*) + ____ (*g*)

A. neutralization reaction; H_2O

B. decomposition reaction; CO_2

C. single replacement reaction; CO

D. oxidation-reduction reaction; OH^-

87

A catalyst increases a reaction rate by

A. increasing the activation energy.

B. increasing the concentration of the reactants.

C. changing the relative partial pressures of the reactants.

D. changing the reaction mechanism.

88

What is the concentration of Ni^{2+} ions in a saturated solution of NiS? (The K_{sp} for NiS is 4×10^{-20}.)

A. 16×10^{-40} M

B. 4×10^{-20} M

C. 2×10^{-20} M

D. 2×10^{-10} M

89

What is the molar mass of $ZnCl_2$?

A. 136.29 amu

B. 100.83 g

C. 136.29 g

D. 100.83 amu

90

According to the ideal gas law, which of the following could NOT happen when the number of moles of a gas increase?

A. Pressure increases as temperature and volume stay constant.

B. Volume increases as temperature and pressure stay constant.

C. Pressure and volume decrease while temperature stays constant.

D. Temperature decreases as pressure and volume stay constant.

91

Which statement about the periodic table is FALSE?

A. While moving from left to right on the periodic table, atomic radii decrease.

B. When moving from top to bottom on the periodic table, atomic radii increase.

C. While moving left to right on the periodic table, the ionization energy increases.

D. While moving from top to bottom on the periodic table, ionization energy increases.

92

What is the name of the acid H_2SO_3?

A. sulfuric acid

B. sulfurous acid

C. hyposulfurous acid

D. persulfuric acid

93

Order these bonds in terms of increasing polarity: C—H, C—C, C—N, C—O, C—F

A. C—H, C—C, C—N, C—O, C—F

B. C—C, C—H, C—N, C—O, C—F

C. C—F, C—O, C—N, C—H, C—C

D. C—C, C—N, C—H, C—O, C—F

94

If the following exothermic reaction is at equilibrium, which of the following statements is true?

$N_2(g) + 3H_2(g) \leftrightarrows 2NH_3(g)$

A. The addition of heat to the system will push the equilibrium in the forward direction.

B. The addition of heat to the system will have no effect on the equilibrium.

C. The addition of heat to the system will push the equilibrium in the reverse direction.

D. The addition of heat to the system will result in a higher equilibrium constant.

95

What will happen to the pH of a nitric acid solution that is diluted by a factor of ten?

A. The pH will go up ten units.

B. The pH will go down ten units.

C. The pH will go up one unit.

D. The pH will go down one unit.

96

In general, the solubility of a

A. solid in a solid decreases with increasing temperature.

B. gas in a liquid increases with decreasing temperature.

C. solid in a liquid decreases with increasing temperature.

D. liquid in a liquid is independent of temperature.

97

Which of the following is a balanced equation?

A. $Cl_2(g) + KBr(aq) \rightarrow KCl(aq) + Br_2(g)$

B. $6CO_2(g) + 6H_2O(l) \rightarrow C_6H_{12}O_6(s) + 6O_2(g)$

C. $C_2H_4O_2 \rightarrow C_4H_6O_3 + H_2O$

D. $Cu(s) + AgNO_3(aq) \rightarrow Cu(NO_3)_2(aq) + Ag(s)$

98

Class D fires involve

A. combustible metals.

B. organic solvents and flammable liquids.

C. electrical equipment.

D. ordinary combustible products.

99

Which atomic model states that electrons move around the orbit in waves and not in defined paths?

A. Bohr model

B. Schrodinger model

C. Rutherford model

D. Dalton model

100

When benzene burns completely in excess oxygen, which combustion products should form?

A. CO_2 and H_2O

B. CH_4 and H_2O

C. CO_2 and H_2O_2

D. CH_4 and H_2O_2

101

In which compound is the oxidation number of As NOT +3?

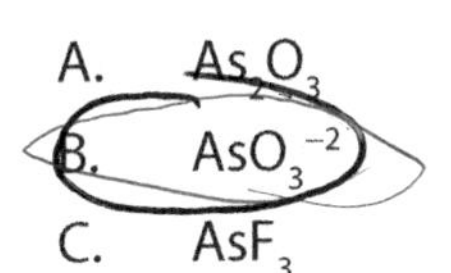

A. As_2O_3

B. AsO_3^{-2}

C. AsF_3

D. As_2H_6

102

The equilibrium constant for the reaction to create sulfur trioxide is $K = 4.0 \times 10^{24}$. Based on the equilibrium constant, which of the following is true about the reaction?

A. The reaction strongly favors the reactants.

B. The reaction favors neither the reactants nor the products.

C. The reaction strongly favors the products.

D. There is not enough information to be able to predict how the reaction will proceed.

Go on

103

Which titration curve could describe the titration of a solution of HCl with the addition of a solution of KOH?

A.

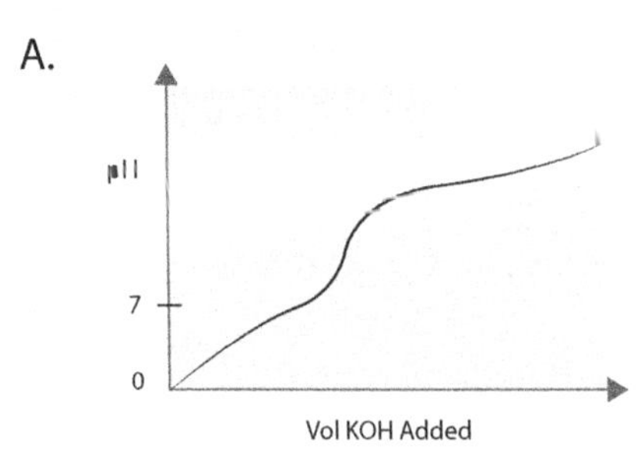

B.

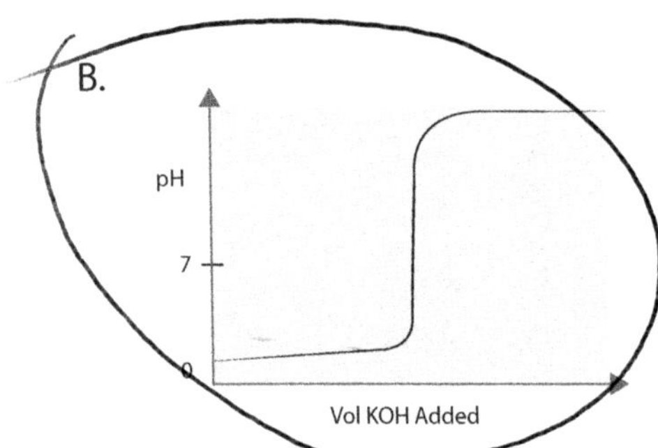

C.

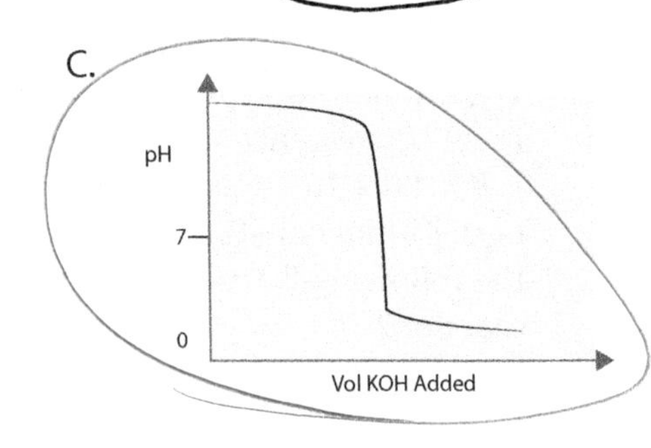

D.

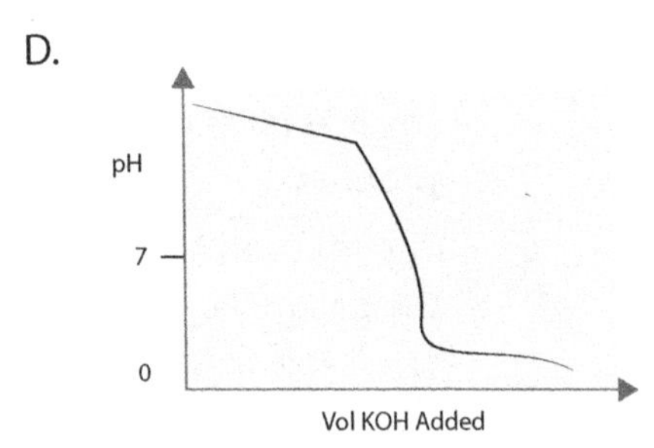

104

When a nonvolatile solute is dissolved in a solvent, which of the following statements is true?

A. The freezing point of the solution is raised.

B. The boiling point of the solution is raised.

C. The osmotic pressure is unchanged.

D. The vapor pressure of the solution is raised.

105

The lines representing a phase transition on a heating curve

A. are vertical.

B. are horizontal.

C. have a positive slope.

D. have a negative slope.

106

What is the IUPAC name of the molecule below?

CH_2 — CH_2—CH—CH—C—C—CH_3

(with CH_3—CH_2—CH_2—CH_3 attached below the two CH groups)

A. 4-methyl-5-n-propyl-6-octyne

B. 5-methyl-4-n-propyl-3-octyne

C. 5-methyl-4-n-propyl-2-octyne

D. 5-methyl-4-n-propyl-2-octene

107

What does Avogadro's number represent?

A. the number of atoms in 1 g of an element

B. the number of atoms in a mole of an element

C. the molar mass of an atom

D. the molar mass of carbon

108

What is the predicted geometry for the molecule SiF_4?

A. tetrahedral

B. trigonal planar

C. seesaw

D. linear

109

What intermolecular forces would need to be considered in predicting the relative physical properties of CH_3F, CH_3Cl, CH_3Br, and CH_3I?

A. London force

B. dipole-dipole and London force

C. dipole-dipole and hydrogen bonding

D. dipole-dipole, hydrogen bonding, and London force

110

How many O_2 molecules are required to balance the following reaction?

$CS_2 + O_2 \rightarrow CO_2 + SO_2$

A. 1

B. 2

C. 3

D. 4

111

Order the following equations and their equilibrium constants from most-favored product to least-favored product.

1. $2H_2(g) + O_2(g) \leftrightarrows 2H_2O(g)$ $K = 3.3 \times 10^{81}$
2. $H_2(g) + I_2(g) \leftrightarrows 2HI(g)$ $K = 2.5 \times 10^{1}$
3. $AgCl(s) \leftrightarrows Ag^+(aq) + Cl^-(aq)$ $K = 1.8 \times 10^{-10}$
4. $HCOOH(aq) + H_2O(l) \leftrightarrows H_3O^+(aq) + HCOO^-(aq)$ $K = 1.8 \times 10^{-4}$

A. 1 > 4 > 2 > 3

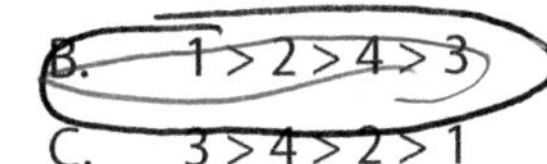

B. 1 > 2 > 4 > 3

C. 3 > 4 > 2 > 1

D. 3 > 2 > 4 > 1

112

Which of the following ALWAYS exists in a state of equilibrium?

I. a weak acid

II. a weak base

III. a hydrolyzed product

A. I only

B. II only

C. I and II only

D. I, II, and III

113

What type of reaction is shown below?

$2Na(s) + 2H_2O(l) \rightarrow 2NaOH(aq) + H_2(g)$

A. neutralization reaction

B. decomposition reaction

C. double-displacement reaction

D. single-replacement reaction

114

What are the products of the complete reaction of NaOH and H_2SO_4?

A. H_2O and $NaSO_4$

B. OH^- and $NaSO_4$

C. H_3O^+ and Na_2SO_4

D. H_2O and Na_2SO_4

115

Which of the following phase transitions passes from a low to high energy phase without passing through an intermediate phase?

A. evaporation

B. condensation

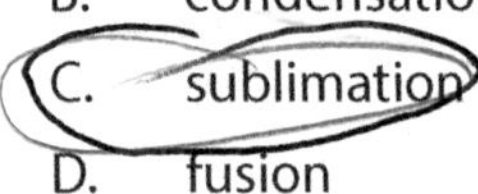

C. sublimation

D. fusion

116

What is the name of the compound below?

$$\begin{array}{l} CH_3CHCH_3 \\ \quad\quad\; | \\ \quad\;\; OCH_2CH_3 \end{array}$$

I. ethyl isopropyl ether

II. 2-ethoxypropane

III. ethyl isopropyl alcohol

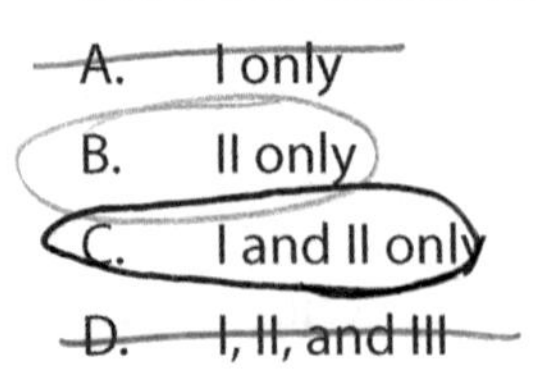

A. I only

B. II only

C. I and II only

D. I, II, and III

117

What is the net ionic equation for the reaction of HNO_3 and KOH?

A. $H^+ + OH^- \rightarrow H_2O$

B. $H^+ + NO_3^- + KOH \rightarrow H_2O + KNO_3$

C. $HNO_3 + OH^- \rightarrow H_2O + K^+$

D. $H^+ + KOH \rightarrow H_2O + K^+$

118

Which is NOT a definition of an acid?

A. A substance that contains hydrogen and produces H^+ in water.

B. A substance that donates protons to a base.

C. A substance that reacts with a base to form a salt and water.

D. A substance that accepts protons.

119

Which of the following compounds contains a π bond?

I. ethylene

II. acetylene

III. carbon monoxide

A. II only

B. I and II only

C. II and III only

D. I, II, and III

120

Place the compounds below in order of increasing melting points.

CCl_4, KCl, and $CaCl_2$

A. KCl, $CaCl_2$, CCl_4

B. KCl, CCl_4, $CaCl_2$

C. CCl_4, KCl, $CaCl_2$

D. CCl_4, $CaCl_2$, KCl

121

Which of the following is NOT a conclusion of the Rutherford model of the atom?

A. Atoms have a positively charged center (nucleus) that contains most of their mass.

B. Atoms are not just empty spaces with electrons distributed around them.

C. The presence of electrons is confirmed for the first time.

D. The positively charged nucleus of an atom is tiny compared with the size of the entire atom.

122

What is the name of the following compound?

H_3C CH_3 CH_3 CH_3

A. decane

B. 3,7-dimethyloctane

C. 3-methylnonane

D. 3,7-dimethylnonane

123

In which of the following mixtures will a precipitate form? Assume equal volumes of 0.1 M solutions.

A. KCl and NH_4NO_3

B. $Ba(OH)_2$ and H_2SO_4

C. Na_2SO_4 and $Al(NO_3)_3$

D. CsI and $MgCl_2$

124

In the reaction $SnCl_2(s) + 2\ Cl^-(aq) \leftrightarrows SnCl_4^{-2}(aq)$,

A. $SnCl_2$ is a Lewis acid, and Cl^- is a Lewis base.

B. $SnCl_2$ is a Lewis base, and Cl^- is a Lewis acid.

C. $SnCl_4^{-2}$ is a Lewis acid, and Cl^- is a Lewis base.

D. $SnCl_4^{-2}$ is a Lewis base, and Cl^- is a Lewis acid.

125

While working in the laboratory, someone breaks a large bottle of chemicals. Which of the following actions must be taken?

A. The spill must be cleaned up appropriately.

B. Everyone must evacuate the laboratory immediately.

C. A qualified person must be called to clean the spill, but work may continue.

D. Experiments should be completed before evacuating.

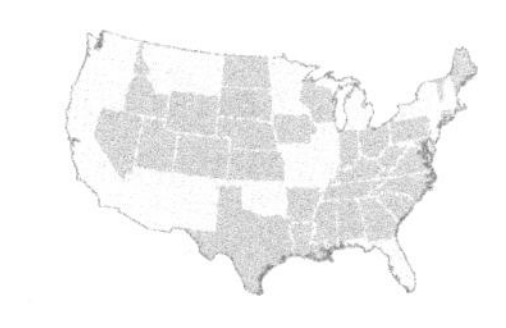

Answer Key

1)

C. **Correct.** Ca^+ has nineteen electrons. All the other ions have eighteen electrons.

2)

B. **Correct.** Use dimensional analysis.

$6 \text{ mol } O_2$	$1 \text{ mol } P_4O_5$	$= \mathbf{2\ mol\ P_4O_5}$
	$3 \text{ mol } O_2$	

3)

A. Incorrect. Hydrogen chloride is an acid, which turns blue litmus paper red.

B. Incorrect. Methane is a neutral compound, which does not turn red litmus paper blue.

C. **Correct.** Ammonia is a base, which turns red litmus paper blue.

D. Incorrect. Helium is a neutral noble gas, which does not turn red litmus paper blue.

4)

A. Incorrect. NH_3 has hydrogen bonding, which increases the boiling point. However, the hydrogen bonding is not as strong as that with water since the three lone pairs on the fluorine atom are more stabilized than the one on oxygen in water, due to fluorine's higher electronegativity.

B. **Correct.** H_2O has hydrogen bonding, which increases boiling point and has two lone pairs on each oxygen atom, one more than that on nitrogen in ammonia.

C. Incorrect. HF has hydrogen bonding, which increases boiling point, but the hydrogen bonding is not as strong as that within water since there is only one lone pair on each nitrogen atom.

D. Incorrect. H_2S does not have hydrogen bonding, thus lowering the boiling point despite having the second-highest molar mass among the chemicals listed.

5)

C. **I and III only**

I. Chromium does not follow the aufbau principle since the ground state electron configuration is $4s^1 3d^5$.

II. Iron does follow the aufbau principle since the ground state electron configuration is $4s^2 3d^6$.

III. Copper does not follow the aufbau principle since the ground state electron configuration is $4s^1 3d^{10}$.

6)

C. **Correct.** An equilibrium always responds to a change by trying to reverse it. The equilibrium will shift to the reactants to increase the number of moles of gases and thus increase the pressure.

7)

A. **Correct.** Because $\Delta T_f = K_f m_{solute}$, the solvent with the largest K_f will have the greatest effect on the freezing point.

8)

A. **Correct.** Because metals tend to consist of ordered, tightly packed atoms, their densities are typically high. The properties in choices B, C, and D apply to metals.

9)

D. **Correct.** Mg has an oxidation number of +2, Na an oxidation number of +1, and O an oxidization number of −2; thus, P has to be +5 to result in a neutral compound.

10)

A. Incorrect. The Roman numeral IV denotes the charge on Sn, not the number of Sn ions.

B. Incorrect. Pentahydrate indicates five H_2O molecules bound per $SnCl_4$.

C. Incorrect. Hydrate indicates water molecules bound not hydrogen atoms.

D. **Correct.** Tin, with a charge of +4, has four Cl^- ions bound to balance the charge, and *pentahydrate* indicates five water molecules bound.

11)

A. **Correct.** Ionization energy increases while moving left to right in the periodic table. As the atomic size decreases left to right, more energy is needed to remove electrons.

12)

A. Incorrect. A solution is a homogeneous mixture.

B. Incorrect. A solution is a mixture, so it cannot have just one kind of atom.

C. Incorrect. A solution is a homogeneous mixture, and it cannot be separated using a filter.

D. **Correct.** A solution is a homogeneous mixture that may be separated using distillation.

13)

A. Incorrect. Deposition is when matter changes from a gas to a solid.

B. Incorrect. Freezing is when matter changes from a liquid to a solid.

C. Incorrect. Condensation is when matter changes from a gas to a liquid.

D. **Correct.** Sublimation is when matter changes from a solid to a gas.

14)

A. **Correct.** The *s* orbital holds a maximum of two electrons with opposite spins.

15)

A. **Correct.** The independent variable is deliberately changed in the course of the experiment.

B. Incorrect. The reaction rate is not directly manipulated or measured in the experiment.

C. Incorrect. The amount of heat produced by the reaction is being measured in the reaction, and is defined as the dependent variable.

D. Incorrect. The product concentration is not directly manipulated or measured in the experiment.

16)

A. **I and II only**

I. True. Hydrofluoric acid (HF) has one proton per formula unit.

II. True. Nitric acid (HNO_3) has one proton per formula unit.

III. False. Phosphoric acid (H_3PO_4) has three protons per formula unit.

17)

D. **Correct.** Oxygen is in the same group as sulfur and is also a non-metal.

18)

B. **Correct.** Lipids are used for energy storage.

19)

D. **Correct.** Plutonium has the highest atomic number out of the actinide elements listed and thus the greatest number of *f* electrons.

20)

A. Incorrect. This is the definition of isobars.

B. **Correct.** This is the correct definition of isotones.

C. Incorrect. This is the definition of isoelectric species.

D. Incorrect. This is the definition of isotopes.

21)

A. **Correct.** This is butanal, which contains aldehyde (—CHO).

22)

C. **Correct.** Subtracting the atomic number from the mass number gives the number of protons: $A - Z = 88 - 38 = 50$.

23)

A. Incorrect. Total Gibbs free energy change is not positive for a spontaneous process.

B. Incorrect. For a spontaneous process, entropy increases.

C. **Correct.** Gibbs free energy change is negative for a spontaneous process.

D. Incorrect. ΔG must be negative for a spontaneous reaction, and may or may not be equal to ΔS.

24)

D. **Correct.** Find the formula mass of ethanol.

CH_3CH_2OH

C = 12.01 amu

H = 1.01 amu

O = 16 amu

$2(12.01) + 6(1.01) + 1(16) = 46.08$ amu

Divide the mass of carbon in ethanol by the total formula mass to find the mass percent of carbon.

$\frac{2(12.01}{46.08} = 0.5213 = \mathbf{52.13\%}$

25)

C. **Correct.** Use the acid dissociation expression.

$HOAc(aq) \rightarrow H^+(aq) + OAc^-(aq)$

$K_a = \frac{[H+][OAc-]}{[HOAc]}$

$[HOAc] = [OAc^-]$ and $K_a = [H^+]$

$pH = pK_a = -\log(1.8 \times 10^{-5}) = \mathbf{4.74}$

26)

A. **Correct.** MRI technology is based on the chemical principle of nuclear magnetic resonance.

27)

A. Incorrect. Boiling point is represented by point E.

B. **Correct.** Melting point is represented by point C.

C. Incorrect. Point C deals with the solid-to-liquid transition, whereas latent heat of vaporization refers to the liquid-to-gas phase.

D. Incorrect. Freezing represents the conversion of liquid to solid, whereas point C represents melting, which is conversion of solid to liquid.

28)

A. Incorrect. This statement is true about point E because point E has more heat added to it compared to point C.

B. Incorrect. This statement is true because at point E, the phase change from liquid to gas takes place.

C. Incorrect. This statement is true because there is more heat at point E and more heat implies more entropy.

D. Correct. This statement is NOT true for point E because evaporation, not melting, occurs at point E.

29)

A. Incorrect. Boiling occurs between points D and E.

B. Correct. The water is melting between points B and C.

C. Incorrect. Deposition—the change from gas to solid—is not shown on the graph.

D. Incorrect. Sublimation—the change from solid to gas—is not shown on the graph.

30)

C. Correct. H_2CO_3 (carbonic acid) is not an organic compound since each H is bonded to an O, not to C. All the others have C–H bonds.

31)

B. Correct. Elements in Group 1 have the lowest first ionization energy because they will form a noble gas when one electron is removed. Elements toward the bottom of a group will have a lower first ionization energy because the valence electrons are farther from the nucleus. Thus, potassium (K) will have the lowest first ionization energy of all the choices.

32)

D. Correct.

$\_P_4 + \_O_2 + \_H_2O \rightarrow \_H_3PO_4$

Add a 4 on the right side to balance the four P atoms on the left.

$\_P_4 + \_O_2 + \_H_2O \rightarrow 4H_3PO_4$

There are now twelve H atoms on the right, so add a 6 to H_2O on the left.

$\_P_4 + \_O_2 + 6H_2O \rightarrow 4H_3PO_4$

There are sixteen O on the right, so add a 5 to O_2 on the left.

$P_4 + 5O_2 + 6H_2O \rightarrow 4H_3PO_4$

33)

D. Correct. Use the equation $E°_{cell} = E°_{cathode} - E°_{anode}$

Cu is the cathode because it has a higher E°.

$0.34 \text{ V} - (-0.76 \text{ V}) = 1.10 \text{ V}$

34)

C. Correct. The benzoate ion does not react with added hydroxide ions, so IV cannot be correct. All the other statements are true.

35)

A. Incorrect. A variable that is directly measured in an experiment is a dependent variable.

B. Incorrect. A variable that is deliberately changed over the course of an experiment is an independent variable.

C. Correct. Confounding variables are not accounted for in the experimental design, but have an effect on the outcome of the experiment.

D. Incorrect. Confounding variables have an effect on the experimental results.

36)

A. Incorrect. Ernest Rutherford's gold foil experiment proved that atoms contain a positively charged nucleus. However, he did not discover electrons.

B. Correct. J.J. Thomson's cathode ray experiment detected the presence of electrons.

C. Incorrect. John Dalton's contribution to atomic theory was the proposition that atoms are indivisible, atoms belonging to the same element are identical, and atoms combine in whole number ratios to form compounds.

D. Incorrect. Niels Bohr developed the quantum model and determined that electrons exist in specific energy levels.

37)

C. Correct. For chemically similar molecules, as molecular weight increases, so do London forces. So, the kinetic energy required to overcome those forces and reach the vapor phase increases with molecular weight.

38)

A. Incorrect. Oxidation to Cu^{2+} results in $3d^9$ as the valence electrons, which is a less stable configuration than $3d^{10}$ with Zn^{2+}.

B. Incorrect. Oxidation to Fe^{2+} results in $3d^6$ as the valence electrons, which is a less stable configuration than $3d^{10}$ with Zn^{2+}.

C. Correct. Oxidation to Zn^{2+} results in $3d^{10}$ as the valence electrons, which is a stable configuration since filled orbitals are preferred.

D. Incorrect. Oxidation to Co^{2+} results in $3d^7$ as the valence electrons, which is a less stable configuration than $3d^{10}$ with Zn^{2+}.

39)

A. Incorrect. This is a synthesis or metathesis reaction.

B. Incorrect. This is a single replacement or displacement reaction.

C. Incorrect. This is a combustion reaction.

D. Correct. This is a decomposition reaction since one reactant gives two products.

40)

A. Correct. Subtract the bond energy for two C=O bonds from the bond energy for O=O.

$$495\frac{kJ}{mol} - 2\left(745\frac{kJ}{mol}\right) =$$

$$\mathbf{-9.95 \times 10^2 \frac{kJ}{mol}}$$

41)

A. Incorrect. Rubidium is a metal.

B. Incorrect. Vanadium is a transition metal.

C. Correct. Antimony is a metalloid.

D. Incorrect. Iodine is a halogen.

42)

A. Correct. Li is an alkali metal, not an alkaline earth metal.

43)

C. Correct. There are three significant figures in this number. Trailing zeros (zeros after the last nonzero digit) are significant when there is a decimal point. So in this case, the nonzero digit *2* and the two trailing zeros count as significant figures—the three underlined digits 0.0<u>200</u>.

44)

C. **Correct.** The values are close to each other (precise) not are not close to the actual value (accurate).

45)

B. **Correct.** The percent dissociation is the percent of the acid that dissociated.

$[H_3O^+] = 7.08 \times 10^{-3} = 0.00708\text{ M}$

$\frac{0.00708\text{ M}}{0.1\text{ M}} = 0.0708 \times 100 = \mathbf{7.1\%}$

46)

A. Incorrect. Ar has eighteen protons and S^{2-} has sixteen protons.

B. **Correct.** They both have eighteen electrons.

C. Incorrect. Ar has twenty-two neutrons and S^{2-} has sixteen neutrons.

D. Incorrect. They are not the same size since S^{2-} has a larger radius because it has two fewer protons than Ar but the same number of electrons.

47)

C. **Correct.** Tungsten carbide is a network covalent solid. All the other statements are true.

48)

B. **Correct.** Divide the molar mass by the mass of the empirical formula and multiply the empirical formula by that ratio.

$\frac{27.67\text{ g/mol}}{13.84\text{ g/mol}} \approx 2$

$2(BH_3) = \mathbf{B_2H_6}$

49)

A. Incorrect. *n* can never equal 0.

B. **Correct.** This set is possible (1s).

C. Incorrect. If $n = 1$, l can only be 0 (and not 1).

D. Incorrect. If $n = 3$, l can only be 0, 1, or 2.

50)

B. **I and II only**

I. A polar covalent bond is a type of intramolecular bond that creates a compound.

II. An ionic bond is a type of intramolecular bond that creates a compound.

III. A hydrogen bond is not a chemical bond, but an intermolecular force that acts between molecules.

51)

D. **Correct.** The acetate ions react with water to form hydroxide ions, which causes the pH to go up.

52)

C. **Correct.** The heat of solution is not a colligative property of a solution because it is determined by the properties of the specific substance being dissolved.

53)

A. **Correct.** VOCs (volatile organic compounds) in breath or intestinal gases contain biomarkers for colorectal cancer.

54)

A. Incorrect. Condensation is the process of conversion from liquid to solid.

B. **Correct.** Evaporation is the process of conversion from liquid to gas that occurs at the boiling point.

C. Incorrect. Melting is the process of conversion of solid to liquid.

D. Incorrect. Sublimation is the process of conversion of solid to gas.

55)

C. **Correct.** Cathode rays are made up of negatively charged particles called electrons.

56)

A. Incorrect. Alpha particles consist of two protons and two neutrons.

B. Incorrect. Alpha particles are positively charged and are deflected by electric and magnetic fields.

C. Incorrect. While beta particles are deflected by electric and magnetic fields, they have a negative charge.

D. **Correct.** Gamma rays are neutral in charge and are not deflected by electric and magnetic fields.

57)

C. **Correct.** The carbonyl group is –C=O. All the other groups are matched correctly.

58)

C. **I and II only**

I. True. Water can form hydroxide or a proton.

II. True. Sodium hydrogen sulfate can form sulfuric acid or a sulfate ion.

III. False. Sodium phosphate can only form an acid such as sodium hydrogen phosphate.

59)

A. Incorrect. Methane burns or combusts by reacting with oxygen to form carbon dioxide and water.

B. Incorrect. The reaction is a combustion reaction since hydrogen is being oxidized with oxygen.

C. Incorrect. The reaction is a combustion reaction since carbon is being oxidized with oxygen.

D. **Correct.** When an egg is boiled in water, the proteins in the egg white and yolk become entangled and clump together. No oxygen is involved in this process.

60)

A. Incorrect. Kinetics can be used to determine the rate determining step, which helps to explain the mechanism of a reaction.

B. Incorrect. The overall order is determined by adding the order of each reactant, which is part of kinetics.

C. Incorrect. Reaction rate can be determined from the rate equation, which includes reactant concentrations.

D. **Correct.** Product concentration is used in equilibrium calculations but not in kinetics.

61)

D. **Correct.** The electronegativity of an element increases up and to the right on the periodic table. Cl is one of the most electronegative elements since it is in group 17.

62)

A. Incorrect. There are no electrons in the nucleus.

B. **Correct.** Atomic number is defined as the total number of protons in the nucleus of an atom.

C. Incorrect. The total number of protons and neutrons in a nucleus is given by the mass number.

D. Incorrect. The total number of orbitals is not given by the atomic number.

63)

A. **Correct.** Barium hydroxide is a strong base and has two hydroxide ions per formula unit.

B. Incorrect. Sodium hydroxide is a strong base but has only one hydroxide ion per formula unit.

C. Incorrect. Potassium hydroxide is a strong base but has only one hydroxide ion per formula unit.

D. Incorrect. Ammonium hydroxide is a weak base.

64)

D. **I and II only**

I. This is a double-replacement reaction: the silver and sodium ions "replace" each other.

II. This is a double-replacement reaction: the hydrogens from the acid and the sodium ions "replace" each other.

III. This is a single-replacement reaction: the aluminum "replaces" the zinc ions, creating a metal and aluminum chloride.

65)

A. Incorrect. Pressure is the force exerted by molecules against a surface.

B. Incorrect. Mass is the amount of matter in a substance.

C. **Correct.** Thermal energy is defined as the average kinetic energy of molecules.

D. Incorrect. Enthalpy is the net heat from the surroundings needed for the reaction.

66)

A. Incorrect. Air is a homogeneous mixture of N_2, O_2, H_2O, and CO_2.

B. **Correct.** Sandy water is not a homogeneous mixture. Sand and water can be easily separated, making it a heterogeneous mixture.

C. Incorrect. Brass is an alloy—a homogeneous mixture.

D. Incorrect. Salt dissolved in water is a homogeneous mixture with salt ions dispersed evenly throughout the mixture.

67)

A. **Correct.** Atomic radius decreases from left to right on the periodic table because, as the number of protons in the nucleus increases, the attraction between the nucleus and the electrons increases.

68)

A. Incorrect. This reaction is a neutralization reaction.

B. Incorrect. This reaction is a combustion reaction.

C. **Correct.** This reaction is a decomposition reaction in which one substance breaks up or decomposes to two substances.

D. Incorrect. This reaction is a simple replacement reaction.

69)

A. **Correct.** The types of radiation in order of increasing frequency are: radio waves < microwaves < infrared rays < visible rays < ultraviolet rays < X-rays < gamma rays.

70)

A. **Correct.** In a closed system, exchange of energy is possible between the system and its surroundings, but exchange of matter is not.

B. Incorrect. This type of system does not exist.

C. Incorrect. In an isolated system, there is no exchange of energy or matter between the system and its surroundings.

D. Incorrect. In an open system, there is exchange of both energy and matter between the system and its surroundings.

71)

A. **Correct.** Mg tends to lose its two valence electrons to form a +2 ion.

B. Incorrect. C does not tend to form ions.

C. Incorrect. Cl tends to gain one electron, forming a −1 ion and completing an octet in the third energy level.

D. Incorrect. Na tends to lose its one valence electron to form a +1 ion. This leaves Na^{+1}, which has a filled second energy level.

72)

A. **Correct.** For binary ionic compounds, the element farther left in the periodic table comes first followed by the root of the second element with an *–ide* suffix.

B. Incorrect. For binary ionic compounds, it is not necessary to specify the number of ions.

C. Incorrect. The element farther to the left in the periodic table is named first.

D. Incorrect. It is only necessary to indicate charge with a Roman numeral for those transition metals that can have multiple charges.

73)

A. Incorrect. There are a total of twenty valence electrons: seven for each Br and six for O. This diagram only shows sixteen. Also, Br does not tend to form double bonds.

B. Incorrect. This diagram only shows eighteen valence electrons. There are twenty.

C. Incorrect. The number of valence electrons is correct, but the least electronegative atom—oxygen—should be in the middle.

D. **Correct.** There are twenty valence electrons. Oxygen being less electronegative than Br is in the middle connected by single bonds to Br. The valence electrons are distributed to give each Br atom an octet and the remaining are placed on oxygen giving it an octet.

74)

B. **Correct.** $K = \frac{[Cl_2][PCl_3]}{[PCl_5]}$ is the equilibrium constant expression for the equation. The expression for the equilibrium constant is the product of the product concentrations divided by the product of the concentrations of the reactants. The coefficients of the balanced equation become exponents of the concentrations in the expression for the equilibrium constant.

75)

A. **Correct.** Colligative properties are changed based on the solute concentration.

B. Incorrect. The solvent mole fraction does not affect the vapor pressure lowering.

C. Incorrect. The overall molality of the solution does not change the vapor pressure.

D. Incorrect. The osmotic pressure is not directly related to the vapor pressure.

76)

A. Incorrect. Systematic errors are the result of faulty experimental design.

B. Incorrect. Systematic errors are reproducible.

C. **Correct.** It is possible to eliminate these errors by correcting the error in the measuring device.

D. Incorrect. It is possible to eliminate systematic errors.

77)

A. Incorrect. Entropy refers to randomness of the system.

B. Incorrect. The specific latent heat of vaporization is the energy required to change a substance from liquid to gas at the same temperature.

C. Incorrect. Sensible heat refers to heat that changes the phase of a substance (as opposed to latent heat).

D. **Correct.** The specific latent heat of fusion is the heat energy required to change 1 g of a substance from a solid to a liquid at the same temperature.

78)

A. Incorrect. Prefixes are not used to denote the number of anions in a salt. The correct number is assumed to balance the charge on the cation.

B. Incorrect. Chromium can have multiple charges. Roman numerals denote the charge.

C. **Correct.** A nitrate ion has a charge of −1, so the Roman numeral III denotes the correct charge on chromium to generate a neutral salt.

D. Incorrect. Chromium has a charge of III not II as in this salt.

79)

A. **Correct.** This concept was introduced by Albert Einstein. Choices B, C, and D were all demonstrated by Niels Bohr.

80)

B. **Correct.** A Brønsted acid-base pair must have hydrogen atoms.

81)

A. **Correct.** The entropy of the universe is increasing.

82)

A. **Correct.** Assume there are 100 g of liquid. Find the moles of each element.

39.99 g C	1 mol C	= 3.33 mol C
	12.01 g	

6.73 g H	1 mol H	= 6.66 mol H
	1.01 g	

53.28 g O	1 mol O	= 3.33 mol O
	16 g	

Divide each number of moles by the smallest number of moles to find the empirical formula.

$\frac{3.33 \text{ mol C}}{3.33 \text{ mol C}} = 1$

$\frac{6.66 \text{ mol H}}{3.33 \text{ mol H}} = 2$

$\frac{3.33 \text{ mol O}}{3.33 \text{ mol O}} = 1$

→ **CH_2O**

83)

A. **Correct.** The molecular weight of CH_2O is 30.03 amu. The subscripts must be multiplied by two to give a compound with a molecular weight of 60.06 amu.

B. Incorrect. CH_2O is the empirical formula, but it only has a formula mass of 30.03 amu.

C. Incorrect. This compound has a greater formula mass than 60.06 amu.

D. Incorrect. The subscripts must all be the same multiple of those in the empirical formula.

84)

A. Incorrect. Br^- has a larger ionic radius than Cl^- being farther down family

7A, so bonds will be weaker in $MgBr_2$ than in $MgCl_2$.

B. Incorrect. Since Mg is to the right of Na in the periodic table, it will have a smaller atomic radius, and the Mg^{2+} ion having a higher positive charge will also have a significantly smaller ionic radius leading to tighter bonding with Cl^-.

C. Incorrect. The more positive charge and smaller ionic radius of Mg^{2+} versus Na^+ is the more significant effect on bond strength.

D. **Correct.** Na only has a +1 charge versus the +2 charge (and smaller atomic radius) of Mg, so Mg^{2+} has a stronger attractive force. Br^- is larger than Cl^-, so it forms weaker bonds.

85)

C. **Correct.** The number at the bottom, 24, represents mass number, or the total number of protons and neutrons.

86)

A. Incorrect. No hydrogen is involved in the reaction.

B. **Correct.** $BaCO_3$ decomposes into BaO (barium oxide) and CO_2 gas.

C. Incorrect. Only one reactant is involved.

D. Incorrect. No hydrogen is involved in the reaction.

87)

D. **Correct.** A catalyst reduces the activation energy by creating an alternative reaction mechanism for the reaction.

88)

D. **Correct.** Use the formula for the solubility product constant.

$K_{sp} = [Ni^{2+}][S^{2-}]$

$4 \times 10^{-20} = [Ni^{2+}][S^{2-}]$

$[Ni^{2+}] = \sqrt{4 \times 10^{-20}} = \mathbf{2 \times 10^{-10}\ M}$

89)

C. **Correct.** The molar mass of $ZnCl_2$ equals the molar mass of Zn (65.38 g) plus two times the molar mass of Cl (2 × 35.453 g). Molar mass is expressed in grams, not in atomic mass units.

90)

C. **Correct.** According to the ideal gas law, $PV = nRT$, if n decreases and T stays constant, then either P or V will have to decrease.

91)

D. **Correct.** This statement is false: moving down the periodic table, the ionization energy decreases because electrons in the valence shells are shielded from the attraction of the nucleus by the core electrons. Choices A, B, and C are true.

92)

A. Incorrect. SO_4^{2-} is the most common oxyanion of sulfur and forms sulfuric acid.

B. **Correct.** SO_3^{2-} has one less oxygen than sulfur's most common oxyanion and forms sulfurous acid.

C. Incorrect. Hyposulfurous acid is H_2SO_2.

D. Incorrect. Persulfuric acid is H_2SO_5.

93)

B. **Correct.** C—C is the least polar bond. C—H is somewhat less polar than C—N, and polarity increases with increasing differences in electronegativities going to the right in the periodic table.

94)

C. **Correct.** An equilibrium always responds to a change by trying to reverse it. Because this is an exothermic reaction, heat is considered a product; the addition of heat will push the equilibrium in reverse to use up the additional heat.

95)

C. **Correct.** The pH will go up one unit because the proton concentration will go down by a factor of 10 ($pH = -\log[H^+]$).

96)

A. Incorrect. Typically, the solubility of two solids would increase with temperature.

B. **Correct.** Decreasing the temperature decreases the ability of gas to escape the liquid, thus increasing its solubility.

C. Incorrect. The solubility of a solid in a liquid typically increases with increasing temperature.

D. Incorrect. The solubility of two liquids is not independent of temperature.

97)

B. **Correct.** This is the balanced equation for photosynthesis.

98)

A. **Correct.** Class D fires involve combustible metals.

B. Incorrect. Class B fires involve organic solvents and flammable liquids.

C. Incorrect. Class C fires involve electrical equipment.

D. Incorrect. Class A fires involve ordinary combustible products.

99)

A. Incorrect. Niels Bohr developed the quantum model and determined that electrons exist in specific energy levels.

B. **Correct.** According to Erwin Schrödinger, electrons move around the orbit in waves and not in defined paths.

C. Incorrect. By performing the gold foil experiment, Ernest Rutherford proved that the atom consisted of a nucleus, a positively charged core at the center.

D. Incorrect. The John Dalton model stated that atoms are indivisible, atoms belonging to same element are identical, and atoms combine in whole number ratios to form compounds.

100)

A. **Correct.** Benzene, like all hydrocarbons, gives carbon dioxide and water when completely combusted.

101)

A. Incorrect. The oxidation number of As is +3 and the oxidation number of O is −2.

B. **Correct.** The oxidation number of As is +4 and the oxidation number of O is −2.

C. Incorrect. The oxidation number of As is +3 and the oxidation number of F is −1.

D. Incorrect. The oxidation number of As is +3 and the oxidation number of H is −1.

102)

C. **Correct.** A large *K*-value indicates the reaction heavily favors product formation. A large equilibrium constant means the concentrations of the products are much larger than the concentrations of the reactants.

103)

A. Incorrect. A strong acid/strong base titration curve would have a very steep equivalence point; this curve is too gradual.

B. **Correct.** The titration curve for a strong acid/strong base titration will have a very steep equivalence point. The addition of the base will result in an increase in the pH.

C. Incorrect. Since the addition of the base will result in an increase in the pH, this curve is incorrect because it shows a decrease in pH.

D. Incorrect. Adding a base causes an increase in pH; this curve is thus incorrect because it shows a decrease in pH.

104)

A. Incorrect. The freezing point is typically decreased.

B. **Correct.** The boiling point is increased with the addition of a nonvolatile solute.

C. Incorrect. The osmotic pressure would be changed.

D. Incorrect. The vapor pressure of the solution would decrease.

105)

A. Incorrect. A vertical line would show that the temperature was increasing without heat being added.

B. **Correct.** Horizontal lines show that heat is being added but the temperature of the substance is not increasing.

C. Incorrect. The slope of the graph shows the change in temperature that accompanies heat transfer within a phase.

D. Incorrect. The slope of the graph shows the change in temperature that accompanies heat transfer within a phase.

106)

A. Incorrect. Counting starts from the end of the straight chain closest to the triple bond.

B. Incorrect. The location of the triple bond is denoted as the position of the first carbon participating in the bond, which is the second carbon in this example.

C. **Correct.** Counting begins at the end closest to the triple bond. The suffix *–yne* indicates a triple bond.

D. Incorrect. The suffix *–ene* denotes a double bond.

107)

A. Incorrect. Avogadro's number is the number of atoms or molecules in a mole of a substance.

B. **Correct.** Avogadro's number is 6.02×10^{23} and is the number of atoms or molecules in a mole of a substance.

C. Incorrect. Each element has its own characteristic atomic mass based on the number of protons, neutrons, and electrons in the atom.

D. Incorrect. The molar mass of carbon is the mass of 6.02×10^{23} atoms of carbon.

108)

A. **Correct.** SiF_4 is tetrahedral with four equivalent bonds and no lone electron pairs on Si.

109)

B. **Correct.** These molecules are polar and so are subject to both dipole-dipole and London forces. There are no hydrogen atoms bound to high electronegative atoms, so there will be no hydrogen bonding.

110)

C. **Correct.** The balanced equation has the coefficients 1:3:1:2.

$\_CS_2 + \_O_2 \rightarrow \_CO_2 + \_SO_2$

Carbon is already balanced (one atom on each side). There are two S atoms on the left, so add 2 to SO_2 on the right.

$\_CS_2 + \_O_2 \rightarrow \_CO_2 + 2SO_2$

There are six O atoms on the right, so add 3 to O_2 on the left.

$\mathbf{CS_2 + 3O_2 \rightarrow CO_2 + 2SO_2}$

111)

[illegible] **Correct.** The larger the equilibrium constant, the more the equilibrium favors products. To order these equations from most product favored to least product favored, the equilibrium constant should be listed from greatest to least.

112)

C. **I and II only**

I. True. All weak acids are in an equilibrium.

II. True. All weak bases are in an equilibrium.

III. False. A hydrolysis process may be irreversible, which means it is not in a state of equilibrium.

113)

D. **Correct.** In the reaction, the Na displaces hydrogen from water in a single-replacement reaction.

114)

D. **Correct.** This reaction is a neutralization reaction, which always produces water and a salt. Sodium is a +1 ion and sulfate is a −2 ion, so the resulting salt is Na_2SO_4.

115)

A. Incorrect. Evaporation is a phase transition from liquid to gas.

B. Incorrect. Condensation does not skip a phase.

C. **Correct.** Sublimation skips a phase—it goes from solid to gas without passing through the liquid phase.

D. Incorrect. Fusion is a phase transition from solid to liquid.

116)

[illegible] **I and II**

I. True. Ethyl isopropyl ether is the correct name using the common names of the simple alkyl groups attached and the word *ether*.

II. True. The smaller —OR group is treated as an alkoxy group that is a substituent of a longer alkane chain. This is technically correct, although this naming technique is more often used for larger ethers.

III. False. This is an ether of the general form R—O—R, not an alcohol of the general form R—OH.

117)

A. **Correct.** The ions that appear on both the reactant and product sides (spectator ions) are not included in the net ionic equation. The solution of HNO_3 is made up of separated H^{+1} ions and NO_3^{-1} ions and the solution of KOH is made up of separated K^{+1} ions and OH^{-1} ions. When these solutions are mixed together, the H^{+1} ions and the OH^{-1} ions combine to make water. The K^{+1} ions and the NO_2^{-1} ions undergo no change and can thus be omitted. This leaves the net ionic equation $H^{+1} + OH^{-1} \rightarrow H_2O$.

118)

A. Incorrect. This is an acid.

B. Incorrect. An acid donates protons to a base.

C. Incorrect. Salt and water are formed when acids and bases react.

D. **Correct.** Acids increase the concentration of hydrogen ions in solution and do not accept protons.

119)

D. **I, II, and III**

I. True. Ethylene contains one double bond and thus has one pi bond.

II. True. Acetylene contains one triple bond and thus has two pi bonds.

III. True. Carbon monoxide contains a triple bond and thus has two pi bonds.

120)

C. **Correct.** CCl_4 is covalently bonded, so the molecules in the solid are held together by relatively weak intermolecular forces compared to the ionic attractions and stabilizing lattice energy experienced by the salts, KCl and $CaCl_2$. $CaCl_2$, with a smaller ionic radius and +2 charge, forms stronger ionic bonds than KCl and so has a somewhat higher melting point.

121)

C. **Correct.** The presence of electrons was first demonstrated by J.J. Thomson. Choices A, B, and D are all part of the Rutherford model.

122)

D. **Correct.** The longest chain is nine carbons long and has single bonds between carbons. The two methyl groups are on the number 3 and 7 carbons.

123)

A. Incorrect. All chlorides and nitrates are soluble.

B. **Correct.** $BaSO_4$ is not soluble.

C. Incorrect. Most sulfates and all nitrates are soluble.

D. Incorrect. All chlorides and iodines are soluble.

124)

A. **Correct.** A Lewis acid accepts an electron pair, and a Lewis base donates an electron pair.

B. Incorrect. The opposite is true.

C. Incorrect. $SnCl_4^{-2}$ is not a Lewis acid or base.

D. Incorrect. $SnCl_4^{-2}$ is not a Lewis acid or base.

125)

B. **Correct.** Immediate evacuation should be the first action.

Follow the link below to take your second Georgia Assessments for the Certification of Educators (GACE) Chemistry Assessment practice test and to access other online study resources:

www.cirrustestprep.com/praxis-chemistry-online-resources

Made in the USA
Monee, IL
17 June 2021

71573597R00122